THE WORKS OF
ARNOLD SCHOENBERG

THE WORKS OF
ARNOLD SCHOENBERG

A Catalogue of his Compositions,

Writings and Paintings

by

JOSEF RUFER

Translated by
DIKA NEWLIN

FABER AND FABER
24 Russell Square
London

First published in England in mcmlxii
by Faber and Faber Limited
24 Russell Square London W.C.1
Printed in Great Britain
by Spottiswoode, Ballantyne and Co. Ltd.
London and Colchester

Originally published in Germany as
DAS WERK ARNOLD SCHÖNBERGS
© *1959 Bärenreiter-Verlag Kassel*
English translation © *1962 Faber and Faber Limited*

TO MY WIFE

PREFACE

There is scarcely any artist whose essence and significance can be captured in a biography for all time. A historical personality appears in a new light to each succeeding generation. Prerequisite to any serious study—not mere subjective evaluation—of such a personality is an exact knowledge of his total *oeuvre*. The basis for musicological research was furnished by bibliographical works, like the Köchel catalogue of Mozart, or Gustav Nottebohm's investigations (impersonal in the best sense of the word) of Beethoven's sketchbooks.

The aim of the present work was to lay a foundation for further research on Arnold Schoenberg's personality and work. The Academy of Arts in Berlin hopes that, with its commission to Josef Rufer to inspect and catalogue the entire legacy of Schoenberg's work, and to issue a complete bibliography, it has taken a step in the right direction.

BORIS BLACHER
Vice-President, Academy of Arts, Berlin

Berlin, March, 1959

TABLE OF CONTENTS

CONTENTS

LIST OF THE FACSIMILE REPRODUCTIONS
AND ILLUSTRATIONS

FACSIMILES OF MANUSCRIPTS

ILLUSTRATIONS

(including reproductions of Schoenberg's paintings)

at end of book

LIST OF ILLUSTRATIONS

FOREWORD

This book contains a bibliographical presentation of all the works of Arnold Schoenberg (1874–1951).

It originated in a commission from the Academy of Arts in Berlin, successor to the earlier Prussian Academy of Arts to which Schoenberg belonged as a member, as a Senator, and as the director of a master class in composition. The fulfilment of this commission, the original aim of which was the inspection, cataloguing, and gathering together of the composer's artistic legacy, took me, in the spring of 1957, to Los Angeles, his final place of residence. In his home there, I found almost all the original manuscripts and sketches (some dating from his early youth) of his compositions and his literary and theoretical works, as well as most of his paintings. My suggestion that the survey of the legacy should be expanded by the inclusion of the few manuscripts in the possession of the Library of Congress in Washington, of a few publishers, and of a Swiss private collector, so that the complete works might be comprehended in this study, was accepted by the Academy, and the terms of my commission were broadened in accordance with this. Thus, I was able to see all of the original manuscripts and documents described in this book, with a single exception. This exception was the short score of the 'Serenade', Op. 24, in the possession of the Library of Congress; the score was not available to me at the time of my Washington visit, but a photocopy of it was sent to me later.

Up till now it has been impossible to determine the whereabouts of the original manuscripts of the following works: the Piano Piece, Op. 33a; two of the Six Male Choruses, Op. 35, 'Das Gesetz' and 'Glück'; the score of the 'Serenade', Op. 24, which seems to exist only in a photocopy.

The following manuscripts have probably been lost or destroyed: the manuscript of 'Accompaniment to a Film-Scene', Op. 34, which was stored in the Stassfurt salt-mines by the publishers (Heinrichshofen) during World War II and, according to them, was destroyed there; the manuscripts (or, more likely, fair copies) of the Six Male Choruses, Op. 35, which were sent to Czechoslovakia for safe-keeping during the war by their publisher, Bote & Bock. However, the loss of these manuscripts is somewhat compensated for by the fact that photocopies of Opp. 24 and 34, and of 'Das Gesetz' from Op. 35 (though not of Op. 33a or of the male chorus 'Glück') were found among the composer's papers, as were first drafts of four of the six male choruses and (in one of the large sketchbooks) of the 'Serenade', Op. 24. An incomplete first draft of Op. 33a has also been preserved.

The initiative to the commission given me by the Academy of Arts in Berlin came from its member, Boris Blacher. During his stay in the United States in the summer of 1956, he had occasion to visit the workroom in Schoenberg's Los Angeles home and to observe that the virtually complete artistic legacy of the composer was still preserved there. His plan won the approval and complete support of Gertrud Schoenberg, the composer's widow, as well as that

FOREWORD

of the President of the Berlin Academy, Prof. Hans Scharoun, and of its Music Division. With this support, and with the financial underwriting of the Berlin Lottery, the completion of my work was assured. Finally, its publication is due to the spontaneous helpfulness and generosity of Dr. Karl Vötterle, owner of the 'Bärenreiter-Verlag'.

The list of those who played a considerable part in the genesis of this work is herewith completed. My gratitude to them, as heartfelt as it may be, is unimportant in comparison with the incalculable service which they have performed for future students of Schoenberg—not to mention all music-lovers, to whom a new road towards the understanding of the most fascinating creative personality of twentieth-century music will now be opened by these documents. My special thanks, however, must go to Gertrud Schoenberg. Without her boundless confidence in me, without her generous help and support in word and deed, I should have been unable to master the task of presenting this material in so complete and accurate a form.

In working on the materials which I had collected, from time to time I was confronted with questions which could be answered only by renewed reference to the manuscripts. For help with these problems, I must cordially thank Dr. Richard S. Hill (Library of Congress, Washington), Jan Maegaard, and Dr. Helmut Wagner.

JOSEF RUFER

Berlin, March, 1959

INTRODUCTION

The following explanations and indications should serve a double purpose in introducing this book:

(1) Several important results of our research, and a number of facts of special interest (e.g., circumstances concerning the ownership and whereabouts of manuscripts), are discussed at this point for special emphasis.

(2) Special characteristics of the presentation and treatment of the text of this book, a knowledge of which is indispensable to its use, are mentioned here, as are the particular methods which had to be used in inspecting and organizing the legacy.

Legacy. All musical and literary manuscripts in Schoenberg's own handwriting (including first drafts and fair copies), as well as all sketches and sketchbooks, and all paintings and drawings listed here, belonged to the legacy (unless another owner is specifically named) at the time this book was first printed. This legacy is in the possession of the composer's widow, Gertrud Schoenberg. A single original manuscript, that of the 'Suite for String Orchestra' (see below), is in other private hands. Furthermore, as already mentioned in the Foreword, there are a number of manuscripts at the Library of Congress in Washington, while several others are in the hands of publishers. These are mentioned in the body of the book when the works in question are discussed.

Original Manuscripts, Fair Copies, Copies. Oftentimes it was impossible to distinguish with certainty between original manuscripts and copies. This would call for careful comparison of the paper and handwriting of the various manuscripts (which are usually in different places). On the other hand, first drafts were very easy to identify, especially when they are in the short-score form which Schoenberg used almost without exception. Everything written by Schoenberg himself (letters, articles, quotations, dates, marginal notes, etc.) has been printed in italics in this book.

Spelling of Words, Names, German and English Titles. The old-fashioned German spelling (differing from present practice) has generally been preserved where Schoenberg used it. From the time of his emigration to the United States in 1933, the composer spelled his name *Schoenberg* rather than *Schönberg*. This spelling has been preserved wherever he used it (i.e., in his own signatures of this period). In his last years, he returned from time to time to the German spelling.

Also, during his American period, Schoenberg gave his works English titles. In his essays and theoretical works of this time, the text is also in English, but from time to time first drafts in German are found.

Dating. Schoenberg sometimes made errors in dating his manuscripts; these are not too hard to detect. However, they have not been corrected here, as reliable bases for correction were generally not to be found.

INTRODUCTION

Numbering. My numbering, in chronological order, of the musical manuscripts without opus numbers was undertaken for practical reasons, above all for the sake of being able to cite these works more readily and accurately. I have preserved Schoenberg's own division of his literary essays, articles and the like into different subject-areas. He had already undertaken this classification before 1933 with a view to the publication of his writings which was being planned at that time. On the other hand, his numbering had to be revised, for many of the several hundred manuscripts (especially those written after 1933) were not included in it. It often happens that the content of an essay touches on two or even more subject-areas. In such a case, Schoenberg would register the essay in each one of these areas (i.e., twice or more). The corresponding duplicates in the individual-subject folders are usually typewritten.

Here, I must also point out that time did not permit me to do more than summarize the contents of a few of the most important writings.

Comments on Individual Works. These are scattered throughout Schoenberg's letters, lectures and articles. They may deal with the genesis of a composition, or with musical, theoretical or interpretative problems. I have included such comments at appropriate points.

Sketches. Of the piles of sketch-sheets, the majority could either be assigned to already-known works or could be included in our list as unknown or unpublished, unfinished, or merely begun. The sketches of unfinished compositions and of mere beginnings (consisting of a few measures only) are listed so completely because they afford very special documentation of the wealth and variety of Schoenberg's inventive powers. Whether, in any individual case, it was the composer's self-criticism or external circumstances which prevented the continuation or completion of a sketch is impossible to determine. The remainder of the sketches, a pile about 10 cm. high, could not be examined thoroughly in the time at my disposal. However, in a cursory examination no new sketches of sizeable dimensions were found.

Music Paper. During the last years of his life, eye trouble forced Schoenberg to use music paper in which the lines were 3 mm. (later even 5 mm.) apart. This, he prepared himself, according to his own design. It is designated in the text as 'hand-lined'. The transparent music paper used for photographic reproduction is here usually called 'blueprint paper'.

Paintings. The paintings at hand in the legacy represent perhaps two-thirds of Schoenberg's work in this medium. The exact whereabouts of the remaining paintings (mostly scattered in private European collections) could not be determined, except for a painting of Alban Berg which may be found in the Historical Museum in Vienna, and three paintings in the possession of Mrs. Jalowetz (which are described in the text). Their existence was determined from a number of exhibition catalogues (dating from the period before 1914) found among Schoenberg's effects.

Library. The legacy contains an extensive collection of music and books, the latter representing the most varied fields of knowledge. Some of the scores, especially the works of Mozart, Beethoven and Bach, contain detailed analyses and comments written in the margins by Schoenberg himself.

ENGLISH PUBLISHER'S NOTE

It will be seen that the terms of reference of this book exclude printed editions, except where copies exist among Schoenberg's papers. (A full-scale account of Schoenberg's publications would require a book to itself.)

There are, however, printed editions which are, for one reason or another, especially relevant to this volume. It is clearly of interest to record, alongside Schoenberg's own corrected manuscripts and printed scores, the few editions in which his revisions reached print. The textual critic will need to relate the two sets of sources, and every reader is likely to want to know what state of the text is present in the score he is using. Autograph facsimiles, too, are of special importance. We have accordingly asked Mr. O. W. Neighbour of the British Museum to add brief notes on printed editions which have a special bearing on the questions with which this book is concerned. His contributions are enclosed in square brackets: [.........]. He has also added one or two arrangements by Schoenberg which appear to survive only in printed editions.

We should also like to thank Mr. Hans Keller for his advice on some problems of translation.

MUSIC

I. PUBLISHED WORKS

A. WORKS WITH OPUS NUMBERS

TWO SONGS for Baritone and Piano, Op. 1
Richard Birnbach (formerly Dreililien-Verlag), Berlin

The two songs 'Dank' ('Thanks') and 'Abschied' ('Farewell'), after poems by Karl Freiherr von Levetzow, are found in a fair copy (ink) on 8 double sheets (upright format, 26·5×35 cm.) bound with sewing-thread. There are occasional small handwritten alterations. Undated.

FOUR SONGS for Voice and Piano, Op. 2
Richard Birnbach (formerly Dreililien-Verlag), Berlin

The manuscripts of the four songs are separate, each one written in black ink on a double sheet (upright format, 26·5×35 cm.).

1. 'Erwartung' ('Expectation': Richard Dehmel); dated *9./8.99*.

2. 'Schenk mir deinen goldenen Kamm' ('Give Me Thy Golden Comb': Richard Dehmel); undated. There are two handwritten copies; one bears the title 'Jesus bettelt' ('Jesus Begs').

3. 'Erhebung' ('Exaltation': Richard Dehmel); dated *16./XI.99*.

4. 'Waldsonne' ('Woodland Sunshine': Johannes Schlaf); undated.

SIX SONGS for Medium Voice and Piano, Op. 3
Richard Birnbach (formerly Dreililien-Verlag), Berlin

The manuscripts of all six songs are bound together; the fair copy, in ink, is on 9 double sheets (upright format, 26·5×34·5 cm.). Also there are individual manuscripts (ink) of the first, second, third and sixth songs (two copies of the first song) on separate double or single sheets (format as above).

1. 'Wie Georg von Frundsberg von sich selber sang' ('How Georg von Frundsberg Sang About Himself': from 'Des Knaben Wunderhorn'—'The Youth's Magic Horn'). The separate copy (these individual copies are evidently earlier drafts than the bound copies) is signed *Berlin 18. März 1903 Arnold Schönberg*.

23

I. PUBLISHED WORKS

2. 'Die Aufgeregten' ('The Excited Ones': Gottfried Keller); individual manuscript dated *9./11.1903.*

3. 'Warnung' ('Warning': Richard Dehmel); individual manuscript dated *7./5. 99.*

4. 'Hochzeitslied' ('Wedding Song': J. P. Jacobsen); manuscript found only in the bound copy containing all six songs.

5. 'Geübtes Herz' ('The Experienced Heart': Gottfried Keller); besides the bound copy, the first 14 measures of this song are written on a sheet dated *2./9. 1903.*

6. 'Freihold' ('Freehold': Hermann Lingg); dated *20./11. 900.*

STRING SEXTET: 'VERKLÄRTE NACHT' ('Transfigured Night'), Op. 4
Richard Birnbach (formerly Dreililien-Verlag), Berlin

The manuscript is in the Library of Congress in Washington; a full-sized photocopy of it is in the legacy. It consists of 24 sheets of 20-lined music paper (upright format, 26·5 × 34 cm.) comprising 39 numbered pages written in ink. No beginning date is given; the date of completion is given as *Fine 1./XII. 99.* The heading, in ink, on the first page of the score reads as follows: *Verklärte Nacht | Gedicht von Richard Dehmel | für sechs Streichinstrumente | von | Arnold Schönberg* ('Transfigured Night' / poem by Richard Dehmel / for six string instruments. . .).

In the manuscript several large cuts have been marked (*vi—de*) with charcoal. Also, this manuscript contains 6 pages of revisions (which have also been photocopied). Attention is called to these in the score with the notation *Einlage* (insertion).

In addition, the legacy includes three loose pages (upright format, 26·5 × 34·5 cm.) of ink and pencil sketches, undated.

No manuscripts of the arrangements for string orchestra were found in the legacy. There are two versions. The first dates from 1917, and was published by Universal Edition, Vienna. The second was published in 1943 by Associated Music Publishers, New York. Both versions include a double-bass part which reinforces the 'celli as needed. In the 1943 version, this part is omitted from two passages where it occurred in the earlier setting.

The following letter from Richard Dehmel, whose poem of the same name furnished the programmatic basis for Schoenberg's sextet, immediately precedes an exchange of letters in which Schoenberg requested the poet to write an oratorio text for him. (See below, Section II B (*e*), p. 117.)

Blankenese b/Hamburg, 12.12.12.

DEAR MR. SCHÖNBERG!

Yesterday I heard 'Verklärte Nacht', and I should consider it a sin of omission if I failed to say a word of thanks to you for your wonderful Sextet. I had intended to follow the motives of my text in your composition; but I soon forgot to do so, I was so enthralled by the music. Besides, Bandler* performed it quite perfectly with his partners; I think that you,

---

* EDITOR'S NOTE: Bandler was the first violinist of the Bandler Quartet.

too, would have enjoyed it thoroughly, even though this work is now ten years behind you. With cordial greetings, your

DEHMEL

> O glorious sound! my words now ring,
> in tones to God reëchoing;
> To you this highest joy I owe;
> On earth no higher may we know.*
>
> D.

PELLEAS UND MELISANDE, Symphonic Poem, Op. 5
Universal Edition, Vienna

Manuscript bound by the composer himself. Title-page in Schoenberg's handwriting: *Pelleas und Melisande / nach dem Drama von Maurice Maeterlinck / für Orchester / von / Arnold Schönberg.* Below this, the complete orchestration is listed.

The manuscript consists of 95 pages of 24-lined music paper, with later corrections added in red pencil. There are 3 loose sheets (pp. 19–20, pp. 65–68).

Date of completion, handwritten on p. 95: *Berlin 28. Februar 1903.* In addition, there exists a bound copy of the large conductor's score, with the following handwritten note by the composer on the title-page: *Dirigierpartitur mit Retouchen 1913 (Berlin)* ('Conductor's score with revisions . . .') *und Prag (1918). (Zemlinsky)*

Universal Edition has the manuscript of Heinrich Jalowetz' four-hand piano reduction (106 pages) with insertions and corrections by Schoenberg.

DRAFTS AND SKETCHES

On 12 single sheets, 6 half sheets and 1 double sheet (upright format, also oblong format, 26·5 × 34·5 cm.) are sketches and drafts of larger sections, mainly written in ink. On one sketch-sheet is the date *4./7. 1902.* Another sheet bears a detailed outline (in pencil) of the organization and content of Maeterlinck's drama; this is the basis for the composition.

[The printed score of 1911 (131 pages) was replaced in 1920 by a new edition (125 pages) containing revisions of instrumentation and dynamic marks. The plates of the later edition were also used for the study score.]

EIGHT SONGS for Voice and Piano, Op. 6
Richard Birnbach (formerly Dreililien-Verlag), Berlin

1. 'Traumleben' ('Dream-Life': Julius Hart); manuscript in ink on 1 sheet of music paper (upright format, 26·5 × 34·5 cm.), with some changes. The last 8 measures have been pasted over with a revised version. Dated *18./12. 1903.*

---

* Translator's note: the beautiful poem of Dehmel should be cited here in the original also:
> Ein Wörtlein Dank—o schönster Schall:
> des Schöpferwortes Widerhall.
> Uns allen ahnt kein höher Glück:
> nun tönt die Welt zu Gott zurück.
>
> D.

2. 'Alles' ('Everything': Richard Dehmel); manuscript in ink on a double sheet (upright format, 26·5 × 34·5 cm.). Note of completion: *Arnold Schönberg Traunstein 6./9. 1905.*

3. 'Mädchenlied' ('Maiden's Song': Paul Remer); manuscript in ink on a double sheet (format as above). Mm. 15–22 (inclusive) are crossed out with pencil; a revised version of this passage (now 9 instead of 8 measures) is pencilled on the third page. Undated.

4. 'Verlassen' ('Forsaken': Hermann Conradi); the first draft of the manuscript is quite different from the published version in mm. 5–6, as well as in mm. 34–39 (inclusive). Dated *19./12. 1903.*

Another draft, in ink, breaks off with m. 17; it is quite different from the above-mentioned version—possibly an earlier draft? It is undated, as is still a third draft written in ink. This third version has pencilled corrections in mm. 5–6 and 34–35 which correspond to the printed version; however, thereafter it, too, differs from the finally published form. Finally, we have a pencil sketch of the beginning of the song (1 page, on a single sheet of music paper).

5. 'Ghasel' (Gottfried Keller); the manuscript is in the same format as the preceding songs of this group. There are slight differences from the published version in the piano part. Dated *23./1. 1904.* A second copy contains the final version of the piano part, with the changes noted in pencil.

6. 'Am Wegrand' ('At the Wayside': John Henry Mackay); manuscript in ink on a double sheet (format as in the other songs of this set). Undated.

7. 'Lockung' ('Temptation': Kurt Aram); manuscript in ink on a double sheet, undated. Later tempo alterations and a new version of the crossed-out mm. 38–44 (inclusive) are written in pencil. In mm. 48–52 (inclusive), 58, and 60–62 the voice part has been altered in pencil; these changes correspond to the final, published version.

8. 'Der Wanderer' ('The Wanderer': Friedrich Nietzsche); manuscript in ink on 2 double sheets; some little handwritten revisions. Dated *Wien 15./10. 1905.*

The first drafts of Nos. 3, 6, 7 and 8 of this set, as well as of Op. 3, no. 1, are found in Sketchbook II (see below).

FIRST STRING QUARTET IN D MINOR, Op. 7
Richard Birnbach (formerly Dreililien-Verlag), Berlin

The manuscript of the score is owned by the Library of Congress in Washington, which also has the handwritten parts. It consists of 30 sheets of music paper (upright format, 26·5 × 34·5 cm.) comprising 55 numbered pages written in ink. The stamped address on the manuscript is Wien IX. Liechtensteinstr. 68/70. Several considerable cuts (marked *vi–de*) in the first section or movement, as well as additional dynamic markings, have been indicated with coloured pencil.

Sketchbook II (see below) contains, from p. 11 onwards (with interruptions up to p. 63), the first draft of the work. Sketches for it already occur on pp. 1 and 3 of this book, as well as in Sketchbook I (see below). A beginning-date for this composition was not found; however, we may make a fairly reliable guess at it, since Schoenberg began to use Sketchbook II in April, 1905. We do have a date of completion, noted on p. 60 of Sketchbook II: *beendigt am 26./9. 1905.*

A. WORKS WITH OPUS NUMBERS

SIX ORCHESTRAL SONGS, Op. 8
Universal Edition, Vienna

1. 'Natur' ('Nature': Heinrich Hart); manuscript (fair copy of the score) in ink on 3 double sheets of 24-lined music paper (upright format, 26×34·5 cm.) bound with white twine. Completed 7. *März 1904*.

2. 'Das Wappenschild' ('The Coat-of-Arms': from 'Des Knaben Wunderhorn'); like No. 1, this is written in ink on 6 double sheets (format as above) bound with white twine. Completed *Wien 25. Mai 1904*. The title-page is crossed out with green pencil; the word *umgearbeitet* (reworked) has been added.

In addition, there are 3 sheets of music paper (format as above) held together with gummed tape, which contain what may be the first draft, written in ink. Various measures have been crossed out in pencil; from time to time comments have been written in such as *ganz neu*, *andere Wendung Dur, E dur, H moll, Cis dur* ('entirely new, a different turn to major, E major, B minor, C sharp major'). Completed *9./4. 04*.

Both manuscripts differ from the published version.

3. 'Sehnsucht' ('Longing': from 'Des Knaben Wunderhorn'); fair copy of the score in ink, on 5 sheets of music paper (format as above) held together with red twine and gummed tape. Completed *Wien 7. April 1905* (however, this date is probably wrong and should be 1904; note dates of the other songs in this set).*

4. 'Nie ward' ich Herrin müd' ('Ne'er, Mistress, Did I Weary': Petrarch); fair copy of the score in ink on 4 double sheets (format as above) bound with blue twine. Completed *Mödling 3. Juli 1904*. Also, there is what appears to be the first draft, written in short-score form, in ink, on a double sheet (26·5×34·5 cm.). The postlude of the song is crossed out, then immediately (with the indication *vi–de*) composed anew. Completed *Juni 1904*.

There is also the manuscript of the piano reduction, written in ink on 2 double sheets and bound with white twine. Furthermore, there is a piano reduction made by Erwin Stein; this manuscript, in ink, has a handwritten note by Schoenberg at the top: *Clavier Auszug von Stein, den müssen Sie überarbeiten!* ('Piano reduction by Stein, you must work over this!') This note was presumably directed to Webern, who made the published piano reductions.

5. 'Voll jener Süsse' ('Filled With That Sweetness': Petrarch); manuscript (fair copy of the score) written in ink on 5 double sheets (format as above), bound with stout white twine. Completed *Wien, November 1904*.

There is also a manuscript of the piano reduction, written in ink on 2 double sheets of 16-lined music paper (format as above).

6. 'Wenn Vöglein klagen' ('When Little Birds Complain': Petrarch); fair copy of the score in ink on 3 double sheets of 22-lined music paper (upright format, 26·5×34 cm.). It breaks off 15 measures before the end. Undated.

Also, there is an undated draft, obviously the first version. It is written in pencil in short-score form, on 3 pages of a double sheet of 22-lined music paper (upright format, 26·5×34 cm.). It, too, breaks off 15 measures before the close.

Finally, measures 1–14 of this song are written in ink, in short-score form, on a double sheet of the same format.

* See Addendum No. 1, p. 77.

I. PUBLISHED WORKS

The first drafts of Nos. 2, 4, 5 and 6 of this set are found in Sketchbook I (see below). The single copies from which the songs were printed are in the possession of Universal Edition, Vienna. These copies (in ink) are not in the composer's handwriting. No. 1 bears a date in his writing: *Wien, 7. März 1904*. Nos. 4, 5 and 6 contain handwritten entries by him.

SKETCHES AND DRAFTS

1. 'Natur.' There is a manuscript fair copy (in ink) of an earlier draft; it contains many corrections in pencil. In addition, there are various other drafts.

2. 'Das Wappenschild.' There is a version for voice and piano, written in ink on a double sheet (26·5 × 34·5 cm.), and dated *26./11. 1903*. It differs from the final version. The accompaniment breaks off at the words 'was die Geduld für Wunder tut' ('what wonders patience does'), the voice at the words 'in den Streit' ('in the fight').

3. 'Sehnsucht.' There is a manuscript for voice and piano, written in ink on a single sheet of music paper (upright format, 26·5 × 34·5 cm.), and undated.

5. 'Voll jener Süsse.' The manuscript of the score is written in pencil on 7 double sheets (upright format, 26·5 × 34·5 cm.) comprising 17 numbered pages. Completed *Wien November 1904*. Also, a single sheet of music paper (oblong format, 27 × 34 cm.) contains a pencil draft, in short-score form but without indications of the instrumentation. Finally, there is a fair copy of the first two-thirds of the song, in ink on a double sheet (upright format, 26·5 × 34·5 cm.).

KAMMERSYMPHONIE FÜR FÜNFZEHN SOLOINSTRUMENTE, Op. 9 (CHAMBER SYMPHONY FOR FIFTEEN SOLO INSTRUMENTS)
Universal Edition, Vienna

ARRANGEMENT FOR ORCHESTRA
Universal Edition, Vienna

CHAMBER SYMPHONY, NEW VERSION FOR ORCHESTRA, Op. 9B
G. Schirmer, New York

An almost complete form of the work is found in Sketchbooks II and III (see below).

Universal Edition, Vienna, has the manuscript fair copy. The score, bound in blue canvas, comprises 56 numbered pages on 30-lined music paper (upright format, 26·5 × 34·5 cm.); it is written in ink. Additions concerning tempi and dynamics have been made in red ink, red pencil, or sometimes in blue pencil. On pp. 3–4 (starting a measure before cue No. 4) 8 measures have been pasted over with a new version. The same thing happens on p. 5 (3 measures in the horns and strings beginning with cue No. 6). A cut from No. 48 to No. 50, marked in red pencil, is cancelled again as the word *bleibt* (remains) is written in several times. The date and place of the score's completion are given at the end: *Rottach-Egern 25. Juli 1906*.

In the legacy, there are also the following materials relating to this First Chamber Symphony:

1. A printed copy of the large score for conductors (revised edition, Universal Edition No. 3667). On the title-page, it bears the note *Bearbeitung für Orchester Arnold Schönberg*, and the stamped address: Berlin-Südende, Berlinerstr. 17a. The score contains the directions for performance with large orchestra, written in red ink. Undated.

2. The photocopy of a manuscript 'arranged for orchestra by the composer', designated as Op. 9B. It contains a title-page and 29 pages of score (numbered 3–31), the last of which bears the notation *Hollywood, April 18, 1935*. In contrast to the orchestral version published by Universal Edition, Vienna, in which the size of the ensemble of Op. 9 is merely enlarged, this version is actually a new transformation for orchestra, with additional subordinate and accompanying voices. This version was published by G. Schirmer, New York. The whereabouts of the blueprint manuscript could not be determined.

3. The manuscript, bound by the composer (the inner title-page is loose) of the four-hand piano reduction. It comprises 59 numbered pages (upright format, 26·5 × 34·5 cm.) written in ink, and is undated and unsigned. It bears the stamped address: Berlin-Südende, Berliner-strasse 17a. On the first page is the following undated note, in red pencil: *Das ist alles viel zu überladen!!! Immer nur halb so viel Stimmen!* ('That is all much too overloaded!!! there should always be just half as many parts!').

4. The manuscript of a version for several (unspecified) instruments, begun on *13./2. 1907* (it progressed no further than m. 14, however).

[The printed score bears the copyright date 1912. The first edition was followed by a 'Verbesserte Ausgabe' ('Improved edition') from the same plates, in which the instrumentation is very considerably revised; many lines previously doubled are entrusted to solo instruments, and the dynamics scaled down. The work was re-engraved for the miniature score (1924) and the dynamics still further reduced.]

SECOND STRING QUARTET IN F SHARP MINOR, Op. 10, with voice (3rd and 4th movements: 'Litanei' ('Litany') and 'Entrückung' ('Rapture'), poems by Stefan George)
Universal Edition, Vienna

The manuscript (fair copy in ink) is in the Library of Congress in Washington. It consists of 24 sheets of 20-lined music paper (upright format, 26·5 × 34·5 cm.), comprising 45 numbered pages; it is undated. A piece of the title-page is torn off. The handwritten title reads as follows: *II. Quartett / für 2 Violinen, Viola und Cello / von / Arnold Schönberg*. Details of tempo and dynamics are written in coloured pencil. (See also Sketchbook III, with the first sketch of the beginning of the composition dated *9./3. 1907*.)

There is a photocopy of this manuscript in the legacy. There is also a pencil manuscript of the third movement ('Litanei') written on a double sheet of 24-lined music paper (oblong format, 28·5 × 36·5 cm.). This manuscript begins with m. 26 and goes to the end of the movement; it was completed on *11./7. 1908*.

In addition, there is a copy of a facsimile edition of the work, 'Im Selbstverlag' (published by the composer himself). This copy contains no additional notations or insertions. Another copy of the same edition is marked (in red pencil) *Dirigierpartitur 3. Juni 1919 Sch.* ('Conductor's score. . . .'); it has additional tempo and dynamic indications and metronome markings. These pertain to the version for string orchestra.

[There are five different printed scores. An autograph facsimile was first published 'Im Selbstverlag' ('Composer's edition'). There followed a corrected reissue which may be distinguished by the imprint of Universal Edition on the title-page and the absence of empty staves between each brace in the first two movements. The first engraved score bears the copyright date 1919, and incorporates metronome markings. It was reprinted with further revisions in 1925, with the information 'Neu revidiert 1921' ('Newly revised 1921'). Finally the string orchestral version was published in 1929.

A copy of the first issue of the facsimile, specially annotated by the composer in 1909 for a performance in Paris, is in the possession of Mr. A. Rosenthal of Oxford, who has kindly allowed me to describe it here. Each page has been extended by a broad margin pasted on to the fore-edge, which gives additional space for elaborate directions for performance. Some of these were taken up in the engraved edition, but others were changed and there were many omissions, particularly from among the copious metronome indications. Many more points were in any case too detailed for inclusion in a printed score.]

THREE PIANO PIECES, Op. 11
Universal Edition, Vienna

1. The first draft of the manuscript is written in pencil on 2 sheets of music paper (on one side of each page, only; oblong format, 14·5×36·5 cm.). The date of completion, *19./II. 1909*, is an important one in the history of music; for this is the first composition to dispense completely with 'tonal' means of organization.

2. Also written in pencil, on 3 sides of 2 sheets of music paper (format as in No. 1). As in the first piece, several small modifications in tempo and many dynamic and phrase markings found in the published version are missing here. Completed *22./2. 1909*.

3. Written in pencil on both sides of a sheet of 24-lined music paper (oblong format, 28·5×36·5 cm.). After m. 4, 12 measures are cut (marked *vi–de*). Completed *7./8. 1909*.

[First published in 1910. Later printings show a few minor revisions and are marked 'Revidiert 1924'.]

TWO BALLADS for Voice and Piano, Op. 12
Universal Edition, Vienna

1. 'Der verlorene Haufen' ('The Lost Battalion': Viktor Klemperer); manuscript written in ink on 7 pages of 2 double sheets (upright format, 26×34·5 cm.). Begun *15./3. 1907*, completed *April 1907*. Five measures have been pasted over with a new version. Later, the words *Original Manuskript* were written in green pencil under the title.

2. 'Jane Grey' (Heinrich Ammann); manuscript on 7 pages of 2 double sheets (format as above); written in ink. Completed *28./4. 1907*. Four measures were pasted over with a new version.

The first drafts of these songs are in Sketchbook III (see below).

FRIEDE AUF ERDEN ('Peace on Earth': C. F. Meyer), Op. 13
for Mixed Chorus a cappella
B. Schott's Söhne, Mainz (formerly Tischer & Jagenberg, Cologne)

The manuscript, in ink, is on 4 loose sheets of 16-lined music paper (upright format, 25·5×34·5 cm.). A handwritten note (initialled) in red pencil, on the right-hand margin of the first page, reads as follows: *Das ist geändert, aber ich weiss nicht wie? Sch.* ('This has been changed, but I don't know how.'). This refers to the alto and tenor parts in the second half of m. 3, which have also been marked in red. Completed *9./3. 1907.* (See also Sketchbook III.)

A second manuscript, apparently a fair copy (bearing two stamped addresses of the 'Gesellschaft der Musikfreunde in Wien'), is written in ink on 11 pages of 16-lined music paper (upright format, 26·5 × 34·5 cm.). Undated.

'Begleitung ad libitum zum Chor "Friede auf Erden"' ('Optional accompaniment to the chorus "Peace on Earth"')—this is the heading of a manuscript in the Library of Congress. It consists of 6 pages written in ink on 4 sheets of music paper (36·5 × 37·5 cm.). Date and place of completion are noted as follows: *Zehlendorf 6./10. 1911 Arnold Schönberg Machnower Chaussee, Ecke Dietloffstr.*

The purpose of this optional accompaniment (double woodwinds, 2 horns and string quintet) is explained fully by the composer in the margin of the score:

Note for the conductor: the purpose of this accompaniment is merely to make clean intonation possible for the chorus singers, if they cannot attain it without this. However, it should in no case have the effect of an obligatory accompaniment; therefore, it should not sound prominent. On the contrary, the effort was made to have it disappear in the sound of the chorus. Therefore, it corresponds to the composer's intent to make this accompaniment as inaudible as possible, so that the sound of the chorus is as pure and unmuddied as possible. To this end, it is recommended that, in general, the accompanying instruments should play considerably more softly, in the first rehearsal, than is indicated here. In the course of the later rehearsals, they may then be asked especially to play louder when it is necessary!

Also, a letter of *16./7. 1913* to the work's original publishers, Tischer & Jagenberg, accompanies the manuscript.

[The posthumous Schott edition (1955) contains some additional markings from an autograph score.]

TWO SONGS for Voice and Piano, Op. 14
Universal Edition, Vienna

The first song, 'Ich darf nicht dankend' ('I May Not Thank Thee'), from 'Waller im Schnee' ('Pilgrim in the Snow') by Stefan George, is found in a manuscript fair copy, written in ink on a double sheet of printed music paper (upright format, 26 × 34 cm.). There is also a transposition from B minor to D minor, made by Erwin Stein, as well as a copyist's transcription from the original (bearing Schoenberg's stamped address: Berlin-Zehlendorf, Wannseebahn, Machnowerchaussee, Villa Lepcke).

The second song, 'In diesen Wintertagen' ('In These Winter Days': Georg Henckel) is written in pencil on 3 loose, numbered sheets of music paper (oblong format, 14·5 × 28·5 cm.). Three measures have been cut and then revised. Completed *2./II. 1908.* Also, there is a copy of the song in Alban Berg's handwriting; it bears Schoenberg's stamped address: Wien XIII Gloriettegasse 43 (not far from Berg's apartment).

The first drafts of both songs are found in Sketchbook III (see below). Universal Edition, Vienna, has a fair copy of the second song. It is in ink, on an 18-lined double sheet (upright format, 26·5 × 34 cm.), and has corrections in pencils of various colours.

I. PUBLISHED WORKS

FIFTEEN VERSES FROM 'THE BOOK OF THE HANGING GARDENS' BY STEFAN GEORGE, Op. 15, for High Voice and Piano
Universal Edition, Vienna

The manuscript is pasted into a thin brown manila folder with gummed tape. It is written on 19 sheets of music paper (upright format, 26·5 × 34·5 cm.) which are bound with white thread. All 15 songs are written in ink and numbered with Roman numerals in blue pencil. Slight changes in dynamics, tempi and phrasing are marked either in blue pencil or in ordinary lead pencil. Undated; stamped address at the end of the manuscript and on the inside back cover: Arnold Schönberg Berlin-Zehlendorf, Wannseebahn, Machnowerchaussee, Villa Lepcke. The title is written in ink on the front of the cover: *Stefan George | Das Buch der hängenden Gärten | (Liederzyklus) | componiert | (für eine Singstimme und Klavier) | von | Arnold Schönberg*

SKETCHES AND DRAFTS

XV, 'Wir bevölkerten die abenddüstern Lauben' ('We lived among the evening-heavy leaves'); first draft in pencil, on a double sheet of 48-lined music paper cut horizontally in half (oblong format, 14·5 × 36·5 cm.). Completed *28./2. 1909*.

XIII, 'Du lehnest wider eine Silberweide' ('You lean against a silver willow-tree'); in pencil on the third page of a double sheet (format as in XV). Completed *27./9. 1908*.

On the first page of the manuscript of Song XV, there is a crossed-out draft of the first 8 measures of Song XIV. They are completely different from the final version. Also quite different is the additional sketch of the first 6 measures of the same song 'Sprich nicht immer von dem Laub' ('Speak not always of the leaves') which we find on p. 4 of the double sheet containing Song XIII; this sketch, however, is not crossed out. On the first page of the manuscript of Song XIII, the first 10 measures of Song XV are sketched; only the first 7 measures of this sketch are identical with the final version.

FIVE ORCHESTRAL PIECES, Op. 16
C. F. Peters, Frankfurt—London—New York

The first drafts of these five pieces, completely worked out in short-score form, were found in the legacy. Also, there are full scores, partly in Schoenberg's handwriting, partly in that of a copyist. These full scores are all written in ink on 30-lined music paper (upright format, 26·5 × 35 cm.), bound, and undated.

I. The short-score manuscript of the first piece is written in pencil on 2½ loose sheets of music paper (oblong format, 29 × 37 cm.; 24-lined). Completed *23. 5. 1909*. The first 5 (numbered) pages of the full-score copy were written by Schoenberg, the remaining 6 by Erwin Stein.

II. The short-score pencil manuscript of the second piece begins at cue No. 8 of the printed score; the first 56 measures are missing. This manuscript, undated, is written on a 24-lined sheet of music paper (oblong format, 29 × 37 cm.). The full-score ink copy (9 pages), made by Erwin Stein, bears a handwritten note by Schoenberg, also in ink: *Diese Abschriften hat Erwin*

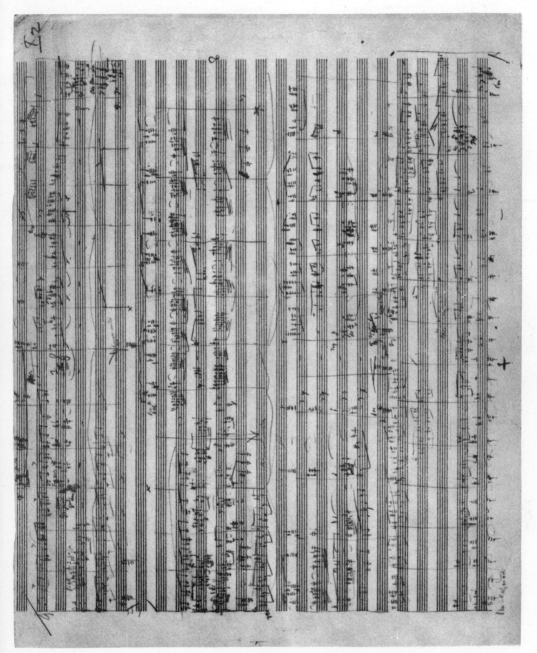

1. A page of short score from the first of the Five Pieces for orchestra. op. 16.

2. The beginning of the fourth of the Five Pieces for piano, op. 23.

Stein hergestellt, als ich einmal genötigt war, die Originalpartitur aus der Hand zu geben.—Sie sind unkorrigiert! Also vielleicht fehlerhaft. Arnold Schönberg. ('Erwin Stein prepared these copies when I once had to let the original score out of my hands. They are uncorrected! therefore possibly contain errors.') Page 9 is in Schoenberg's handwriting, except for a few parts which Stein continued from the preceding page.

III. Schoenberg wrote the short score of the third piece in pencil on a single sheet of music paper (oblong format, 28 × 35 cm.). The full score of 5 pages on 3 sheets of music paper (upright format, 26·5 × 35 cm.) was also copied by him. Also, a strip of music paper (14·5 × 36·5 cm.) bears a very sketchy version of the first few measures, noted first in ink, then in pencil. All this material is undated.

IV. The first draft of the fourth piece is written in pencil, in short-score form, on 4 loose strips of music paper (oblong format, 14 or 11·5 × 36·5 cm.). After the first 21 measures, the next 10 (only the principal voice of which is noted) are crossed out, and, with the indication *vi–de*, reformulated on another strip of paper. Completed *17./7. 1909.*

V. The short-score manuscript of the last piece is written in pencil on both sides of a sheet of music paper (oblong format, 29 × 37 cm.), on three staves throughout. Some of the indications of instrumentation are written in ink. Undated.

There are also two printed scores with numerous entries in red pencil concerning changes in instrumentation and additional metronome marks. One of these scores bears the notation *Reduktion für Standard-Orchester und andere Verbesserungen / September 1949, Arnold Schoenberg* ('Reduction for standard orchestra and other improvements . . .') In this reduced setting, the work was again published by Peters, as 'New Version'. Note on the last page of the score: *revidiert und reduziert zur normalen Besetzung September 1949 A. Sch.* ('revised and reduced to normal orchestral size. . . .')

Finally, the legacy contains another printed score, designated as *meine Vorlage für Kammerorchesterbearbeitung* ('my basis for an arrangement for chamber orchestra') (single woodwinds, piano, harmonium and string quintet). It bears the stamp of the 'Verein für musikalische Privataufführungen in Wien' (Society for Private Musical Performances in Vienna), and was used by the composer for the performance of the work in this Society, which was founded and directed by him (1919–1922). The third piece (stapled together with metal clamps in this score) was omitted from this performance, since, in it, the function of the orchestral tone-colour is an essential one.

The original manuscript of the score is with Edition Peters in New York. It consists of 26 loose sheets of music paper (upright format, 26·5 × 34 cm.), comprising 48 numbered pages of score. Two sheets are used as a cover, and bear the title of the work, written in Gothic characters. The manuscript, written throughout in ink, has the following note (in red) on p. 1: *was ich hier rot eingetragen, ist nachträgliche Verbesserung (betr. später: 8va, Vorzeichen, Lagenversetzung, ergänzende Tempoangaben, dyn. Ergänzungen, Angabe ob solo oder alle, vergessenen Wechsel der Schlüssel).* ('What I have inserted in red here are later corrections—e.g., octave-signs, accidentals, changes of register, additional indications of tempo and dynamics, indications of solo or tutti passages, omitted clef-changes.') At the ends of individual pieces are noted their completion-dates: I: *9./6. 1909*; II: *15./6. 1909*; III: *Steinakirchen 1./7. 1909*; IV: *18./7. 1909*; V: *Steinakirchen 11. August 1909.*

3

I. PUBLISHED WORKS

FACSIMILE PLATE I

From a diary of Schoenberg, *27. I. 1912*:

Letter from Peters, making an appointment with me for Wednesday in Berlin, in order to get to know me personally. Wants titles for the orchestral pieces—for publisher's reasons. Maybe I'll give in, for I've found titles that are at least possible. On the whole, unsympathetic to the idea. For the wonderful thing about music is that one can say everything in it, so that he who knows understands everything; and yet one hasn't given away one's secrets—the things one doesn't admit even to oneself. But titles give you away! Besides—whatever was to be said has been said, by the music. Why, then, words as well? If words were necessary they would be there in the first place. But art says more than words. Now, the titles which I may provide give nothing away, because some of them are very obscure and others highly technical. To wit:

  I. Premonitions (everybody has those)

  II. The Past (everybody has that, too)

  III. Chord-Colours (technical)

  IV. Peripetie (general enough, I think)

  V. The Obbligato (perhaps better the 'fully-developed' or the 'endless') Recitative.

However, there should be a note that these titles were added for technical reasons of publication and not to give a 'poetic 'content.

[The score was published in 1912. Later a 'Verzeichnis der Berichtigungen und Verbesserungen' ('List of corrections and improvements') of a 1922 revision was inserted. These changes, largely affecting dynamics, and the titles of the pieces, were subsequently incorporated in a 'Neue revidierte Ausgabe'. The reduction for normal orchestra was published posthumously in 1952.]

ERWARTUNG ('Expectation'), MONODRAMA, Op. 17
(Libretto by Marie Pappenheim)
Universal Edition, Vienna

The manuscript of the first draft is written in short-score form, in pencil, on 4 or 5 staves. Of the 6 double sheets of 24-lined music paper (oblong format, 29 × 36 cm.), bound with heavy thread, one is used as a cover, with the inscription *'Erwartung'* (*Monodram*). The pages of the score are numbered from 1 to 19 (with 12a instead of 13). The date of the beginning of the composition is noted at the upper right of p. 1: *27./8. 1909*. Completed *12./9. 1909*.

The legacy also includes the manuscript of a piano reduction prepared by Schoenberg, which begins with m. 6. It is written without the voice part, in pencil, on 14 numbered pages of 24-lined music paper (oblong format, 29 × 36·5 cm.; 4 double sheets). Also, there is the handwritten text of Marie Pappenheim, with many cuts and alterations in Schoenberg's handwriting, and several musical sketches at various points in the text.

The (originally bound) manuscript of the score is with Universal Edition in Vienna. It is written in ink on 34 sheets of 30-lined music paper (upright format, 26·5 × 34 cm.) comprising 67 numbered pages. Additions and corrections are inserted in coloured pencil or red ink. In addition to the title of the work written in India ink, the title-page contains exact directions for printing, written in red pencil. A separate, unnumbered sheet of music paper contains instructions for the music engraver.

On p. 16, mm. 142–147 (inclusive) have been pasted over. The same thing has been done on p. 29, m. 225, in the trombone, harp, and celesta parts. In addition, exact metronome markings have been added later, in green pencil. A slip of paper pasted on p. 41 bears the following notation in red ink: *Nachträgliche Zusätze oder Verbesserungen trage ich in meine Originalpartitur mit roter Tinte ein. Schönberg. Bitte die Anmerkung auf Seite 41 des Correktur Abzugs zu beachten und überall durchzuführen.* ('I am indicating later additions or corrections in red ink on my original score. Please note the remark on p. 41 of the proof sheets and observe it throughout.')

At the end, the score bears the signature *Arnold Schönberg Wien 4. Oktober 1909.*

From a letter of Schoenberg, *14. IV. 1930*, to Ernst Legal, the Intendant of the Kroll-Oper in Berlin, with detailed directions for the performance of the two operas 'Erwartung' and 'Die glückliche Hand':

. . . But what I can already say about questions of production is this:

The most important thing: I believe that you are not one of those stage directors who look at a piece only for the possibilities of making something quite different out of it. This is wrong, and never more wrong than when done to me, for I have an unusually precise picture of the staging in mind while composing.

In 'Erwartung', these are the greatest problems:

I. It is necessary always to see the woman in the forest, in order to understand her fear of it! for the whole piece can be understood as a nightmare. But, for that very reason, it must be a real forest, and not just an 'abstract' one! That kind of abstraction is gruesome, but not frightening.

II. In composing, I left hardly any time for the three scene-changes, so that they must happen on an 'open' stage.

III. On top of that, the background becomes important only in the final (fourth) scene; then the foreground must be empty, and everything that could impede the view must be removed.

While one can manage the first two changes by showing different views of the path which the woman must follow (simply by means of lighting), can have her enter from different sides, and, for the rest, can picture various sections of the forest simply by using a few practical objects which can be pushed or revolved, in the fourth scene the house in the background ought to become visible, while the forest disappears.

This problem is not easy to solve.—At home, I began to build a little model which represents the attempt to set up two or more little turntables on the stage, in such a way that, if they are turned all the way to the side, everything which might obstruct the view of the background is moved out of the way. Basically, this can be like the enclosed paper model. Here I have arranged two little turntables. But perhaps there can be several. Their size can be determined by the stage technician. Four sections are constructed differently. By having the turning-point off-centre, it is possible to get a narrow, completely empty area for the fourth scene. The turntables can be small enough to be operated by hand. What do you think of this idea?

— — — — — — — — —

I. PUBLISHED WORKS

In the 'Glückliche Hand', the following factors are especially important:

I. The play of coloured light. This calls for very strong lights and good colours; the stage-decoration must be so painted that it takes the colours!

II. The construction of the stage, and the stage-picture, must follow my directions exactly, for a thousand reasons; otherwise, nothing will work. Once, I prepared pictures of it, but I would have to hunt them out, now. In any case, I ought to receive your sketches in plenty of time to look them over.

III. I have also fixed the exact positions of the actors and the precise paths which they should follow on the stage. I am convinced that these directions must be observed exactly, if everything is to come out right.

IV. It is very difficult to illuminate the twelve faces in the first and fourth scenes, to have them disappear and reappear in a flash. This must be discussed further.

V. The mythical animal must be very large. The efforts to have it represented by a person, as was done in Vienna and Breslau, have been completely unsuccessful up till now. Especially at the end of the third scene, where the stone begins to glow, falls on the man and then turns into the mythical animal. Above all, no actor has been able to make such a big leap (about 2½–3 metres). Besides, a leap does not look like a fall. Here, the best idea would probably be to go back to my original description.

VI. At the end of the first scene, the curtain should tear. This has never even been indicated in any of the previous performances. My wife thinks that the illusion of this could be given by lighting. I think that a skilful upholsterer could work out something with a combination of Venetian-blind cords.

VII. Also at the end of the first scene, 'black veils' descend upon the man. This problem, too, was unsolved up till now.

VIII. The 'sun' in the second scene is also not easy to represent. It must be very low!

Now I think I have pointed out most of the spots which have caused difficulties up till now.

I am no friend of so-called 'stylized' decorations (what style?). In a picture, I like to see the good, practised hand of a painter who draws a straight line straight and does not take children's drawings or primitive art as a model. The objects and places in my dramas are part of the story and therefore one should be able to identify them as clearly as the notes. If the onlooker has to ask himself, as in a picture-puzzle ('Where is the hunter?') what the stage-setting means, he fails to hear part of the music. That may be pleasant for him, but it is not what I want.

DIE GLÜCKLICHE HAND ('The Hand of Fate'), DRAMA WITH MUSIC, Op. 18
Universal Edition, Vienna

The manuscript, which is in the Library of Congress, consists of 14 pages of score, written in ink (36·5 × 37·5 cm.). They are bound in a double sheet, on the second (inside) page of which the title *Die Glückliche Hand* is written in pencil. The date of beginning is marked *angefangen Freitag 9. September 1910*; the date of completion is marked and signed *18./XI. 1913 Arnold Schönberg*. The handwritten note (in ink) on an accompanying sheet of paper may be translated as follows:

The title 'Hand of Fate' is chiefly symbolic.

But once it showed its miraculous power in an astounding way.

When I was finishing the composition of this work, I lived in a house that stood alone in the middle of a large garden.

It was summer, and I had worked hard on a sultry, hot day.

The next morning, the gardener knocked and asked, 'Is this yours, Mr. Schönberg? I found it in the garden, about 15 metres from the house!'

It was this manuscript.

I had left it on my writing-table in the evening. Because of the heat, the windows were open. In the night, a thunderstorm broke out, and the manuscript was blown out of the window.

The traces of rain are to be seen on several pages.

I have wanted to write this down for a long time!

8. July 1948   Arnold Schoenberg

In the legacy, there are sketches for the text as well as for the music. Of the latter, there are 11 sheets of music paper (oblong format, 20·5×36·5 cm.), with sketches written in pencil throughout. These comprise the following:

(a) 4 sheets, numbered with red pencil from I to V (V on the reverse of IV), notated in short score on 5 to 8 staves, include mm. 166–200 (202);

(b) 1 sheet has mm. 224–245;

(c) a sketch shows the beginning of the final chorus (mm. 214 ff.) in an earlier version differing from the final form.

Furthermore, 6 measures of the beginning are notated in pencil on each of 2 double sheets (oblong format, 29×37 cm.); one of the sheets bears the date *11./10. 1908*. Also, there is a strip of music paper (14·5×37 cm.) on which three schematic ideas, each from 3 to 6 measures long, were jotted down. Alongside them are written the words *Thaten, Beschwichtigung, Schein—Glück*. ('Actions, Appeasement, Illusion—Fortune.')

Finally, there are two typewritten copies of the text with handwritten corrections, alterations and additions. One of these copies has the following handwritten note on the first page: *Dieses Maschinenschrift-Exemplar mit einigen Durchschlägen hat Mathilde hergestellt. Schönberg.* ('Mathilde prepared this typed copy with several carbon copies.' Mathilde was Schoenberg's first wife.) P. 5 contains a plan for the staging; on p. 2, some of the orchestration is indicated in the margin at one point in the text. In addition, one copy of the text bears the Vienna address (both handwritten and stamped) *Schönberg XIII Hietzinger Hauptstrasse 113*, as well as the stamped address: Berlin-Südende, Berlinerstrasse 17a, I. The manuscript fair copy of the score, which is with Universal Edition in Vienna, consists of 31 loose single and double sheets of 36-lined music paper (upright format, 27×35·5 cm.), and is written in ink. It comprises 60 pages of score numbered from 2 to 61. The last page bears a note as to date and place of completion: *Berlin-Südende 20. November 1913 Arnold Schönberg*. Signed corrections and additions were made in red ink, in red or blue pencil, in copying-ink pencil, or in ordinary lead pencil. On p. 27, a passage in mm. 112–114 (inclusive) has been pasted over; there are changes in the bass clarinet, first and second bassoons and contrabassoon, and the parts for four horns. This alteration is marked with a signed marginal note, *Instrumentationsänderung Schönberg*. On p. 49, there is a more detailed direction to the performers than that found in the published score. It should read: . . . *gesprochen werden sollen, so dass gleichsam Akkorde entstehen. Das gilt stets für die betreffende Phrase (auch wenn die Akkorde nicht mehr notiert sind) und wird durch 'unisono' aufgehoben.* ('. . . should be spoken so that quasi-chords are formed. This always applies to the phrase in question (even when the chords are no longer notated) until it is cancelled by the word "unisono".'). Finally, p. 1 contains numerous observations and directions to the music engraver, for the copying of parts, etc.; these are written partly in ink, partly in pencil.

SIX LITTLE PIANO PIECES, Op. 19
Universal Edition, Vienna

The manuscript of the 'Six Little Piano Pieces', Op. 19, is written in ink on 3 pages of a double sheet of 18-lined music paper (upright format, 26 × 34 cm.). The first 5 pieces are numbered with Roman numerals. The manuscript is dated *I. 19./2. 1911—II. 19./12. 1911*; a later addition in pencil reads, *wahrscheinlich auch 19./2. Sch.* ('probably also written on Feb. 19'). The third, fourth and fifth pieces are all dated *19./2. 1911*. The final, unnumbered piece is dated *17./6. 1911*.

In the legacy, there is also a copy of an edition of this work printed in Moscow in 1933.

HERZGEWÄCHSE ('Foliage of the Heart'), Op. 20
for high soprano, harp, celesta and harmonium (Maurice Maeterlinck)
Universal Edition, Vienna

The undated manuscript is written in black ink on 6 pages of 18-lined music paper (upright format, 26·5 × 34 cm.). Later (apparently for a performance from the manuscript) directions for the registration on the harmonium were added in red and blue pencil.

Universal Edition, Vienna, also possesses a manuscript of Op. 20. It is written in ink, on all 4 pages of a double sheet of 18-lined music paper (oblong format, 26·5 × 37 cm.), and bears the completion-date *9./12. 1911*.

> [The first edition was an autograph facsimile included in 'Der blaue Reiter', edited by Kandinsky and Marc, published by R. Piper & Co., Munich, 1912, reissued 1914.]

PIERROT LUNAIRE, Op. 21
for speaking voice, piano, flute (alternating with piccolo), clarinet (alternating with bass clarinet), violin (alternating with viola) and 'cello. 21 Melodramas after Albert Giraud, translated by O. E. Hartleben
Universal Edition, Vienna

The manuscript, in the possession of the Library of Congress (a photocopy is in the legacy), consists of 24 sheets of music paper, bound by Schoenberg himself. The pieces listed as Nos. 1–11 in the manuscript (which were then arranged in a different order in the published version) are written on paper of oblong format, 37 × 29 cm.; the remaining pieces are also written on paper of oblong format, but larger (36·5 × 34·5 cm.). Nos. 1, 3, 4 and 5 are written in pencil, all the others in ink. The 13th, 23rd and 24th sheets of paper are blank.

The musical manuscript itself comprises 37 pages (inaccurately numbered 38 by Schoenberg). In addition, there are the title-page and two other pages. On one of these, the 21 pieces are listed in their order of composition, with indication of their page-numbers in the manuscript; on the other, the order in which they were finally published is listed, along with their division into three sections of seven pieces each, their page-numbers in the manuscript, and the instrumentation of each piece. Schoenberg has given the dates of composition for each piece. From these, we learn that the entire work (with the exception of 'Kreuze', which was not completed until July 9) was composed between March 12 and May 30, 1912, and that most of the pieces (14) were written one a day.

The dates, noted in Schoenberg's own handwriting, are as follows:

1. 'Gebet an Pierrot' ('Prayer to Pierrot'): *angefangen 12./3. 1912 || beendet 12./3. 1912*
2. 'Valse de Chopin': *7./5. 1912*
3. 'Dandy': *begonnen 1./4. 1912*, completed *2./4. 1912*
4. 'Colombine': *20/4. 1912*
5. 'Mondestrunken' ('Moon-Drunk'): *17./4. 1912–29./4.*
6. 'Rote Messe' ('Red Mass'): *22./4. 1912–24./4. 1912*
7. 'Parodie': *4./5. 1912*
8. 'Der kranke Mond' ('The Sick Moon'): *18./4. 1912–18./4. 1912*
9. 'Die blasse Wäscherin' ('The Pale Washerwoman'): *18.4. 1912–18./4. 1912*
10. 'Enthauptung' ('Decapitation'): *23./5.*
11. 'Nacht' ('Night'): *9./5. 1912–21./5. 1912*
12. 'Serenade': *25./4.*
13. 'Heimfahrt' ('Homeward Journey'): *9./5. 1912*
14. 'Gemeinheit' ('A Dirty Trick'): *26./4.–6./6. 1912*
15. 'Kreuze' ('Crosses'): *27./4.–9./7. 1912*
16. 'O alter Duft' ('O Fragrance Old'): *30./5. 1912–30./5. 1912*
17. 'Mondfleck' ('A Fleck of Moonlight'): *28./5. 1912*
18. 'Madonna': *9./5.*
19. 'Raub' ('Theft'): *9./5. 1912*
20. 'Heimweh' ('Nostalgia'): *5./5. 1912–22./5. 1912*
21. 'Galgenlied' ('Gallows Song'): *12.5.*

In the possession of Universal Edition, Vienna, there is an additional manuscript, bound in thin brown pasteboard, accompanied by an undated slip with the signature of Felix Greissle, Schoenberg's son-in-law: 'nur "teilweise" Autograph' ('autograph only "in part"'). The title-page is written in Schoenberg's hand. On the 43 sheets of music paper (some of which have become loosened in the cover) 85 pages have been numbered; of these, 73 have been written on. 'Kreuze' (No. 14), however, is written on 3 tipped-in sheets (Nos. 1–4 of 6 numbered pages). The first 2 of these sheets are in upright format (25·5 × 33 cm.); the third is also in upright format (27 × 34 cm.). Of the 43 numbered sheets of music paper, some are in upright format (26·5 × 34 cm.), others in oblong format (34·5 × 26·5 cm.). The entire manuscript is written in black ink; only No. 4 ('Die blasse Wäscherin') has a piano reduction, written below the score, in red ink. Occasional corrections or additions have been made in red pencil or copying-ink pencil. Mm. 16–19 (inclusive) of 'Valse de Chopin' (p. 16) are pasted over with a new version; the same thing has been done to m. 19 in 'Heimweh' (p. 55).

Nos. 5, 7 and 11, which are signed, are unquestionably autographs; all the others are probably so, with the following exceptions: No. 6, No. 8 (with autograph corrections), the postlude to No. 13 from m. 4 onwards, the first 4 pages of No. 14, at least the first 18 measures of No. 15, and the transition to No. 18. These are in another's handwriting. The manuscript also contains two stamped addresses in Berlin, where the work was composed: Berlin-Südende, Berlinerstrasse 17a/I, and Berlin-Zehlendorf, Wannseebahn, Machnowerchaussee, Villa Lepcke.

In the legacy, there is also a copy (not in the composer's handwriting) of Giraud's original 50 poems in the German translation; from these, Schoenberg made his choice. The first musical ideas are sketched in the margins of several poems.

From a letter of Schoenberg, *31. August 1940*, to the conductor Fritz Stiedry and his wife, the actress Erika Wagner (formerly of the 'Volkstheater' in Vienna), who had already performed the speaking part of 'Pierrot Lunaire' under Erwin Stein in Europe:

We must thoroughly freshen up the speaking part, too—at least that, for this time I intend to catch perfectly that light, ironical, satirical tone in which the piece was actually conceived. Then, too, times and ideas have changed a lot, so that what might have sounded Wagnerian or at worst Tchaikovskian to us then would remind us of Puccini, Lehar or worse today. It is hard to prepare this in two weeks so that it is worthy of being immortalized on records as the authentic performance.

(The above-mentioned recording was made and released by Columbia Records, U.S.A.)

Postscript to a letter from Schoenberg to Daniel Ruyneman, of the Secretariat of the Nederlandse Vereniging voor Hedendagse Muziek, Amsterdam; *23. Juli 1949*:

I note with pleasure that you intend to engage Frau Marya Freund for the performance. I should merely like to emphasize that none of these poems is meant to be sung, but must be spoken without fixed pitch.

From a letter of the composer, *15.2. 1949*, to the conductor Hans Rosbaud:

I do not know whether you are familiar with the records that I made of it. In some respects—tempo, presentation of mood, and above all the playing of the instrumentalists—they are really good, even very good. They are not so good with respect to the balance of instruments and recitation. I was a little annoyed by the idea of overemphasis on the speaker—who, after all, never sings the theme, but, at most, speaks against it, while the themes (and everything else of musical importance) happen in the instruments. Perhaps, because I was annoyed, I reacted a little too violently, out of contrariness, and forgot that one must, after all, be able to hear the speaker. So now she is really drowned out in several places. That should not be. Now, in the concert-hall this is somewhat easier, for one can either place the speaker somewhat nearer to the audience or move the instruments somewhat farther away. This contributes a great deal to the distinctness of the speaking part, and also gives the instruments their due, so that the music can really come into its own. It is not very easy to achieve this, but I really do believe that the balance can be perfect.

FOUR SONGS, Op. 22, for Voice and Orchestra
Universal Edition, Vienna

The manuscripts of the four songs are written on loose sheets of music paper.

1. 'Alle welche dich suchen' ('All who seek thee') is written in ink, in short-score form, on 1 page of 18-lined music paper (upright format, 26·5×34·5 cm.). The heading reads:

A. WORKS WITH OPUS NUMBERS

Aus dem Stundenbuch von Rainer Maria Rilke Seite 59/30. XI. 1914 ('From Rainer Maria Rilke's "Book of Hours", p. 59 . . .'). Note of completion: *Arnold Schönberg 3./XII. 1914.*

2. 'Mach mich zum Wächter deiner Weiten' ('Make me the watcher of thy distances') is written in ink, in short-score form, on 2 pages of 18-lined music paper (oblong format, 34·5 × 26·5 cm.). Heading: *Rilke, Stundenbuch Seite 80*; at the upper right of the page, the date *3./XII. 1914*; completed *1./I. 1915*. There is a pasted-on slip of paper showing which instruments are used in which measures, and the number of staves needed. (N.B.: here, for the first time, Schoenberg used his short-score form in the printed version.)

3. 'Vorgefühl' ('Premonition'). The heading of this third song reads *Rilke, Buch der Bilder | 19.VII. 1916* ('Book of Pictures . . .'). It is written in short-score form, in black and violet ink, on a page of 24-lined music paper (oblong format, 29 × 36·5 cm.). Date of completion: *28./VII. 1916 Arnold Schönberg.*

There is a slip of paper pasted on the manuscript, with notations similar to those found in the preceding song.

4. 'Seraphita' (Ernest Dowson, translated by Stefan George). The manuscript of this song is written in short-score form, in ink (with the exception of a few measures at the entrance of the voice, which are in pencil). It is on 6 sheets of music paper of varying sizes, which are numbered in blue pencil and held together with red silk cord. Sheet I: 24-lined paper, oblong format, 34·5 × 29 cm.; Sheet II: 18-lined, upright format, 34·5 × 26·5 cm.; Sheets III, IV and V: 17-lined, oblong format, 36·5 × 19 cm.; Sheet VI: 20-lined, oblong format, 33 × 27 cm. Completed *6./X. 1913.*

Schoenberg rearranged these separate, unnumbered manuscripts in chronological order for publication, as follows: 1. 'Seraphita'; 2. 'Alle welche dich suchen'; 3. 'Mach mich zum Wächter deiner Weiten'; 4. 'Vorgefühl'.

There is also a sketch for 'Seraphita' written on a page of 28-lined music paper (upright format, 26·5 × 34·5 cm.), begun in pencil and continued in ink. The sheet is headed *Seraphita von Dowson*. This sketch contains the complete voice part, followed by a first draft of the orchestral introduction which differs from the final version. The orchestration is indicated.

The copies of the four songs in the possession of Universal Edition, Vienna, are not in the composer's handwriting, with the exception of 'Seraphita'.

'Alle welche dich suchen' comprises 4 pages written in ink on 3 bound sheets of music paper (upright format, 26·5 × 34 cm.). Date and place of completion: *Berlin-Südende, 8. Jänner 1915 Arnold Schönberg.*

'Mach mich zum Wächter deiner Weiten' comprises 7 pages written in ink on 5 sheets of music paper (upright format, 26·5 × 34 cm.). Date and place of completion: *Berlin-Südende, 14. Jänner 1915 Arnold Schönberg.*

'Vorgefühl' consists of 6 pages written in ink on 5 sheets (upright format, 26·5 × 34 cm.). Date and place of completion: *Arnold Schönberg, Wien 1. November 1916.*

The manuscript of 'Seraphita' consists of 4 bound sheets of 24-lined music paper (upright format, 26·5 × 34 cm.); it is written in ink. M. 44 has been pasted over, in the clarinet parts. The designation Ӈ ('Hauptstimme') for the principal voice has been added later, in blue pencil. Completed and signed *9./XI. 1913 Arnold Schönberg.*

All four songs bear the stamped address: Wien XIII Gloriettegasse 43.

I. PUBLISHED WORKS

FIVE PIANO PIECES, Op. 23
Wilhelm Hansen, Copenhagen

The first drafts of the third, fourth and fifth pieces are found in Sketchbook V (see below).

The legacy contains fair copies, in ink, of the first, second and fourth pieces. The first is written on a 12-lined double sheet (upright format, 24·5 × 34 cm.). It bears no beginning date; the date of completion is marked *9. VII. vollendet Juli 1920*, and the stamped address Mödling bei Wien has been added. The second piece, on a 14-lined single sheet, also bears the date of completion only: *27./VII. 1920 Arnold Schönberg*. The fourth piece is written on a double sheet (upright format, 26·5 × 34 cm.; 14-lined). Date of beginning (written in pencil): *26./7. 1920*; date of completion (written in ink): *13./II. 1923 Arnold Schönberg*. On the first page, two measures have been crossed out and replaced by a new version.

The manuscript of the fourth piece comes from a period when Schoenberg was about to discover and formulate his 'method of composition with twelve tones related only to one another'. The preceding phases were already governed by the idea of the so-called 'Grundgestalt' (basic set), which was the germ from which an entire piece was to be developed. These basic sets did not yet consist of all twelve tones, but of a smaller or larger number (cf. theme of the Variations in Op. 24), or of motifs which, together with the entire basic set, were to be as obligatory throughout the course of the piece in question as the 'twelve-tone row' was later to become. This is especially clear in the manuscript of the fourth piece. We see the basic set in the first two measures; Schoenberg has outlined its various complexes of motifs and intervals in pencils of various colours.

FACSIMILE PLATE II

In the unclassified pile of loose sketches (see above, Introduction), the Danish musicologist Jan Maegaard found, on a more careful inspection, a sheet dated *8./7. 1920* with sketches for the second piece which differ from the final version.

Schoenberg gave a copy of Op. 23, along with sketches for the 'Serenade', Op. 24 (see below), to the Prussian State Library (now German State Library) at its request. We learn this from the letter of thanks written by the director of the Music Division of the (then) Prussian State Library on July 30, 1925. This copy of Op. 23 is in the composer's handwriting; it is bound in score-paper, with wrapping-twine. The title-page, written in ink, reads as follows: *Fünf Klavierstücke / opus 23 / von / Arnold Schönberg*; on the lower margin is written *II. Exemplar* ('Second copy'). On the inside of the title-page are pasted the typed instructions ('*Anmerkungen*') for the performer.

The music manuscript itself is written in ink, and comprises 10 sheets of music paper (upright format, 26·5 × 35 cm.; 16-lined), i.e., 20 numbered pages, the last of which is blank. The third, fourth and fifth pieces contain initialed corrections (wrong notes, omitted accidentals) in red ink; some slurs, tempo markings, rests, etc., have also been added. The fifth piece has pencilled annotations on the lower margins of pp. 16–17; these have to do with accentuation, and refer back to the directions pasted on the inside of the title-page.

The following dates are given at the ends of the individual pieces:

I. 2. *Abschrift* ('Second copy') / *18. IV. 1923 / Arnold Schönberg*
    At the bottom of p. 1, in pencil: *II Exemplar*

2. *abgeschrieben* | *am 30.*|*IV. 1923* | ('copied on April 30, 1923') *Arnold Schönberg*
3. *abgeschrieben* | *17. III. 1923* | *Arnold Schönberg*
4. *abgeschrieben 14.*|*III. 1923* | *Arnold Schönberg*
5. Heading: *Walzer*
   Note of completion: *Arnold Schönberg* | *II. Abschrift* | *14. III. 1923*

SERENADE, Op. 24

for clarinet, bass clarinet, mandolin, guitar, violin, viola, 'cello and baritone voice (4th movement: Sonnet of Petrarch)

Wilhelm Hansen, Copenhagen

In the legacy, there is only a photocopy of the manuscript of the full score; it is loose in a pasteboard cover. On the cover, Schoenberg wrote in green pencil: *Photographie des Serenaden-Manuskripts. Das Original habe ich Dr. Schwarzmann geschenkt* ('Photograph of the manuscript of the Serenade. I gave the original to Dr. Schwarzmann'). (The world première took place on May 2, 1924, before invited guests in the home of Dr. Norbert Schwarzmann, Vienna I, Krugerstrasse 17; the first public performance was on July 20, 1924, in Donaueschingen.) This manuscript which was given to Dr. Schwarzmann has not been found up till now.

The photocopy (white on black) comprises 62 pages of score. On the first and last pages, there is a stamped address: Arnold Schönberg Mödling bei Wien Bernhardgasse 6; on the last page, there is a note of completion: *Abschrift vollendet 27.*|*IV. 1923 Arnold Schönberg*. The photocopy shows subsequent handwritten corrections, either indicated in the score itself or written on the backs of the photocopied pages.

The legacy also includes a large printed conductor's score (bound in bright blue canvas by the composer) which bears numerous corrections of printer's errors, in red or black ink or in pencil.

Large portions of a first draft of the work are found in Sketchbook V (see below). The first sketches for the Sonnet, in which the final form of the row does not yet appear (the Sonnet is the only movement of the work which uses a twelve-tone row) were found by the musicologist Jan Maegaard in a little sketchbook from the year 1922, which turned up in the unclassified pile of sketches (see Introduction).

A manuscript of the *short score* of Op. 24 is in the possession of the Library of Congress. It comprises the following:

(1) A typed title-page, listing the movements.

(2) Typed directions for performance (underlined by hand at various points) on the back of the title-page ('Anmerkungen auf *der Innenseite des Titelblatts der Serenade*'); also, a short typed addition to these directions.

(3) Forty-five pages of short score, notated on 3–5 staves, with complete indications for the instrumentation. The third movement is written in pencil on four pages (oblong format, 26·5 × 34·5 cm.); everything else is written in ink (on paper of oblong format, 20·5 × 37 cm.). Occasional improvements, cuts, and (always initialled) corrections of wrong notes give rise to the supposition that this is the first draft of the short score after the incomplete one in Sketchbook V. According to its dating, it immediately precedes the manuscript of the full

score described above. Accompanying the short-score manuscript is a programme for the performance of May 2, 1924 (at I. Krugerstrasse 17—Dr. Schwarzmann's Vienna address; see above); this concert included the 'Serenade' followed by 'Pierrot Lunaire'.

The seven movements of the short-score manuscript in the Library of Congress are numbered with Arabic numerals.

1. Above the tempo-indication at the beginning, there is the following note: *angefangen 27. IX. 1921*. At the end of this movement, the date and place of completion are noted: *beendet 6.X. 1921 | Arnold Schönberg | Traunkirchen*.

2. Note of completion: *Arnold Schönberg | Abschrift vollendet 20./III. 1923*. (The number 20 is hard to read.)

3. *Abschrift vollendet am 19./III. 1923 | Arnold Schönberg*.

4. At the beginning, in the right-hand margin: *Petrarca Sonett 217*. The first two words of the tempo indication *Nicht zu rasch* ('Not too fast') are crossed out. Note of completion: *Abgeschrieben am 16./April 1923 | Schönberg*.

5. Below m. 122 is an initialed correction of wrong notes, with the remark *siehe I. Niederschrift* (probably the draft contained in Sketchbook V). Note of completion: *Abschrift beendet 18./IV. 1923*.

6. Heading: *Lied (ohne Worte)* ('Song Without Words'). Note of completion: *abgeschrieben* (day and month illegible, possibly 19. IV.) *1923*.

7. Heading: *Finale*. Mm. 45–148 (inclusive) are blank. In each measure, the number of the corresponding measure in the first movement is written: e.g., m. 45 bears the number 33 (from the first movement), etc. Thus, the Finale proves to be an extensive reprise of the first movement, with the exception of mm. 1–44, which are new, as are mm. 149–154 (a reminiscence of the sixth movement). Measures 155–163 are again blank, bearing only the numbers (137–145) of the corresponding measures in the first movement. This last movement is undated and unsigned.

SKETCHES

In the legacy there are 26 small and large sheets of music paper bearing sketches; there are also 9 sheets with fair copies of parts of the score. These are written in ink; the sketches are written partly in ink, partly in pencil. The fair copies include, among other material, 69 measures of the third movement, 26 measures of the first movement, and 29 measures of 'Tanzschritte' ('Dance-Steps', the fifth movement). A sketch with the beginning of the first movement bears the date *27./IX. 1921*: on other sheets are found the dates *6./VIII. 1920, 3./8. 1920, 27./IX. 1921*.

The German State Library (Berlin, Unter den Linden) possesses 5 sheets of sketches for Op. 24, written in pencil, numbered from 1 to 5, and bound with wrapping-twine. Schoenberg gave them to the library (then the Prussian State Library) in 1925, along with a copy in his own handwriting of Op. 23 (see above). These are all sketches for the second and fifth movements in short-score form. Sheets 1 and 2 (oblong format, 35·5 × 13 cm.) have been used on one side only; page (sheet) 1 bears the date *6.VIII. 1920*, written at the upper left of the page in green pencil. Sheet 3: *Menuetto*. Several places have been traced over in ink. Sheet 4, side 1: *Menuett Trio 1*; on the lower right of the page: *folgt Trio II*. Sheet 4, side 2: upper left-hand margin: *1) Menuett/8.10. 1921*. Sheets 3 and 4 are in oblong format, 35 × 20·5 cm. Sheet 5, side 1 (oblong format, 33·5 × 24 cm.): at upper left: *Menuett/Trio II*; at lower right: *Fortsetzung/ siehe Skizzenbuch / 1922/1923 / Seite 18* ('For the continuation see sketchbook of 1922–1923, p. 18') (see below, Sketchbook V).

SUITE FOR PIANO, Op. 25
Universal Edition, Vienna

The first draft of 4 of the 6 movements—Minuet, Musette, Gavotte and Gigue—is included in Sketchbook V (see below). A single sheet of 20-lined music paper (upright format, 26 × 34·5 cm.) probably gives the first draft of the Prelude; it is written on one side of the paper, in pencil. There is no heading; on the upper left-hand side of the page is a stamped address (Arnold Schönberg Traunkirchen No. 29 Villa Josef, Ob.-Öst.). At the upper right is written *Traunkirchen 24. VII. 1921* (the word *Traunstein*, written above, is crossed out). At the end of the page is written *Traunkirchen 29. Juli 1921 Schönberg*. The four pieces of the sketchbook are undated.

A cover made of music paper, with the inscription *Suite für Klavier opus 25*, contains (with the exception of the Intermezzo, which was found separately) copies of the movements in the composer's own hand. They are written in ink on 12-lined music paper (upright format, 15 × 34 cm.) and bound with thin wrapping-twine. Here, the date given at the end of the Prelude is *Traunkirchen Juli 1921*. The Gavotte is undated; in the next-to-last measure there is an initialled correction with the note: *g(statt ges) siehe Skizzenbuch* ('G instead of G flat—see sketchbook'). Note at the end of the Musette: *abgeschrieben 18.III./ 1923 Arnold Schönberg*. This date probably applies to the copies of the two preceding pieces as well. The Minuet and Trio are signed: *copiert 22./III. 1923 Arnold Schönberg*. The copy of the Gigue breaks off with m.12. All the copies contain initialled corrections made subsequently in red ink.

The separate copy of the Intermezzo (upright format, 26·5 × 35·5 cm.; in ink) bears the following note of completion: *abgeschrieben 26./II. 1923 Arnold Schönberg*. The date *Traunkirchen 25./7. 1921* (added later: *Juli*) found on the upper right of page 1, with the first few measures of the Intermezzo following it, has nothing to do with this copy. Presumably, Schoenberg used a sheet that had already been written on for his copy. This note does indicate that the Intermezzo was composed in July, 1921; such indications are lacking for the other movements, since—as mentioned above—their first drafts in Sketchbook V are undated.

Also, the row-charts and sketches with various combinations of the row still exist, as do the typed instructions to the music engraver.

The author may add this personal note. It must have been about the time of the composition of the Prelude (end of July, 1921) when Schoenberg told me, during a stroll in Traunkirchen, 'Today I have discovered something which will assure the supremacy of German music for the next hundred years.' It was the method of composition with twelve tones related only to one another. Considering the date of the Prelude, it seems uncertain whether this or (as previously believed) the Waltz from Op. 23 (see above) is the first twelve-tone composition.

I. PUBLISHED WORKS

A copy of Op. 25 in the composer's own handwriting is with Universal Edition in Vienna. The 6 movements are written individually in ink on loose sheets of 14-lined music paper (upright format, 26·5 × 34 cm.). There are 21 numbered pages in all. At least in the case of the last 4 movements, it is evident from the notes at the end—*abgeschrieben 5. III* (or *27. III, 5. III, 8. III,* respectively), signed *Arnold Schönberg,* that these are copies. Diagonally across the title-page (on which the names of the 6 movements are given) is written in pencil: *Wo sind meine Anmerkungen?? Schönberg* ('Where are my directions?...'). (These 'Anmerkungen' were the directions to the player; see also below.) There is also a stamped address: Mödling bei Wien Bernhardgasse 6.* Page 2 bears the following note in red pencil: *Ich bitte dringendst, mir mitzuteilen, wer es sich herausgenommen hat, an meinem Manuskript Änderungen, die deutlich gegen meine Absicht gerichtet sind, vorzunehmen! Arnold Schönberg.* ('I demand to know who has taken it upon himself to make alterations in my manuscript which go exactly contrary to my intentions!')

QUINTET, Op. 26
for flute, oboe, clarinet, bassoon and horn
Universal Edition, Vienna

Sketchbook V (see pp. 128–130) contains, on pp. 41–113 inclusive, not only sketches but also the first draft of the work. The first sketches are dated *14./IV. 1923*; the first movement was begun on *21./IV. 1923*, the last movement completed on *26./VII. 1924*.

The fair copy of the score is in the possession of Universal Edition, Vienna. It is written in ink on 40 loose sheets of 18-lined music paper (upright format, 27 × 35·5 cm.), comprising 79 numbered pages. Corrections and additions (signed) have been made in ordinary lead pencil, red pencil, and black or red ink.

Page 1, upper right: *angefangen am 1. Mai 1923.*
Page 18: *Abschrift beendet 9.6. 1923 Arnold Schönberg.*
Page 48: the top voice in m. 44 has been pasted over.
Page 55: beside the flat preceding the *d* (second quaver in the flute) Schoenberg wrote: *das ist nicht meine Hand!!! Schönberg* ('that is not my handwriting!!!...').
Page 79: *Abschrift beendet am 27. August 1924 Arnold Schönberg.*

Besides the above-mentioned sketches in Sketchbook V, the legacy also contains sketches on 3 sheets of music paper (oblong format, 20·5 × 34·5 cm.); two of these pages are written in pencil, one in ink.

FOUR PIECES FOR MIXED CHORUS, Op. 27
Universal Edition, Vienna

1. 'Unentrinnbar' ('Inescapable'; text by composer).

The first draft is written in black ink on 2 pasted-together strips of 10-lined music paper (12 × 34·5 cm.). Date of completion: *30.9. 1925.* The composition is written on the first and third pages; the second contains the basic row together with its inversion transposed a fifth

* See Addendum No. 2, p. 77.

lower, as well as the retrograde forms. Dynamic markings have been added later in red ink or green pencil. In the left-hand margin of the first strip of music paper, Schoenberg's text is written in ink. It contains some trifling corrections and is probably also a first draft.

2. 'Du sollst nicht, du musst' ('Thou Shalt Not, Thou Must'; text by composer).

The first draft is written in pencil on 2 loose sheets of music paper (oblong format, 19×34·5 cm.). The dynamic markings are in black ink. Date of beginning: *16./X. 1925*; date of completion: *17./X. 1925*. The words of the text are written down only here and there, as though for purposes of orientation; they were obviously scribbled very rapidly. The complete text, typed on a single sheet of paper, is pasted to the side margin of the music paper; also, a strip of music paper (4 staves), with the row and its mirror-forms, is pasted to the upper margin. Two measures (3 and 4) have been crossed out and rewritten.

3. 'Mond und Menschen' ('Moon and Mankind'; by Tschan-Jo-Su, from Hans Bethge's 'Die chinesische Flöte').

The manuscript, written alternately in pencil and ink, is a first draft. It is written on 2 sheets of music paper (oblong format, 19×34·5 cm.), which are pasted together with the typed sheet of text. Date of beginning: *14./X*; date of completion: *16./X. 1925 Arnold Schönberg*.

Several measures are crossed out and rewritten. Later, initialled corrections have been added in red ink.

Nos. 1–3 of this set are a cappella choruses. However, we now come to:

4. 'Der Wunsch des Liebhabers' ('The Lover's Wish'; by Hung-So-Fan, from Hans Bethge's 'Die chinesische Flöte'), with ensemble of mandolin, clarinet, violin and 'cello.

The manuscript is written in score-form, in ink, on 3 double sheets (oblong format, 25·5× 34·5 cm.), comprising 9 pages; it is bound with white wrapping-twine. There are several slight corrections in red ink. Date of completion: *10./XI. 1925 Arnold Schönberg*.

In addition, there are sketches on 7 sheets and strips of music paper.

The manuscript fair copy of Op. 27 is in the possession of Universal Edition, Vienna. The first three pieces are written in ink, each on a separate 16-lined double sheet (upright format, 26·5×34 cm.); they display minor, signed additions and corrections in red or black ink and green pencil. The fourth piece is written in ink on 7 loose sheets of 24-lined music paper (upright format, 26·5×34 cm.), comprising 13 pages of manuscript. The cover, a double sheet of music paper, is stamped with the Mödling address, to which has been added in pencil *derzeit Berlin Charlottenburg Steinplatz 2* ('present address: Berlin . . .').

No. 1 comprises 3 pages. Date of completion: *30./IX. 1925*.
No. 2, also 3 pages; signed date of completion: *Arnold Schönberg 17./X. 1925*.
No. 3, 4 pages; signed date of completion: *16.X. 1925 Arnold Schönberg*.
No. 4, unsigned and undated, has only the stamped Mödling address.

With this manuscript belong 3 bound sheets of lined writing-paper (21·5×28 cm.). On the first page, there is a pen-and-ink sketch for the cover design. There is also a note in pencil: *Diese . . . (illegible) . . . umfasst 3 Blätter und enthält u.a. 1. die Gesangstexte 2. und die Vorbemerkungen 3. ferner: Inhaltsverzeichnis 4. und Innentitel.* ('This . . . contains 3 pages which include, among other things, 1. the texts of the songs, 2. the introductory remarks, 3. furthermore, the table of contents and 4. inside title-page.') Another pencilled note, also written diagonally across the page, pertains to the signed instructions for the engraving of the music. Next to a correction made by somebody else on this third page—'Ausführenden' instead of 'Spieler'—Schoenberg has written in red ink: *Diese Verbesserung ist zwar gut. Aber ich bitte doch in Hinkunft in meinem Manuskript keine Änderungen vorzunehmen, sondern das irgendwo anders anzumerken. Ein Manuskript ist immer nur vom Autor; mit seinen Vorzügen und Fehlern. Sch.* 'This correction is good, granted. But in future please do not undertake *any* alterations in my manuscript—rather, note them down somewhere else. A manuscript is always by the author *only*—with its merits and mistakes'.

THREE SATIRES for Mixed Chorus, Op. 28
Universal Edition, Vienna

1. 'Am Scheideweg' ('At the Crossroads'; text by composer, as in all these Satires).

The first draft of the manuscript is written in pencil on a half-sheet of 15-lined music paper (oblong format, 25·5 × 34·5 cm.). In the upper left-hand corner, the text is written in ink, and followed by the date of completion: *12. XI. 1925 Arnold Schönberg.* On the back of the page are sketches.

There is also a manuscript 'Tonal oder atonal?' (first line of text; title later altered to 'Am Scheideweg'). This is on a single sheet of music paper (oblong format, 26 × 35 cm.). Date at upper right: *12./XI. 1925.* The measures (1–18) are written on 4 staves, and numbered in green pencil. Handwritten text at upper left of page.

2. 'Vielseitigkeit' ('Versatility').

The manuscript is on a 20-lined sheet of music paper (upright format, 27 × 35 cm.). The heading, and the date of completion (*fertiggemacht 31./XII. 1925*), as well as the middle voices, are written in ink; the outer voices are in pencil. With this are 4 sheets of sketches, written on one side of the page, partly in ink and partly in pencil; 2 of these differ from the final form and are obviously first drafts.

Nos. 1 and 2 are 'a cappella' choruses.

3. 'Der neue Klassizismus' (a little cantata for mixed chorus, accompanied by viola, 'cello and piano).

The manuscript consists of 9 sheets of 18-lined music paper (used on both sides; oblong format, 25·5 × 34·5 cm.), bound in a cover of doubly folded brown wrapping-paper. Begun *13./XI. 25. Sch.*; finished *22. XII. 1925 Arnold Schönberg* (this note is continued in ink: *fertiggemacht 30./XII. 1925 Schönberg*).

To judge by these dates, the parts of the manuscript written in ink were most likely finished on December 30, 1925. This refers especially to the instrumental accompaniment from m. 113 to the end; the choral parts are written entirely in pencil, and only occasionally traced over in ink. Throughout the manuscript we find notes of the row-forms and transpositions used. There is also a row-chart, drawn up in ink on a piece of thin cardboard (upright format, 11 × 37 cm.).

There are 11 pages of sketches for this piece. They are noted on half-sheets of music paper (oblong format, 26 × 34·5 cm.). One sheet bears the notation: *noch mit Blinddarm begonnen 13./XI. 1925*; another sheet, *15./XI. 1925!! in der Nacht!* These were written in hospital, before and after an operation for appendicitis ('Blinddarm').

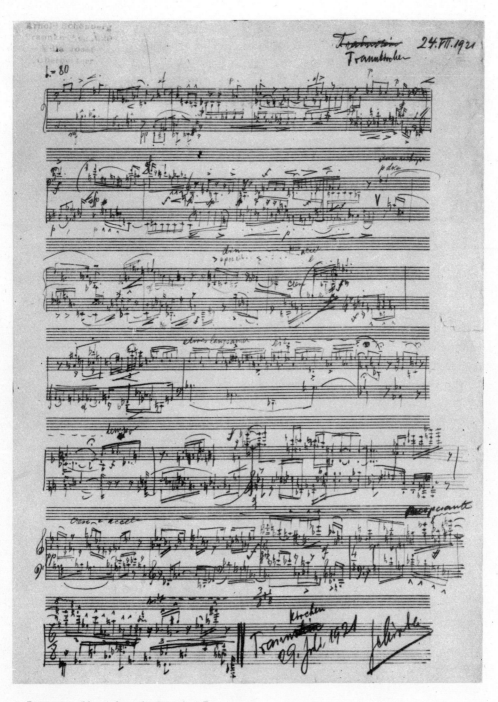

3. Präludium (No. 1) from the Suite for piano, op. 25.

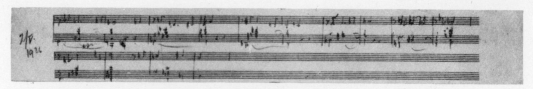

4. First draft of the theme of the Variations for Orchestra, op. 31.

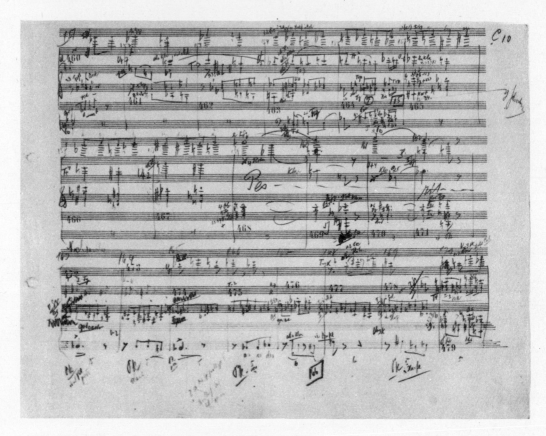

5. A page of short score from the Variations for Orchestra, op. 31.

A. WORKS WITH OPUS NUMBERS

'Anhang' (Appendix) to the Satires.

1. 'Ein Spruch und zwei Variationen über ihn' ('A Proverb and Two Variations on it')
The following materials were found:

(a) A manuscript fair copy, in ink, written on the first 2 pages of a double sheet (upright format, 27×35·5 cm.); a piece of paper with the typed commentary is pasted on. Undated.

(b) A manuscript first draft, written in ink on paper of oblong format (25·5×34·5 cm.), contains the first canon. Date of completion, written in pencil: *9./12.25 Sch.* On the left-hand side of the page, above the canon: *Etwas einfach* ('Rather simple'). Under this is the third canon. It is written in score-form, in ink, and headed: *Nicht ganz strenger Satz; aber immerhin: ein ganz genauer Doppelkanon.* ('Counterpoint not quite strict; but for all that a very exact double canon.') There is a crossed-out passage from the middle of the third measure to the middle of the sixth; underneath this, a somewhat different version has been added in pencil.

(c) The manuscript of the first draft of the second and third canons, in score-form, is written in pencil (text in ink) on 2 pasted-together sheets (oblong format, 31·5×34·5 cm.). At the end of each canon Schoenberg wrote *10./12.25 Sch.*

Below this is another improved draft of the canon No. 3 (in score-form). This bears the note: *nicht ganz rein, aber immerhin ein Doppelkanon* ('not quite strict, but anyway a double canon'). Next to this is a note in ink: *folgt noch eine verbesserte Form / fertiggemacht 1./I. 1926* ('following is still another improved form completed Jan. 1, 1926'). On the back of the page are pencil sketches.

(d) Two additional sheets (oblong format, 26·5×34·5 cm.) of pencil and ink sketches for the canons and for the text of the commentary.

2. 'Canon für Streichquartett'.
Manuscript in ink on a strip of music paper (oblong format, 11·5×34·5 cm.); 2 little passages are pasted over with revisions. Note of completion: *Berlin 14./II. 1926 / in einer Stunde fabriziert!! Jetzt gehts schon ziemlich schnell Schönberg.* ('Produced in an hour!! Now it's going rather quickly.')

3. 'Legitimation als Canon' (und vice versa).
A half-sheet of music paper (oblong format, 25·5×34·5 cm.) bears the first pencilled draft, written in six voices in score-form. 2½ measures are crossed out and rewritten. Date of completion: *29./IV. 26 Sch.* On a second sheet of the same format, the canon is written in pencil, as a riddle-canon. It includes the text (the word-order was later changed because of the notes), and the text is also written by itself at the bottom of the same page, with the remark: *in Ewigkeit—ohne Ende! Schluss nur im Notfall.* ('In eternity—without end! Ending only in case of emergency.') On the other side of the sheet, the canon is written on four staves, in the treble and bass clefs; the ending (7 measures) is written in ink. With this are 2 sheets of hand-lined paper (carbon copies, upright format, 20×33·5 cm.) on which the canon is noted in pencil as a riddle-canon, with text and heading; 2 sheets (25·5×34 and 14×32 cm.) with sketches, and 2 slips of paper with rough drafts of the text.

A fair copy of Op. 28 is in the possession of Universal Edition, Vienna. The title-page is a sheet of paper with the title written in ink; on its inner side is the table of contents. There are some pencilled notations.

No. 1, 'Am Scheideweg' (the original title 'Tonal oder atonal' is crossed out), is written in India ink on a sheet of 16-lined music paper (upright format, 26·5×34 cm.). There are minor corrections in red ink. Signature: *12.XI. 1925 Arnold Schönberg*.

No. 2, 'Vielseitigkeit', is written in India ink on one side of a sheet of music paper (upright format, 26·5×33·5 cm.). The corrections, in red, are signed. Undated.

No. 3, 'Der neue Klassizismus', is written in ink on 14 loose sheets of 24-lined music paper (upright format, 26·5×34 cm.), comprising 27 numbered pages. The upper margin of p. 20 shows a pencilled change in the text: *sie geht wohin sie will (überall!) Sch*. ('it goes wherever it will—everywhere!'). On p. 26, mm. 166–168, inclusive, are pasted over: a revision? Note of completion: *Abschrift beendet Berlin 19./I. 1926 Arnold Schönberg*. Under this is the stamped address: Mödling bei Wien, Bernhardgasse 6, with the handwritten addition *derzeit Charlottenburg Steinplatz 2, Pension Bavaria*.

Appendix to Op. 28: 2 double and 2 single sheets of music paper (upright format, 26·5×34 cm.) comprise 7 pages written in India ink. There are detailed marginal notes, and a little pasted-on slip of paper with directions for the music engraver. Also pasted on is the text (typed) of 'Ein Spruch und zwei Variationen über ihn.' The typed foreword with handwritten additions and corrections, the introductory remarks, and the texts of the three choruses and of the Appendix also belong to this material.

From a letter to Mr. Amadeo de Filippi, May 13, 1949:

It is very interesting to me that you like these Three Satires and especially that you find that the technique is similar to the Third String Quartet and the Wind Quintet. It is true—they must have been written about the same time. I think it was 1926. I wrote them when I was very much angered by attacks of some of my younger contemporaries at this time and I wanted to give them a warning that it is not good to attack me.

The title 'Manysided', means only that it can be used by turning around the paper and reading it from the end to the beginning and the same music (if you call it music) would come out. This piece was never intended by myself to be sung or performed. It is merely on paper. But if one would try to perform it I think about 60 to the quarter-note would be a good tempo.

The Cantata is the piece which could and should be performed and I am ready to do as much as I can, if you send me your copy with your remarks. It will interest me very much.

(Schoenberg's original English)

For further hints on the performance of Schoenberg's choruses, see also below, discussion of 'De Profundis', Op. 50 B.

SUITE, Op. 29
   for piano, piccolo clarinet, clarinet, bass clarinet, violin, viola and 'cello
Universal Edition, Vienna

The first part of the manuscript, a fair copy written in ink, appears in score-form on 11 pages of 3 unbound double sheets (oblong format, 29×34·5 cm.). Undated, with the following note at the upper left of the first page: *Eigentum meiner lieben Trude (geb. Kolisch) aus der Wiedner Hauptstrasse 18./III. 25 Arnold Schönberg aus Mödling, Bernhardgasse 6* ('Property of my dear Trude, née Kolisch . . .').

The continuation is on 4 unbound double sheets (upright format, 26·5×34·5 cm.); a single sheet is pasted to the last double sheet. In all, there are 17 pages of this portion of the score, ending with the close of the first movement, 'Ouvertüre'. The first 149 measures of the second movement, 'Tanzschritte' ('Dance-Steps'), appear on a sheet of oblong format, 29×34·5 cm.; the remainder comprises 10 pages of 5 double sheets (upright format, 26·5× 34 cm.) bound with wrapping-twine. The third movement, 'Theme with Variations' (on 'Ännchen von Tharau') is on 21 pages of bound double sheets (upright format, 26·5×34 cm.); the fourth movement, 'Gigue', comprises 27 bound pages (format as in the third movement).

This material is undated. There are corrections of trifling errors, in ordinary lead pencil as well as in red, blue and green pencil. The row-forms and transpositions used are indicated virtually throughout the entire manuscript. Frequently, the sheets of music paper bear the stamped address: Arnold Schönberg Charlottenburg, Steinplatz, Pension Bavaria.

The first draft of the work, with the exact dates of composition, is found in Sketchbook V (see below). Also, the legacy contains two printed, bound copies with handwritten corrections of printer's errors; one of these has, in addition, a separate list of such errors. On the cover of one copy, the timings of the individual movements are listed: *I. 9 min., II. 9 min., III. 8 min., IV. 6 min.*

SKETCHES

In all, there are 12 sheets of sketches, mostly written in pencil, sometimes in ink. Four of these (1 double sheet, oblong format, 17×34·5 cm.; 2 single sheets, same format) contain the sketch of the fourth movement ('Gigue') with notes on its formal organization. Also, there are two row-charts.

THIRD STRING QUARTET, Op. 30
Universal Edition, Vienna

The manuscript, in the possession of the Library of Congress, consists of 37 loose sheets of music paper (oblong format, 34·5×26·5 cm.), laid in a letter-file; 36 of these sheets are numbered. The music is written on one side of the page only, in pencil. The title and dedication are written in ink: *III. Streichquartett opus 30 | Frau Elizabeth Sprague-Coolidge gewidmet | Arnold Schönberg.*

This manuscript contains the following dates:

At the end of the first movement: *10./II. 1927 Schönberg.*

At the beginning of the second movement: *4./II. 27*; at the end: *20./II. 1927 Schönberg.*

At the beginning of the third movement: *3./II. 27*; at the end: *4./III. 1927 Schönberg.*

At the beginning of the fourth movement: *5./II. 27* and *3./III. 27.* At the end of this movement, i.e., of the whole quartet: *8./III. 1927 Arnold Schönberg.*

Marginal note next to m. 73 in the third movement: *hier acht Tage krank gewesen* ('ill for a week at this point').

I. PUBLISHED WORKS

SKETCHES for the Third Quartet are found, in the legacy, on 3 single sheets and 1 double sheet (oblong format, 26·5 × 34·5 cm.). These are probably first sketches; they are dated *28.I. 27.* They include beginnings of the Intermezzo (26 measures, differing in part from the later version), 19 measures of the Adagio, and 6 measures of the Rondo. On one (otherwise blank) page of the double sheet are 11 measures of a string quartet in G major. Also, there are 4 row-charts; one of these is written in ink on hand-lined blueprint paper (upright format, 18 × 31·5 cm.).

VARIATIONS FOR ORCHESTRA, Op. 31
Universal Edition, Vienna

The first draft of the complete work is notated in short-score form, on 5 or 6 staves, with detailed indications of the instrumentation. It is written in pencil on 30 loose sheets of music paper (11 of oblong format, 19·5 × 34·5 cm., the others 26·5 × 34·5 cm.) comprising 32 numbered pages. These are numbered from I to XX, then (in the Finale) from C_1 to C_{12}. Two pages have been used on both sides, the others on one side only; all have perforated margins and are fastened as in a letter-file. The gray cardboard cover bears, in red pencil, the inscription *Variationen für Orchester.* Below, in pencil, is the following note: *angefangen in Berlin 1926 Frühjahr ca. 200 Takte componiert fortgesetzt und beendigt Roquebrune, Cap Martin, Frankreich, Juli und August 1928* (continuation in ink): *dort mehr als 300 Takte komponiert und die Partitur angefertigt* ('Begun in Berlin, spring of 1926, about 200 measures composed. Continued and completed at Roquebrune, Cap Martin, France, July and August 1928; there more than 300 measures composed and the score prepared').

On the inside back cover is pencilled an exact calculation of the timings of the individual sections of the score. The allover timing is given as *16′ 12″.*

The original *full* score is in the possession of Universal Edition, Vienna. On the title-page is written in ink: *Variationen für Orchester von Arnold Schönberg opus 31.* Also, there is a stamped address: Charlottenburg 9, Nussbaumallee 17. Below, and on the back of the page, there are pencilled directions (concerning the low notes of the bass clarinet, etc.) which are to be included in the score.

This fair copy of the score consists of 37 sheets of 30-lined music paper (upright format, 26·5 × 34 cm.), comprising 73 numbered pages. The first 7 are written in ink, the rest in pencil. The complete manuscript is bound in 2 volumes. At the bottom of the first page of the score, there are pencilled directions to the music engraver, and hints for performance (from the viewpoint of instrumental technique). Page 73 bears the note of completion *beendet: Roquebrune, 20. September 1928 Arnold Schönberg.* Two strips of music paper, laid between pages of the score, bear corrections for m. 286 and mm. 290–292, respectively.

There is a photocopy of this score in the legacy. Schoenberg made later corrections in the photocopy. Fastened to the first page are typed *Anweisungen für den Stich der Variationen für Orchester* (instructions for the engraver), as well as the detailed orchestration—5 sheets of paper in all.

While the actual composition of this work was completed on *21. VIII. 1928* (see short score), the full score was not finished till *20. September.*

A. WORKS WITH OPUS NUMBERS

SKETCHES for Op. 31

Including 4 narrow (4-lined) strips of music paper, there are, all told, 36 sheets of sketches. Most of these are on paper of oblong format (26×35·5 cm.); most of them are written in pencil (a few in ink).

On a narrow strip of music paper dated *2./V. 1926* we find the first, incomplete draft of the theme of the Variations. On another sheet of the same date is a first draft of its continuation; this, however, is crossed out. On the back of this sheet is the complete, final version; the numbering of its measures corresponds to that of the published form.

A sheet of music paper, the upper left-hand corner of which has been cut off, bears the following note (translated):

I had forgotten this guide-sheet, which sketches the construction of a variation, when, after an interruption of several months, I tried to finish the variation in 1926. In vain I tried to deduce the principle according to which I had chosen ★ etc., from the already-completed portion. I interrupted the work, and tried to resume it in the following years, but still in vain.—This time too; but, since I had given up these efforts as valueless, I decided to base the variation on a new constructive idea. When I had found one, I carried it out in the form of a sketch. Suddenly I decided to compare this with the enigmatic portion that I had already composed. It came out that I had once more found the supposedly 'lost' idea—or, rather, I had to conceive the same logical thought, after I had given up trying to remember it! 28./VII. 1928 Arnold Schönberg.

VON HEUTE AUF MORGEN ('From Today till Tomorrow'), Op. 32
Opera in 1 Act (Text by 'Max Blonda', *recte* Gertrud Schoenberg)
B. Schott's Söhne, Mainz

The first draft of the manuscript, bound in heavy cardboard by the composer, includes (inside the cover, in front of the first page of music) the row-chart of the work, with two different second halves of the row. Then, there are a total of 72 numbered pages of short score (1131 measures). These are written in ink, usually on 5–6 staves. 16–19-lined music paper (oblong format, 25·5×34·5 cm.) was used. Begun *25./X. 1928*; signed and completed *1. Jänner 1929 Arnold Schönberg* $3^h15(15^h15)$.

Handwritten insertions in the manuscript:

Page 1 (pencil): *beim Partitur schreiben Doppelstriche bloss anwenden um 1. Formteile (neue Sätze) zu kennzeichnen 2. Recit. von Arie und Arioso nach Möglichkeit zu trennen.* ('In writing the full score, use double-bars only (1) to indicate formal divisions (new sections), (2) to separate recitative from aria and arioso as much as possible.')

Page 13 (blue pencil): *einen Tag stecken geblieben!* (red pencil) *Seite 13 dreizehn Takte auf dieser Seite* (blue pencil) *allerdings auch auf Seite 11.* ('Stuck for a day here! Thirteen measures on p. 13—though also some trouble on p. 11.')

Page 31, m. 493 (pencil): *die durchgehenden 8. Töne sind hier richtig* (ink) *weil nämlich die Gesangsstimme selbst eine 12 Ton-Reihe ist.* ('All right for the 8th tone to continue through here as the voice part itself is a 12-tone row.')

Page 34, bottom (ink): *Anstelle der Takte 534 bis 540 kann auch ein anderer Modetanz gespielt werden wahrscheinlich aber doch besser nicht. Denn dieser ist hier (bewusst und unbewusst) motivisch zu fest verankert! Schönberg.* ('Instead of mm. 534–540, some other popular dance can also be played; however, probably better not. This one (consciously and unconsciously) is too firmly integrated into the whole from a motivic point of view!')

Page 43 (ink): *Ich kann den Tenor im Violinschlüssel gar nicht mehr lesen. Ich muss hier einen Ausweg finden. In der Partitur schrieb ich ihn unbedingt im Tenorschlüssel.* ('I just can't read the tenor part in the treble clef any more. I'll have to find a solution here. In the score, I simply must write it in the tenor clef.')

Page 49, m. 768 (*Sehr lebhaft*): (ink): *ohne Taktteilbetonung! hier immer: Cel. 8va höher als geschrieben, aber nur an dieser einen einzigen Stelle* nur die Akkorde. ('No accentuation of the beats, celesta an octave higher than written *only in the chords* of this one passage.') N.B.: The quavers $c\sharp^1$–b^1–$c\sharp^2$, between the chords, are also placed an octave higher in the score. However, in the short score, Schoenberg's downward-pointing brackets clearly indicate that he wanted these notes played *at the written pitch*.

Page 59, m. 942 (ink): *Achtung, Sänger doch im Violinschlüssel (dass kein Irrtum mit den* 𝄢 *entsteht).* ('Attention: singers in the treble clef after all (so as to avoid confusion with the 𝄢 clefs).') M. 941 (pencil): *die ganze Tenorstimme sorgfältigst revidieren, ob ich nicht hie und da eine Note im Tenorschlüssel geschrieben habe.* ('Revise the whole tenor part most scrupulously lest there be an occasional note in the tenor clef left.')

On pp. 15, 16, 30, 66, 67 and 68 there are numerous indications of instrumentation, and a few added notes, in red ink. At the bottom of p. 68 is written in red pencil: *seit 10 Tagen: Textänderungen!* ('for the past 10 days; *textual changes!*').

Mm. 1–452 of the manuscript of the piano reduction are missing. Mm. 453–613, written in pencil on 15 sheets of music paper, were done by Karl Rankl, a pupil of Schoenberg and at that time conductor at the Kroll-Oper in Berlin. As this reduction had to be prepared very rapidly, he helped Schoenberg with it. Schoenberg could not get together with Universal Edition on a contract. At that time, Schott turned the work down, and for a short time Schoenberg toyed with the idea of publishing it himself. However, he finally turned it over to a Berlin publisher, Benno Balan.

The portion of the piano-reduction manuscript in Schoenberg's handwriting extends from m. 614 to the end. It is written on 50 sheets of music paper. The first 8 of these are numbered with Roman numerals, in red pencil, from IX to XVI; they include mm. 615–729. The remaining pages are numbered in pencil from 1 to 42.

M. 614 is written in pencil by Schoenberg—it is the last measure on the final page of Rankl's portion of the piano reduction. Mm. 615–624 are still written in pencil, but from there on the remainder is written in ink. Date of completion: *30./IX. 1929.*

There are a few initialled corrections. Pp. X, XI, and XII are in oblong format, 27 × 35 cm.; all the others are in upright format of the same dimensions. There is a detailed set of directions for the blueprinter, written in ink on one side of a single sheet of paper.

Also, we find a photocopy (white on black) of the short score—72 pages. On the cardboard binding, there is a note in ink: *bitte: schonend behandeln! provisorisch eingebunden. Schönberg.* In pencil: *Diese Fotografie ist vor Fertigstellung der Partitur gemacht und differiert in einigen Kleinigkeiten mit der Partitur! Schönberg.* ('Please handle with care! temporary binding. This photograph was made before the score was prepared and differs from the score in several small particulars.')

The legacy also contains a printed conductor's score, in which were found two tinted sketches by Schoenberg. One is a water-colour (7 × 10 cm.), the other a pastel (11 × 8 cm.). Finally, there are two printed piano reductions, with corrections of errata.

[The work was first printed in vocal score, with the copyright date 1929. Bars 1–452 are reproduced from the corresponding section of the autograph, which now appears to be missing (see above). There followed a corrected vocal score, reproduced from entirely different MSS, and a full score, partly in Schoenberg's hand, both with copyright date 1930. All three publications bear the words 'Im Selbstverlag des Komponisten' ('Composer's edition'), the two 1930 scores adding 'Auslieferung und Bühnenvertrieb Edition Benno Balan' ('Material Benno Balan'). The Ars Viva full and vocal scores were reproduced in a reduced format from these editions, the latter unfortunately from the 1929 text.]

From a letter of Schoenberg, *4. X. 1929*, to the conductor at the Frankfurt Opera House, Wilhelm Steinberg, concerning the coming stage première of 'Von Heute auf Morgen':

Above all: my music calls for singers who are able to sing 9/10 of their parts between pp *and* mf, *in order to achieve appropriate climaxes with an occasional* forte *and with very few* fortissimos. *In other words, they must not (as is all too customary in Berlin and elsewhere in Germany) do nothing but scream the text all evening, so that the stage-directors are quite right when, in opera too, they take the whole responsibility on themselves instead of allowing music and song to have their full effect. My opera is vocally conceived from A to Z—in fact, to such an extent that there are hardly any longer instrumental interludes. The singers must be able to sing piano and mezza voce, and legato when that is called for; even in 'détaché' passages, their style must remain cantabile. They must cut their tones short only where staccato is indicated; but this is for purposes of special musical characterization, not because of the text.*

The singing and acting must always remain dignified. The singers must never 'characterize' at the expense of vocal beauty, must never exaggerate. Better colourless than crude—better no humour than this disgusting slapstick which is rampant in Berlin. They do not need to worry—it is not necessary to 'help out' my music; in itself it is so characteristic that, when it is performed correctly, all the characterization is automatically present. This has proved to be the case with all my works up till now.

Let me begin with the two comic parts, the girl-friend and the singer.

The girl-friend should pretend to be very witty, without being so in the least. She should be rather insipid, affected, superior, 'sophisticated', false; but all of this should not be too greatly underlined.

The comic effect of the singer is based on his self-satisfaction; there should be nothing overdone or coarse about it, though. He is very witty, knows that he has all kinds of success and uses what he has without forcing it at all. I should prefer a very successful tenor who simply plays himself as we see him. He must sing especially beautifully, smoothly, sweetly, and expressively—something like Tauber.★ It is not necessary for the audience to roll in the aisles laughing at these characters; in fact, the whole setup makes that impossible—it is good enough if they have plenty of occasion to smile. The outcome of the play makes the tenor as ridiculous as he ought to be, in any case; anything more would merely detract, for it has not been composed into the music. And that is the most annoying thing—to arouse an expectation that one cannot fulfil.

★ AUTHOR'S NOTE: Richard Tauber was a greatly admired tenor around 1930.

The man is also comical, up to a point. Especially because of his wavering attitudes, his easy irascibility and his self-importance. If he collapses in the second third of the opera, and then becomes rather haughty when things go somewhat better for him again, I think that is enough contrast for this character; anyway, his music is richly varied enough to provide everything necessary for his complete portrayal.

On the other hand, the most prominent characteristics of the wife, who is not supposed to be funny in any way, and who, therefore, cannot and should not have a comic success, are intelligence, naturalness and tenderness. Without ever being sentimental, she should always show warmth. However, the temperament which she must display in the 'disguise' scenes will be most convincing when it is seen to conceal anger, stubbornness, and a desire for revenge. Nevertheless she is quite uncomplicated (while the other three characters are all more or less 'pseudo-complex' in the modern manner) and transparent.

In characterizing the voices, I would describe the tenor simply as 'Tauber', the girl-friend as 'coloratura-soubrette', with the 'coloratura' more important than the 'soubrette'—in other words, a light, not too warm, bright voice. The man should have a rich, dark baritone voice, but with some lightness as well (therefore, not too dark).

I think that only singers who can sight-read these parts and who have absolute pitch can really learn them reliably. I know several such. But I hope that you have even better ones.

They will certainly not be able to tackle the ensembles, duets and quartets until they have learned their parts perfectly. But then the difficulties should no longer be especially great.

For the orchestra, I should like to recommend to you the individual preparation of the smallest possible groups. This has already worked out very well on several occasions. In my estimation, you can probably make out with 9–12 orchestral rehearsals (including the stage rehearsals) by using this method. The 'Glückliche Hand' in Vienna (Stiedry) and the 'Erwartung' in Prague (Zemlinsky) were rehearsed in this manner: flutes alone, oboes alone, etc., horns alone, trumpets alone, etc., harp and celesta alone, percussion alone, first violins alone, second violins alone, etc. (all the string groups). Perhaps that is a lot of work for the conductors and coaches, but it is very rational for the orchestra. Only then were the three large groups—woodwinds, brass and percussion, and strings—rehearsed. In the third rehearsal, the whole orchestra came together for the first time. Thus, three rehearsals only were used!

Here, you might rehearse oboes, flutes, and saxophone together, and then clarinets and bassoons. Perhaps the brass can be taken in two sections. But the strings as thoroughly as possible: perhaps first and second violins together, but violas alone, 'celli alone, and basses (whose task here is not very easy) also alone.

It would be good to have these preliminary rehearsals some time in advance, for then the orchestra men will be frightened and will practise their parts. All that is necessary is for the gentlemen to be able to play what is written there!

Piano, harp, guitar and mandolin should also be rehearsed in two groups, if possible; but the percussion should be rehearsed alone, if only to check the cues.

Now I think that I have said everything of importance that occurs to me.

Just one more thing: the tone of the whole should actually be very light. But one ought to feel, or sense, that behind these simple events something else is hidden; that these everyday characters and happenings are being used to show how, above and beyond this simple story of a marriage, the so-called modern, the merely modish exists only 'from today till tomorrow', from a shaky hand to a greedy mouth—not only in marriage, but no less in art, in politics and in attitudes towards life.

A. WORKS WITH OPUS NUMBERS

I should be happy if you would bring these viewpoints to the attention of the other participants in and directors of this performance. I have turned to my colleague first; for, if the music is good, the rest can hardly go wrong.

PIANO PIECE, Op. 33a
Universal Edition, Vienna

In the legacy there was found only a first draft, begun on *25./XII. 28*. It includes the first 25 measures of a total 40 measures, written in ink. Though many of the actual notes are different in the final version, the character and formal outline of the first 19 measures are identical in both versions. The possibilities of comparison thus afforded are very instructive from the viewpoint of compositional technique.

At the end of the sketch, which covers one side of a piece of music paper, several row-forms of the piece are notated. The whole is written in ink; the paper is of oblong format, 35 × 27 cm.

The whereabouts of the original manuscript could not be determined. Universal Edition possesses only a copy in another hand, signed by Schoenberg and with handwritten entries by him.

PIANO PIECE, Op. 33b
Publisher's rights presently belong to Gertrud Schoenberg
Formerly: New Music Society of California

The manuscript, dated *8./X. 31*, is written in pencil on an 18-lined double sheet (oblong format, 26 × 33·5 cm.). Date of completion: *10.X. 31 Barcelona Arnold Schönberg*. The first 6 tones of the basic row are noted over m. 1, the remaining 6 over m. 4.

A slip of paper inserted between the pages of the double sheet bears this notation in Schoenberg's handwriting: *Takt 37 b? ces? // Takt 63 l. H. 32tel statt 16tel? // Takt 22 l. H. untere Stimme a(statt b)?*
        b(statt h)?
('m. 37; B flat? C flat? m. 63, left hand: demisemiquavers instead of semiquavers? m. 22, left hand, lower voice: A (instead of B flat)?
        B flat (instead of B)?')
Also, there is a printed copy ('New Music', April, 1932), with a correction of the lower part in m. 63 made by Schoenberg in red.

BEGLEITUNGSMUSIK ZU EINER LICHTSPIELSZENE ('Accompaniment to a Film-Scene'), Op. 34
Heinrichshofen's Verlag, Wilhelmshaven

There is a photocopy of the manuscript, bound by Schoenberg: 33 sheets, pasted on white music paper. At the upper left of the first page: *15./X. 29*. After the final measure of p. 33: *Arnold Schönberg, Berlin, 14. Februar 1930*.

Later handwritten corrections of errata are written on the white music-paper backing; all are initialled individually. In the right-hand margin, p. 1: *für einige schwierige Figuren werde ich mit farbiger Tinte Erleichterungen eintragen.* ('I shall write in simplified versions of several difficult figurations, in coloured ink.')

A copy of the printed score is designated, in red pencil, as *Handexemplar A. Sch.*; it contains corrections of notes and indications of principal voices.

The original manuscript, which was in the possession of the publishers, was destroyed, as a result of the war, in the rock-salt mines at Stassfurt.

SKETCHES FOR OP. 34

There are 7 sheets of music paper, laid in a bright yellow cardboard cover (oblong format, 36·5 × 27·5 cm.). The sketches are written in ink, sometimes on both sides of the page. On one of these sheets is the row-chart of the work; a pasted-on slip of paper gives exact calculations of the timing of the individual sections (mm. 1–8, etc.). This sheet is of upright format (26·5 × 34 cm.). On another sheet (oblong format, 24 × 35 cm.) are sketches and the beginning of the work. On another (upright format, 26·5 × 34·5 cm.) we find a section marked *Molto allegro* (corresponding to mm. 44–59 of the score, different thereafter). Also, on 4 of these 7 sheets, numbered IX (oblong format, 25 × 34·5 cm.), X (upright format, 23·5 × 35·5 cm.), XI (upright format, 26·5 × 34·5 cm.) and XII (oblong format, 25·5 × 34·5 cm.) is written the section extending from m. 128 to the end. These 4 sheets are fastened together with wrapping-twine. The sheets with mm. 1–127 are missing. In addition, there is a little sheet of music paper (its corner torn off) with the row of the work and its inversion transposed a fifth down.

SIX PIECES FOR MALE CHORUS A CAPPELLA, Op. 35
(Texts by the composer)
Bote & Bock, Berlin-Wiesbaden

I. 'Hemmung' ('Restraint')

The manuscript is written in pencil on a double sheet (upright format, 26·5 × 34 cm.). The measures are numbered in red pencil. Date of completion: *19.II. 1930 Arnold Schönberg.*

II. 'Das Gesetz' ('The Law')

Photocopy (black background) of the manuscript, full size (oblong format, 26·5 × 35·5 cm.), on 3 pages. Date of beginning: *5./III. 1930.* Date of completion: *Berlin Charlottenburg 9./III. 1930 Arnold Schönberg.*

III. 'Ausdrucksweise' ('Means of Expression')

Manuscript written in pencil, in choral score-form, on 3 pages of a double sheet (oblong format, 26·5 × 34·5 cm.). Mm. 23–28 were evidently left out in copying, and are appended on the third page. Date of beginning: *4./III. 30*; date of completion: *4./III. 30 Arnold Schönberg.*

There is also a sketch-sheet with the row-forms, headed *Masseninstinkt.* (The text begins: 'Aus uns, im Masseninstinkt...') ('From us, in mass instinct...').

A. WORKS WITH OPUS NUMBERS

IV. 'Glück' ('Happiness')

Schoenberg gave the manuscript to Frau Charlotte Dieterle, as appears from a letter to her written on February 7, 1939. There is no photocopy.

V. 'Landsknechte' ('Yeomen')

The fair copy of the manuscript, in choral score-form, is written in black ink on 7 pages of 2 unbound double sheets (oblong format, 27 × 35 cm.). Date of beginning: *5./III. 1930*; date of completion: *8./III. 1930 Berlin Charlottenburg Arnold Schönberg*. There are also 2 sketch-sheets (with the row-forms).

VI. 'Verbundenheit' ('Obligation')

The manuscript still bears the title *Jeder—jedes—jedem* ('Each man—each thing—to each'). It is written in ink, on a double sheet (oblong format, 26·5 × 34·5 cm.). It was begun on *16./IV. 1929*. The date of completion, *19./IV. 1929 Arnold Schönberg*, is written in red ink, as is the notation below: *Die erste Strophe samt den 5 Texten am 16. IV. nachmittags in etwa 2 Stunden geschrieben. Die 2. Strophe dieses Stückes erst heute (Text sowohl, als auch Musik) aber nicht wegen 'Schaffensqual', sondern weil ich durch Besuche etc abgehalten wurde. Arnold Schönberg.* ('The first stanza and the 5 texts were written in about 2 hours on the afternoon of April 16. The second stanza of this piece (text and music) was not finished till today—however, not because of 'creative woes', but because I was interrupted by visits, etc.')

One negative and two positive photocopies of the manuscript also exist.

DRAFTS OF OP. 35

The draft of the first chorus, 'Hemmung', is written in ink on both sides of a single sheet of music paper (oblong format, 25 × 35 cm.), in sections: mm. 1–10, 11–15, 16–22, 23 to the end. There are slight deviations from the final version.

'Das Gesetz' is complete, on a sheet of music paper that has been pasted together in a number of places. This draft is written in both ink and pencil. At the beginning, there is a handwritten note: *flüchtige Abschrift (in der Skizze) wahrscheinlich sehr fehlerhaft. Sch.* ('hastily copied (in sketch form), probably very inaccurate . . .'). At the end, undated: *Achtung, bei eventuellen Korrekturen: diese Partitur ist vom Original, das in [𝄢 9/8] geschrieben ist, abgeschrieben. Bei der Umschreibung auf [𝄞] können Fehler entstanden sein. Schönberg.* ('Attention, in case of proof-reading: this score is a copy of the original, which is written in [𝄢 9/8]. The rewriting in [𝄞] may have produced errors'.)

'Ausdrucksweise': this draft is completely different from the original (see above). It comprises the first 10 measures; these are written on blueprint paper (oblong format, 32 × 43 cm.) headed with the title following the opening words *Aus uns. . . .*

There is also a draft of the chorus *Glück* which differs completely from the original (see above). It is incomplete, comprising mm. 1–20 only. With it are found a row-chart, and the handwritten text.

A section of the sixth chorus, 'Verbundenheit' (m. 19 to the end), is written in ink on 2 staves, on strips of music paper (oblong format, 12 × 25 cm.). Presumably this is part of the first draft. Except for negligible changes, it is identical with the original.

I. PUBLISHED WORKS

[Apart from the Bote & Bock edition (1930) of the complete set, 'Verbundenheit' was published by Deutscher Arbeiter-Sängerbund, Berlin. The edition is numbered 1382, dated VII 1930, and contains the following note: 'Kann von Vcl. und Kbs. (3:1 oder 2:2) begleitet werden, eventuell aber auch vom Klavier' (Can be accompanied by 'cellos and basses (3:1 or 2:2), or possibly also by a piano).]

CONCERTO FOR VIOLIN AND ORCHESTRA, Op. 36
G. Schirmer, New York

(N.B.: from here on the English titles given are those under which the works were published.)

The manuscript, notated in short-score form on 5–6 staves, is loose in a cardboard cover, on which is written *Violin-Konzert erste Niederschrift Sch.* ('Violin Concerto, first draft . . .'). The paper used is surprisingly varied in format and quality. This first draft must have been the basis for the printed conductor's score; this, also in short-score form, was prepared from blueprints which are not in the composer's handwriting.

The first movement of the manuscript begins on two sheets of 18-lined music paper (upright format, 28 × 33 cm.), pasted together with gummed tape. The top half of the first page is covered with pencil sketches, while the bottom half is blank. The second page, too, shows sketches (in pencil and ink) on the upper 6 staves. Only then does the manuscript score proper begin. At this point, the page-number 1 is written in red pencil and encircled. Page 2 of the short score is on side 3 of these 2 music-paper sheets; side 4, again, contains pencil sketches only. A double sheet of 24-lined music paper (oblong format, 27 × 34 cm.) is attached to these sheets with heavy white wrapping-twine. On side 1 of this double sheet, the *fourth* page of the score is notated. Side 2 contains more sketches, side 3 is blank except for a few notes in the upper left-hand corner, and side 4 contains the *third* page of the short score.

Then, bound with the same sort of twine, there are several sheets of the above-mentioned 18-lined music paper, bearing pp. 5–16 of the short score. The date of completion of the first movement is noted after m. 265: *11./9. 1934.*

The second movement begins (pp. 17–19) on 3 pasted-together sheets of blueprint paper (oblong format, 22 × 34 cm.)—18-lined. The sheet bearing p. 19 is stuck to a double sheet (24-lined, upright format, 27·5 × 34 cm.) with gummed tape in such a way that manuscript p. 20 is on side 2 of the double sheet and p. 22 on side 1, while the fourth side is blank. Attached to this with gummed tape we find photocopies of pp. 21–22. Manuscript pp. 23–27 are on white, transparent paper of oblong format (22 × 35·5 cm.), bound with gummed tape. P. 25 contains the end of the second movement, while the third movement begins on p. 26. Pp. 28–41 (41 being the last page) are written on yellowish blueprint paper (oblong format, 25 × 31·5 cm.). Some of these sheets are loose, while others are fastened together with gummed transparent tape (Scotch tape).

The first movement is written in pencil. So is the second movement, through m. 416 (though some spots are either written in ink or traced over in ink; m. 392, written in ink, is pasted on). The first 3 measures (417–419) of p. 23 are also written in pencil, but from there on to the end of the second movement, the manuscript is written in India ink. The third movement, beginning on p. 26 (see above), is written in pencil up to m. 501. From m. 502 (middle of p. 27) to the end, it is written in India ink.

Dates noted in this manuscript are as follows:

First movement: no heading or beginning date: completed *II./9. 1934.*

Second movement: heading, *Concerto for Violin and Orchestra by Arnold Schoenberg.* No beginning date; date of completion: *27. August 1936 Arnold Schoenberg.*

Third movement: again, no beginning date; date of completion: *beendet 23.IX. 1936 Arnold Schoenberg.*

The following handwritten annotations deserve special attention:

1. On p. 9, after m. 169, the following 5 measures (170–174) are crossed out. Over these, the following note has been made in pencil (rather hard to read, as it has been partially rubbed out): *längere Unterbrechung, nach dieser entdeckte ich, dass 169 = 13 × 13 | Klavierauszug bis Takt 176(?) sind 13 geschriebene Zeilen | ebenfalls Unterbrechung nach Partiturseite . . .* (hard to read, could be either 10 or 16). ('Long interruption—thereafter I discovered that 169 = 13 × 13. Thirteen lines of the piano reduction written up to m. 176(?) Another interruption after p. (?) of the score.')

The newly composed measures 170–174, which follow the crossed-out measures, are completely different from these first attempts.

2. On p. 13, in black India ink: *Hier habe ich gehalten, als ich noch 29 hier bloss skizzierte Takte auszufüllen hatte und mich am 15. September für fast 3 Wochen (bis heute sind es schon 19 Tage) ins Bett legen musste: Seite 13 Arnold Schoenberg—3. X. 1935 Ich versuche (!) heute weiterzuarbeiten Arnold Schoenberg.* ('I stopped here when I still had 29 sketched measures to fill in. On the 15th of September, I had to take to my bed and have been there for nearly 3 weeks (19 days today): *Page 13. 3. X. 1935:* trying (!) to go on with my work today.')

3. At the bottom of p. 13 is the following note in ink: *Niemand wird es glauben wollen, dass ich, als ich in die Partitur die Nummer des Taktes 222 schrieb, ich mir dachte: 'Bis jetzt habe ich mich diesmal noch nicht in der Taktnumerierung geirrt.' Und sofort darauf dachte ich: 'So, jetzt ist's aus' und entdeckte eine Minute später, dass ich beim 223ten Takt die Nummer ausgelassen habe und auf Seite 13! eben dort, wo ich unterbrochen habe! | 11./X. 1935.* ('Nobody will believe me—but when I numbered measure 222 in the score, I thought to myself, "Up till now I haven't made any mistakes in the measure-numbering this time." And then I thought at once, "But it couldn't last". And a minute later I discovered that I left out the number in measure 223—and on *page 13*, where I interrupted my work!')

(See earlier instances of Schoenberg's belief in the baleful influence of the number 13 on his life, as noted in other manuscripts.)

In addition, the manuscript contains numerous corrections (some initialled) made with pencils of various colours, as well as indications of the different row-forms used. From time to time the pages are stamped with Schoenberg's address.

Also, there is a row-chart of the work with the manuscript. It is written on narrow-lined music paper (upright format, 15 × 23 cm.). Then, there is a photocopy of the manuscript, comprising 11 pages only, and ending with m. 330 in the second movement. It is in oblong format (30·5 × 40 cm.) and contains corrections of errata, made in several colours.

Finally, there is a fair copy of the piano reduction—29 unbound pages, breaking off at m. 329 in the second movement. The first 9 pages (through m. 88) are written on regular music paper (upright format, 24 × 31·5 cm., except for pp. 7–8 which measure 26·5 × 33 cm.), in ink, pencil, and crayon (?). From p. 12 onwards, yellowish blueprint paper (24 × 31·5 cm.) and black India ink are used. There are photocopies of pp. 6–11.

SKETCHES FOR OP. 36

A large portfolio contains numerous sketches for the Violin Concerto, and a chart for the third movement in which the transpositions and mirror-forms of the row used in mm. 474–686 are set down. This portfolio also contains the blueprints of mm. 1–330, made by a copyist.

FOURTH STRING QUARTET, Op. 37
G. Schirmer, New York

The manuscript is in the possession of the Library of Congress. It consists of 28 sheets of music paper (oblong format, 34 × 22·5 cm.) comprising 54 numbered pages, written in ink throughout. The cardboard-bound photocopy in the legacy shows several corrections made later in red pencil.

At the beginning and ending of each movement, the following dates are given:

1. *April 27, 1936 | 12.VI. 1936*

2. *24./V. 36 | 10. Juni 1936.*

3. No beginning date is given; apparently Schoenberg simply continued composing without interruption after finishing the second movement. Date of completion: *18. Juni 1936.*

4. *18.6. 1936 | finished July 26, 1936 Arnold Schoenberg.*

At several points in the manuscript, there are marginal notes, as follows:

At the top of the first page: *fulfilling with pleasure the commission of the great patroness of music Mrs. Elizabeth Sprague-Coolidge. Arnold Schoenberg.*

At measure 22: *nach 10tägiger Pause fortgesetzt am 9. V. Umzug!* (Moving caused a 10-day interruption of work.)

At m. 206: *hier wieder einen Tag stecken geblieben* ('stuck here for a day again') (with an arrow pointing to the page-number 13, which once more had, presumably, caused the composer to 'get stuck' at a critical point).

At m. 725 (in pencil): *perhaps this ought always to be noted so as in 717.* At m. 788: *bis 25. Juni bis hieher gelangt, am 8. Juli wieder angefangen!* ('got this far by June 25, began anew on July 8!').

SKETCHES AND DRAFTS

The legacy contains 14 loose sheets of music paper (upright format, 27 × 34·5 cm.), and 4 smaller slips of paper pertaining to this work. These are obviously parts of an earlier draft. The material at hand begins with a group of measures numbered 683–691, which present a somewhat different form of mm. 681–689 in the published version. Immediately following, on the same page, there begins the fourth movement, with the annotation *IV./18.VI. 36.* It, too, differs from the final version at several points. The section from m. 776 (774 in the published version) to 788 (786) inclusive is either missing or lightly sketched only. Then, the draft extends from m. 789 (787) to 893 (891), again with some variants. On an additional sheet are mm. 894 (892)–937 (935), carrying us to the end of the fourth movement. The mistake in measure-numbering came about because Schoenberg at first left out 239 and 378 when numbering the measures.

CHAMBER SYMPHONY NO. 2, Op. 38
G. Schirmer, New York

The composition of this work is unusual in that it extended over a span of 33 years, with interruptions of many years. The composition was begun in August, 1906, immediately after the completion of the First Chamber Symphony; it was then continued in 1911 and 1916, and—at the suggestion of the conductor Fritz Stiedry—finally completed in 1939. On December 18, 1947, Schoenberg wrote to me: *Ich habe es vollendet (2 Drittel war vorhanden) im Stil in dem es konzipiert war.* ('I have completed it in the style in which it was originally conceived [two-thirds of it was already finished]'.) In this connection one should remember that the year 1906 still belongs to Schoenberg's first, 'tonal' period; 1911 and 1916 fall in his 'non-tonal' period, while 1939 is deep in his 'twelve-tone' period (during which, however, several tonal compositions were written after 1934).

The first sketches, as well as more extensive drafts, are found in Sketchbook III (see below). There, they begin on p. 32, with the date *1.8.1906*, and on p. 33 with the remark *angefangen 14.8. 1906 in Rottach.*

The first (incomplete) manuscript of the score contains mm. 1–145 of the first movement, written in ink on 16½ pages of 18-lined score-paper (oblong format, 26 × 44 cm.). After this, a note was added: *there follow ms. 146–165.* After 3½ blank pages, the second movement (through m. 251) follows, on 12 pages. On the first page of the manuscript, we find the dates *29./8. 1908* and *14./I. 1907.* There are also pencil sketches, and a note: *Der erste Es moll Akkord erst im 11. Takt* ('The first E flat minor chord only in measure 11') (N.B.: the first movement is in E flat minor). On p. 5, in place of mm. 39–40, is noted: *vielleicht die nächsten (4) Takte lieber 36–39 wiederholen die Harmonie beibehalten und die Hauptfigur als Contrapunkt.* ('Perhaps repeat mm. 36–39 in the next 4 measures—keep the harmony and use the principal figure as a counterpoint.') In addition, there are a few slight instrumental retouches in the manuscript.

The manuscript of the completion of this composition (1939) is loose in a cardboard cover bearing the inscription *IInd Chamber Symphony.* It consists of 12 sheets of music paper and is written in pencil on one side of the page. The first 10 sheets are of oblong format (29·5 × 35·5 cm.); the last 2 (21·5 × 34·5 cm.) are fastened together with gummed tape. This manuscript begins with m. 309 in the second movement and goes to the end of that movement. (In this connection, see below, letter of Schoenberg to Fritz Stiedry.) The date at the end of this manuscript—*12./X. 1939*—does not correspond with that of the facsimile edition—*October 21, 1939.* Probably the former refers to the completion of the composition, the latter to that of the fair copy.

The publisher G. Schirmer, New York, owns the manuscript of this fair copy. It comprises the complete score, and consists of 32 loose numbered pages of blueprint paper, white or yellowish (oblong format, 35·5 × 22·5 cm.; from p. 25, oblong format, 35·5 × 25 cm.; last page, 35·5 × 17 cm.), with perforated left-hand margins. It is written in India ink; a few corrections and additions in brown pencil (occasionally in ordinary lead-pencil) refer to rests, dynamics, phrasings, slurs, etc. The first movement bears the date of completion *Brentwood Park August 15, 1939*; the second (last) is signed *Arnold Schoenberg Brentwood Park October 21, 1939*.

The same publisher has the composer's fair copy of the version for two pianos, Op. 38B (hitherto unpublished). It is written in India ink on 41 loose, numbered pages of blueprint paper (oblong format, $38 \cdot 5 \times 26 \cdot 5$ cm.). The date at the end of the first movement is *XII, 25, 1941*; at the end of the second movement is the signature *finished Brentwood Park January 12, 1942 Arnold Schoenberg*, along with a handwritten notice of copyright and the complete address in block letters.

From the correspondence of Schoenberg with Fritz Stiedry, it appears that, at first, 3 movements were planned, and the work was to end with an Adagio. This plan was finally given up; however, the following sketches or drafts found in the legacy pertain to it:

(*a*) A page of score written in India ink on blueprint paper (oblong format, $26 \times 35 \cdot 5$ cm.), and pasted on cardboard with gummed tape. It contains the first 19 measures (numbered 490–508) of the Adagio. (N.B.: the first 2 movements are numbered consecutively, from 1 to 489.)

(*b*) Five sketch-sheets, one of which bears the date *November 5, 1939*.

(*c*) A draft comprising 127 measures, written in short-score form on loose sheets. On the first page, next to the tempo indication (Adagio, $\matho = 42$) there is the following handwritten note: *XI./5. 1939 after 536 pause of more than 10 weeks | changed an(d) started anew January 27 1940*. This draft begins in black India ink on 2 sheets of blueprint paper (oblong format, $35 \cdot 5 \times 22 \cdot 5$ cm.). From m. 533 onwards, it is written on 5 pages of 2 double sheets of music paper (oblong format, $34 \cdot 5 \times 25 \cdot 5$ cm.), mostly in India ink but sometimes in pencil. The first 8 measures (490–497) are completely different from the corresponding passage in draft (*a*); the following measures, however, are identical. Up to m. 542, the composition is completely carried out, on 3 or 4 staves. From there on, the principal voice continues to m. 618, while countermelodies and harmonization are only partially carried out. A separate sheet (blueprint paper, as above) contains another version of mm. 534–535. See also Sketchbook III.

Also, the legacy contains a copy of the printed edition (bound by Schoenberg) with several corrections of errata, and additional dynamic indications.

HISTORY OF THE WORK'S ORIGIN. SCHOENBERG'S IDEAS ON MUSICAL PERFORMANCE PRACTICE IN GENERAL

From a letter of Schoenberg to the conductor Fritz Stiedry (undated):

Dear Dr. Stiedry:

For the past month I have been working on the Second Chamber Symphony. I spend most of my time trying to find out: 'What did the author mean here?'

After all, in the meantime my style has become much more profound and I have much difficulty in making the ideas which I wrote down years ago without too much thought (rightly trusting to my feeling for design) conform to my present demand for a high degree of 'visible' logic. This is now one of my greatest difficulties, for it also affects the material of the piece.

However, this material is very good: expressive, characteristic, rich and interesting. But it is meant to be carried out in the manner which I was capable of at the time of the Second Quartet.

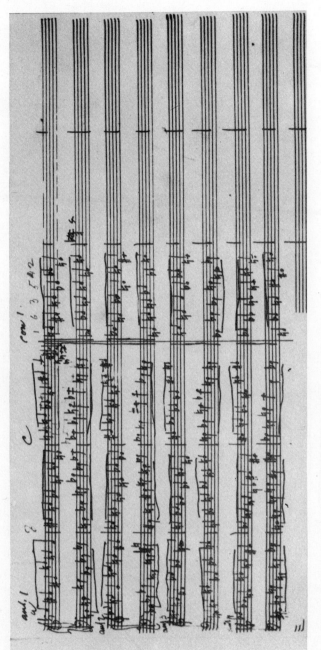

6. Table of sets for the ODE TO NAPOLEON, OP. 41.

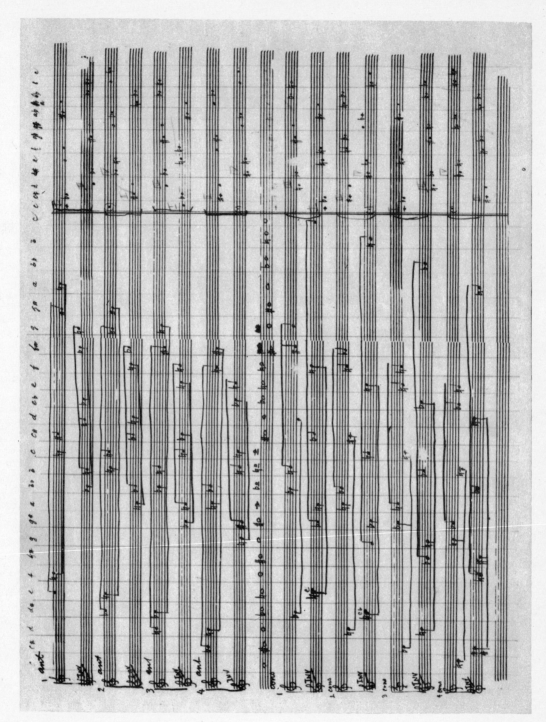

7. Table of sets for the ODE TO NAPOLEON, OP. 41.

A. WORKS WITH OPUS NUMBERS

The first movement is finished. I have altered very little; only the ending is entirely new, and the instrumentation. In a few places I have altered the harmonization, and I have changed the accompaniment figures rather frequently. After numerous experiments, I decided to rework these completely.

I am very well satisfied with the movement. Besides, it is easy to play; very easy. Duration: 7½ to 8 minutes.

Now I am working on the second movement. If I succeed in finishing it, it will be quite effective: a very lively Allegro.

Whether I shall write a third movement (or even a fourth or fifth, which is also not out of the question) is not yet certain. I have not yet been able to find my old sketches—it is too hot to look for them. So I have no idea whether or not I can resume with one of the many plans which exist for the completion. My preliminary idea is to have a slow third (final) movement, a heroic Maestoso. *Whether that is a good plan, I shall know only in four to six weeks; by then, I shall hope to have the second movement finished.*

From a letter of April 2 (?) to Dr. Stiedry:

Dear Dr. Stiedry:

The last movement is an 'epilogue', which does bring thematically new material (developed from preceding material) but which, nevertheless, is not unconditionally necessary. The musical and 'psychic' problems are presented exhaustively in the two completed movements; the final movement merely appends, so to speak, certain 'observations'.

From a letter of Schoenberg to Fritz Stiedry, January 8, 1941, concerning the latter's performance of the Second Chamber Symphony and using this as a basis for comments on musical performance practice:

. . . But I must react against what you say about the passages mm. 72–76 and mm. [?]. On the contrary, I find the strings too noisy in both cases, and this is because each of the staccatos marked ▼ is played sforzato *instead of being played as an unusually* short *note. For me, the noise of the strings is so disturbing that the winds do not come out plastically enough.—*

. . . Yesterday, January 2, I played the records once more, and then remembered that I wanted to mention one more point. It has to do with the detached notes, which were mostly played as staccatos. This is wrong—at least in my music. I really mean only that each note should be bowed—or breathed— separately. I do not like excessive, mushy legato, but these notes should in no case be shortened.

Then the little crescendo-decrescendos; these are almost always exaggerated and make so much noise! Likewise the marcatos. A sfz *is something else; that is a strong accent. But in* fp *(I tell musicians) the* p *is important, not the* f. *Then, especially in cantabile melodies (but also everywhere else) one should absolutely* not *accentuate the 'strong' beats. In one phrase, I say, there is only* one *strong beat.*

KOL NIDRE, Op. 39
for speaker, mixed chorus and orchestra
Boelke-Bomart, Inc., Hillsdale, N.Y.

In the legacy, we find the first, completely worked-out draft, which shows only slight deviations from the published version. The manuscript is written in pencil, in short-score form, on 11 sheets of music paper (16 pages numbered with Roman numerals; upright format, 26·5 × 34·5 cm.). The sheets, not all of the same make and with different numbers of lines, are held together with a strip of linen. The text of the speaker is written in red pencil. The date on the first page: *begun Aug. 1, 1938*. On the last page, the signature reads: *Sept. 8, 1938 Arnold Schoenberg.*

The published full score—consisting of a title-page (with precise indications of choral setting and orchestration, as well as a note concerning copyright, and the composer's Los Angeles address) and 28 pages of score—was prepared from the blueprint sheets written by Schoenberg. The last page is signed: *September 22, 1938 Arnold Schoenberg.* This is obviously the date when the fair copy was completed. It was impossible to learn the whereabouts of this blueprint manuscript.

The legacy also contains the following materials pertaining to Op. 39:

A fair copy of mm. 1–19, written in ink on music paper (upright format, 43 × 32 cm.), and dated *August 1, 1938.*

Three sheets of transparent music paper (upright format, 31·5 × 42·5 cm.) without superscription, containing the same 19 measures written in short-score form in India ink; dated *September 1938.* Identical with the final version.

Ten sketch-sheets, predominantly of upright format (26 × 33 cm.), written in pencil; one of the sheets bears the date *1. VIII. 38.*

Also, typed copies of the text in English and Hebrew, as well as a German version of the 'Kol Nidre' made by Schoenberg himself. (The following is the English text of the published version.)

All vows, oaths, promises and plights of any kind wherewith we pledged ourselves counter to our inherited faith in God, Who is One, Everlasting, Unseen, Unfathomable—we declare these null and void.

We repent that these obligations have estranged us from the sacred task we were chosen for. We shall strive from this day of atonement till the next to avoid such and similar obligations so that the Jom Kippur to follow may come to us for good.

Whatever binds us to falsehood may be absolved, released, annulled, made void and of no power.

Hence all such vows shall be no vows, and all such bonds shall be no bonds, all such oaths shall be no oaths.

From a letter to Paul Dessau, New York, November 22, 1941:

Dear Mr. Dessau:

I wrote the 'Kol Nidre' for Rabbi Dr. Jakob Sonderling, 525 S. Fairfax, Los Angeles, Cal. — — — At my suggestion, the text of the 'traditional' 'Kol Nidre' was altered; but the introduction was an idea of Dr. Sonderling's.

When I first saw the traditional text, I was shocked by the 'traditional' conception that all obligations which one has undertaken during the year should be dissolved on the Day of Atonement. I consider this conception false, for it is truly un-moral. It contradicts the high ethical quality of all Jewish commandments.

From the first moment that I began to read it, I was convinced that the 'Kol Nidre' comes from Spain; it later came out that I was right. This made it clear to me that the meaning was simply as follows: all who had, willingly or unwillingly (apparently), gone over to Christianity—and who, therefore, were supposedly excluded from the Jewish community—might, on this day, once more become reconciled with their God; all other vows and promises were to be dissolved. This has nothing to do with commercial 'deals'!

There are two difficulties connected with the use of the traditional melody:

(1) Actually there is no 'melody' as such, but only a number of melismas which resemble each other up to a point without, however, being identical; also, they do not always appear in the same order.

(2) This melody is monodic and is not based on harmony in our sense—perhaps not even on polyphony.

I selected the phrases which a number of versions have in common and put them together in a reasonable order. One of my principal tasks was to 'vitriolize away' the 'cello-sentimentality of the Bruchs, etc., and to give this DECREE the dignity of a law, of an edict. I think that I have succeeded in this. These measures 58 to 63 are at least not in sentimental minor key. . . . I am sure, too, that you will see much of what I have added to the total effect by providing a motivic basis.

VARIATIONS ON A RECITATIVE FOR ORGAN, Op. 40
H. W. Gray Company, New York

The manuscript, a blueprint fair copy on 15 loose pages (20-lined, upright format, 28 × 38 cm.), has a cardboard cover. Date on first page: *August 25, 1941*; at the end: *Oktober 12, 1941 Arnold Schoenberg.* In addition, both these pages bear the composer's stamped address.

There are 43 sheets of sketches, on music paper of various sizes. 5 sheets of hand-lined music paper (13-lined, upright format, 21·5 × 29·5 cm.) contain the section from m. 134 to the end. These sheets are written entirely in pencil, and held together with two metal rings from a letter-file. They are bound in brown paper, which bears the legend: *Sketches of Variations for Organ 1941.* Date of completion on the last of these 5 sketch-sheets: *October 12, 1941.*

In addition, we find passages (with analysis by measures) from Op. 40 written in pencil on a sheet of transparent music paper, hand-lined with a distance of 3 mm. between the lines. These passages, numbered continuously in Roman numerals, were evidently intended for a motivic-thematic analysis.

The indications for registration given in the published version come from the organist Carl Weinrich. They were included without the knowledge of Schoenberg and in complete opposition to his artistic intentions. The following passages from letters prove this. The first, taken from a letter to the present writer, gives the composer's answer to questions on this point. The second comes from Schoenberg's answer to the Berlin musicologist Dr. David, who had brought about the work's first performance in Berlin (in the Paulus-Kirche, Zehlendorf).

From a letter to Josef Rufer, February 8, 1949:

The organ does not need to be an American one. Through the registration of a Mr. Weinrich, who has an unusually large organ in Princeton, the whole picture of my music is so confused that most people cannot make it out; but Mr. Stein [Ed. note: the publisher?] *has promised to give me a list which shows my original version. — — — If I were doing the registration, I should work it out only in such a way that all the voices come out clearly. But that seems to be impossible on the organ.*

From a letter to Dr. David, Berlin-Zehlendorf, May 10, 1949:

I consider the organ, in the first place, as an instrument with keyboard, and I write for the hands in the way that they can be used at a keyboard. I am little interested in the instrument's colours—for me, the colours have a meaning only when they make the idea clear—the motivic and thematic idea, and eventually its expression and character.

I wrote this piece at the suggestion of the Gray Company, which has published a series of modern organ pieces. Actually, I was supposed to write a short piece, but the variations interested me very much and it became a long piece.

Actually, I have set down my views about the organ more than forty years ago in an article which I never finished and therefore never published. Among other things, I demanded that such a huge instrument should be playable by at least two to four players at once. Eventually, a second, third or fourth set of manuals could be added. Above all, the dynamics of the instrument were very important to me, for only dynamics make for clarity and this cannot be achieved on most organs.

If one did not remember the splendid organ literature and the wonderful effect of this music in churches, one would have to say that the organ is an obsolete instrument today. No one—no musician and no layman—needs so many colours (in other words, so many registers) as the organ has. On the other hand, it would be very important to have the instrument capable of dynamically altering each single tone by itself (not just an entire octave-coupling)—from the softest pianissimo *to the greatest* forte.

Therefore, I believe that the instrument of the future will be constructed as follows: there will not be 60 or 70 different colours, but only a very small number (perhaps 2 to 6 would certainly be enough for me) which would have to include the entire range (7–8 octaves) and a range of expression from the softest pianissimo *to the greatest* fortissimo, *each for itself alone.*

The instrument of the future must not be more than, say, $1\frac{1}{2}$ times as large as a portable typewriter. For one should not strike too many wrong keys on a typewriter either. Why should it not be possible for a musician, also, to type so accurately that no mistakes occur?

I can imagine that, with such a portable instrument, musicians and music-lovers will get together in an evening in someone's home and play duos, trios and quartets; they will really be in a position to reproduce the idea-content of all symphonies. This is, naturally, a fantasy of the future, but who knows if we are so far away from it now? If tones can be transmitted quite freely into one's home (much as the radio transmits tone now) all that will probably be possible.

The registration of my Organ Variations is apparently designed for the Princeton University organ. This does not suit me at all and so many people have complained about it. I have asked my publisher to bring out an unregistered edition also, so that each player can make his own registration. For me, an edition in which the bass is often higher than the tenor is really unreadable. It seems unmusical to me, and, besides, I do not believe that a well-educated musician needs this.

In my original draft, I included an occasional indication of sonority. But this is only to indicate whether something should be played tenderly and cantabile, *or more roughly and* staccato, *or energetically—nothing more than that.*

A. WORKS WITH OPUS NUMBERS

ODE TO NAPOLEON BUONAPARTE (Lord Byron) for String Quartet, Piano and Reciter, Op. 41. The same for String Orchestra, Piano and Reciter, Op. 41b
G. Schirmer, New York

The manuscript, written in pencil, consists of 33 loose numbered pages of 16- or 17-lined music paper. Pp. 1–12 are of oblong format, 20×34·5 cm., while the remaining pages, also of oblong format, have the dimensions 25·5×34·5 cm. This appears to be the first draft; the first page of the score bears no title but has the date *March 12, 1942 (III/17)*. At the end of the manuscript is the date and signature *Brentwood Park June 12, 1942 Arnold Schoenberg*. The sheets of music paper, which have perforated margins, are held together with thin white twine.

Also, many sketches exist. Among these is a row-chart, which shows the structure (unusual in many respects) of the row on which the work is based.

FACSIMILE PLATE VI

On a second sheet of music paper, this row is placed in a very significant relationship to the chromatic scale.

FACSIMILE PLATE VII

A rough draft of the reciter's part (carried out from measures 1 to 171) and a typed copy of the text give information about Schoenberg's method of composing this work. Alongside the text, Schoenberg made various notes on the musical organization, and indications as to corresponding parts and motivic relationships. Furthermore, the text is divided up into measures, and there are some keywords to indicate the musical characterization.

The manuscript of the blueprint fair copy is in a letter-file. On top, we find a typed copy of the German text, fastened with wire to a metal ring. Then, on blueprint paper, there are the title page (22×30 cm.) and the Explanatory Notes (22×28 cm.); there are two versions of the Notes—obviously a first draft was later improved upon. Then, in quarto format (30×34 cm.), there are 36 pages of hand-lined blueprint paper (12-lined) laid in the file. The first page bears Schoenberg's stamp and copyright indication; the last (36th) page is signed and dated *June 12, 1942 | Brentwood Park | Los Angeles, | California*. Every two sheets of manuscript are separated by a sheet of white paper. On p. 5 there is an initialled correction in m. 38 (a quarter-rest in the 'cello). On p. 16, m. 116, the *marcato* signs (>) in the piano part are changed, with red pencil, into accentuation signs (—).

From a letter of Schoenberg to H. H. Stuckenschmidt, January 15, 1948:

I think that, as speaker for the 'Ode', only a very musical singer can be considered. The declamation is not so difficult as that of 'Pierrot'. But, nevertheless, it is necessary that the speaker remain in strict time everywhere except in the 'colla parte' passages. Many things in the music, which continually paints a background, underlines and illustrates, would be incomprehensible, even senseless, if word and note did not coincide at the right moment. I once compared this sort of error to the clown's joke: first the man falls down, then he raises his arm with the pistol, then one hears the shot.

...Lord Byron, who had at first admired Napoleon greatly, was so disappointed by his simple resignation that he made him the object of his bitterest scorn. I do not think that I failed to reflect this in my composition.

I. PUBLISHED WORKS

On December 16, 1949, Schoenberg wrote to George Barati in Oakland, California, concerning the version for string orchestra (original letter in English):

The Ode is originally written for string quartet and piano. Only to give Rodzinsky a chance to perform it, I added the bass voice. I personally prefer, of course, the solo performance, in which case I recommand the following sitting positions: . . . In case you want to use the orchestra, you must get the bass part and change the sitting of the performers correspondingly, always trying to have the speaker a little apart from the instrumental body.

CONCERTO FOR PIANO AND ORCHESTRA, Op. 42
G. Schirmer, New York

The manuscript was bound by Schoenberg himself. On the front of the heavy pasteboard cover, the title is printed in charcoal block-letters: *Piano Concerto (transparent Originals)*. The inscription on the inner title-page, also done in block-letters (in India ink), reads as follows: *To Henry Clay Shriver | Concerto for piano and orchestra by Arnold Schoenberg.* Alongside this, in script: *first performance by Stokowsky and Steuermann New York, broadcast NBC, February 6, 1944, NBC Studio* (the preceding words *Carnegie Hall* are crossed out). The 46 pages of the manuscript are written in short-score form, in black India ink on white blueprint paper with pre-printed lines (upright format, 28 × 38 cm.). Each sheet is attached to a sheet of white paper with gummed tape. Handwritten note on p. 1: *July 5, 42 begun first sketches—July 10, 42 by Arnold Schoenberg opus 42.* P. 40, upper right: *after an interruption of about six weeks. December 26, 42.* P. 46 (closing page): *finished December 29, 1942 || score finished December 30, 1942 Arnold Schoenberg.*

An additional fair copy, obviously not in Schoenberg's handwriting (in India ink on white blueprint paper, upright format, 33·5 × 43·5 cm.) is with G. Schirmer, Inc., in New York. It shows several corrections made in blue pencil by Schoenberg, and bears, in block letters, the completion-date *December 30, 1942.*

SKETCHES FOR OP. 42

There are 23 pages of sketches, on paper (including some blueprint paper) of varying sizes. Also, there is a row-chart. Most of this material is written in pencil, but some pages are written in India ink.

At m. 33 (the last measure of the melody played by the piano) there is the following note: *repeated in orchestra, piano adds a countermelody, this countermelody is repeated in orchestra, piano adds a second countermelody, all three together.* In these words, Schoenberg has briefly sketched the form of the first movement.

After m. 117 there is the following note: *13 mal 9 = 117!!! It costs two days to find out, what was wrong. A great error in construction at measure 13 × 9 = 117.*

A first draft of mm. 117–144, as well as m. 338 to the end, is written on 7 sheets (oblong format, 27 × 34 cm.) of music paper, usually on both sides of the page. Note of completion: *December 29, 1942.* With this are several sketch-sheets. On a first draft of the piano melody which opens the work, the date *July 5, 1942* is noted.

One sheet bears the following notes, with the corresponding musical sketches:

> *Life was so easy*
> *suddendly* [sic] *hatred broke out* (*Presto ♩= 72*)
> *a grave situation was created* (*Adagio*)
> *But life goes on* (*Rondo*)

The explanation is found in a letter to Oscar Levant, for whom the concerto was originally intended, but who later gave up the idea of playing it. Schoenberg wrote him that he had tried to find a few explanatory phrases for the piece, as this would probably be very much to Levant's taste.

THEME AND VARIATIONS for band, Op. 43A
The same for orchestra, Op. 43B
G. Schirmer, New York

The manuscript is bound. On the binding: *Theme and Variations for Windband Original on Transparentpaper*, initialled.

Title-page: *Theme and Variations for Windband by Arnold Schoenberg opus 43, Copyright 1943 by Arnold Schoenberg.*

On the back of the title-page, in ink: *Duration approximately 11 minutes.* This note is followed by an exact listing of the duration of the theme, of the individual variations and of the five parts of the Finale—in all, 11 minutes.

The manuscript consists of 42 pages of blueprint paper. The first 4 are written in ink, in ordinary score-form, on 32-lined paper with pre-printed lines (upright format, 28 × 38 cm.), while all the others are written in pencil, in short-score form, on hand-lined blueprint paper (24 × 34 cm.). All pages are affixed with gummed strips to pieces of white paper. Date of completion on p. 42, handwritten: *finished July 3, 1943 | score finished | August 24, 1943 | Arnold Schoenberg* (there is also a notation of copyright).

SKETCHES FOR THE VERSION FOR LARGE ORCHESTRA, OP. 43B

There are numerous pencil sketches of varying extent; also, there is an almost complete short score (beginning with m. 25), written in pencil on 22 loose sheets. The paper is hand-lined, 18 × 21·5 cm. in dimensions, partly in upright and partly in oblong format; only two sheets have been widened to 29 cm. by the pasting on of additional paper. The first sheet of this short score bears the note: *after a long interruption started here June 20, 1943*—the following page expands this statement with the added words: (*counterpoint textbook*). Note at the end: *ending sketched July 3, 1943.*—The third sheet (Variation II) again shows the date *June 20, 1943.*

In addition, there are 3 sheets of music paper with sketches of mm. 163–168, 1 sheet with mm. 148–162 and 1 with mm. 156–163. Also there is a table (accurate to seconds) with the duration of the individual variations, and 10 sheets of varying sizes with sketches pertaining to the original composition.

The composer on Op. 43A (original English):

My dear friend, the late Carl Engel, then President of the G. Schirmer, Inc. had asked me frequently to write a piece for wind band. He complained that the great number of such bands had an important influence on the development of love for music in America, but unfortunately there are only a small number of good original compositions available, while for the most of their playing they are limited to arrangements. A considerable part of these arrangements reveals a poor or at least a low taste; and besides they are not even well orchestrated.

I know from my own experience that, though the imbalance inherent in this combination of instruments is one of the basic factors of the poor, unclear and trivial sound, the technique of orchestration has not changed there considerably during the last about sixty years. Compare to that the great development in orchestration which took place through the achievements of Mahler, Strauss, Debussy and their successors.

When I promised to write such a piece, I knew at once that my ordinary manner of writing would be much too difficult, except for a very small number of the best bands and their conductors. Accordingly I decided I had to resolve a pedagogical task, and by this decision also a number of other problems were decided.

From a letter to the conductor Fritz Reiner, October 29, 1944 (translated):

. . . it is not one of my principal works; anybody can see that, for it is no twelve-tone composition. It is one of those works that one writes in order to enjoy one's own virtuosity and, in addition, to give a group of amateurs—in this case, wind bands—something better to play. I can assure you, and I think I can prove it—that as far as technique is concerned it is a masterpiece, and I believe it is also original, and I know it is also inspired. Not only because I cannot write even 10 measures without inspiration, but I really wrote the piece with great pleasure.

PRELUDE, Op. 44, for mixed chorus and orchestra
Edition Shilkret, Malverne, Long Island, N.Y.

The 'Prelude' is the first piece in a suite for chorus and orchestra to which several contemporary composers, commissioned by the publisher Nathaniel Shilkret, contributed one movement apiece. The basic idea was to select Biblical texts. Schoenberg's composition was conceived by him as a prelude to the Creation ('Genesis'). Accordingly, the mixed chorus which enters near the end of the piece does not sing words, but (on vowels) only notes.

The manuscript is written in crayon (?) and pencil, in short-score form, on one side of each of 19 numbered, loose sheets of blueprint paper. These are in oblong format, 28 × 44 cm., with 3 holes in the left-hand margin. The 13th page is numbered 12a; several pages bear the stamped address. Every now and then, the notes are traced over with black India ink. The first 6 pages are written on heavier paper, having 4 or 5 staves with 5 mm. space between the lines; all the other pages are on hand-lined blueprint paper.

On p. 3, there is a ★ at m. 12, referring to the following handwritten footnote (original English): *always without Hollywood style of vibrato and portamento; even large intervals must not be connected by gliding, but, if necessary by strecking. This gliding is of a detestable sentimentality. Sch.* The later photocopied draft of the score shows a shortened version of this comment, without mention of the 'Hollywood style'.

No date is given for the beginning. Date of completion: *September 30, 1945.*

A. WORKS WITH OPUS NUMBERS

The beginning of the four-voiced double fugue is sketched in pencil on two hand-lined sheets of music paper (upright format, 23 × 30·5 cm.; 4 staves, 5 mm. space between lines) written on one side of the page only. An additional sketch-sheet of hand-lined transparent paper (upright format, 28 × 34 cm.), contains, on one side of the page, mm. 47–59, on the other, mm. 76–79—all written in pencil.

STRING TRIO, Op. 45
Boelke-Bomart, Inc., Hillsdale, N.Y.

The manuscript, written in pencil, consists of 21 numbered loose sheets of blueprint paper (upright format, 42 × 60 cm., 5 mm. space between lines, 12-lined). Handwritten note on first page: *August 20, 1946;* on last page: *Arnold Schoenberg September 23, 1946.* At lower left of page; *Ossia Measures 28–29 (Viola and 'Cello).*

Also, there are several row-charts, and a detailed time-chart, as well as 4 sketch-sheets (hand-lined with 5 mm. space between lines, oblong format, 29 × 43 cm.), one of which bears the date *June 7, 1946.* All of this material is written in pencil.

A SURVIVOR FROM WARSAW, Op. 46
for Narrator, Men's Chorus and Orchestra
Boelke-Bomart, Inc., Hillsdale, N.Y.

The manuscript is in the Library of Congress. It is written, sometimes in pencil and sometimes in ink, one one side of each of 20 sheets of thin white paper (oblong format, alternating between 27·5 × 37·5 and 28 × 43 cm., 5 mm. space between lines). It is in short-score form. The music-sheets are pasted to brown wrapping-paper. The title, in ink, reads as follows: *A survivor of* [*!*] *Warsaw | by Arnold Schoenberg | opus 46.* Note on the first page: *begonnen 11. August 1947;* on the last page: *finished August 23, 1947 | Arnold Schoenberg.*

The legacy also contains a photocopy of the manuscript. This copy, which is bound with gummed tape, shows a number of small corrections and alterations made in black, red or blue pencil; several badly reproduced passages have been traced over. The handwritten title-page of the cover of this photocopy reads as follows: *Dedicated to the Koussevitzky Foundation who commissioned it | A Survivor from Warsaw | For narrator and Mens Choir and | Orchestra* [the precise orchestration follows] *| op 46 | by Arnold Schoenberg | Copyright 1947 by Arnold Schoenberg.*

At the lower right of the title-page is the following note: *This text is based partly upon reports which I have received directly or indirectly A. Sch.*

The same title for the work, printed in block letters, is found on the brown cardboard cover of a photocopy of the score made by René Leibowitz from the short score. This photocopy, which is also in the Library of Congress, consists of 21 pages (upright format, 27·5 × 37·5 cm.). It bears the note: 'Score made by René Leibowitz, Hollywood December 1947 | Finished August 23, 1947.' On the first page is Schoenberg's handwritten note: *Copyright by Arnold Schoenberg 1947.*

The row-chart of the work is found in the legacy, both in the original (white blueprint paper with 5 mm. space between lines, oblong format, 28 × 43 cm.) and in a photocopy.

Also, there are many sketches for both text and music, as well as a printed score *with corrections* (these words appear in red pencil on the title-page). These rather extensive corrections pertain almost exclusively to the German translation by Margaret Peter.

PHANTASY FOR VIOLIN with piano accompaniment, Op. 47
C. F. Peters, Frankfurt—London—New York

Since Schoenberg wanted to write a phantasy for violin *with piano accompaniment* and not a duo, he first composed the entire violin part alone. It is written in pencil on 3 sheets of hand-lined blueprint paper of different sizes, as follows: I, 43 × 56 cm., II, 43 × 37 cm., and III, 43 × 75 cm. The first page bears the handwritten note *begun March 3, 1949*; on the third page is written *March 22, 1949 Arnold Schoenberg*. During the course of the violin part, the row-forms which are being used, as well as those which are planned for the piano part, are noted in red, green or black pencil.

The manuscript of the whole work (i.e., including the piano accompaniment) consists of 10 loose sheets of blueprint paper (upright format, 43 × 56 cm.), lying in a loose pasteboard cover. This manuscript is written in pencil, and the paper is hand-lined as in Op. 45 and Op. 50b. Handwritten note on the first page: *Copyright 1949 by Arnold Schoenberg*. There is also the stamped address, and, at the upper left of the page, the note *March 3 (March 5) 1949*. Both violin and piano parts contain subsequent insertions, ossia indications, etc. A metronome mark is added to the 'Meno mosso' at m. 34 ($\downarrow$ = 46). Each page bears the composer's stamped address.

THREE SONGS, Op. 48, for low voice
Boelke-Bomart, Inc., Hillsdale, N.Y.

The manuscript of the first draft of the 'Three Songs' (texts by Jakob Haringer) consists of a double sheet (upright format, 34·5 × 51 cm.), and contains the following compositions, written in ink or India ink:

Page 1: *Mädchenlied* ('Maiden's Song'). Upper right of page: *18.II*—date of completion: *23.II. 1933 Arnold Schönberg*.

Page 2: Continuation and close (mm. 16 ff.) of the song 'Sommermüd' ('Weary of Summer'), the beginning of which occupies the lower half of

Page 3: This song is dated *14.I.–15.I. 1933*. On the upper half of p. 3 is the song 'Tot' ('Dead'), dated *17.II.–18.II. 1933*. Also there is a small sheet with sketches for the songs.

In addition, we have a fair copy in Schoenberg's own hand, with each song dated and signed, written on music paper of upright format (34 × 26·5 cm.) and bound with stout twine.

These songs, first composed in Berlin, were forgotten by Schoenberg under the strain of the happenings of the following years. He found them only later, by chance, among his manuscripts. This accounts for the high opus-number, which he added many years after the songs had been composed.

A. WORKS WITH OPUS NUMBERS

THREE FOLKSONGS, Op. 49, for mixed chorus a cappella
Edward B. Marks Music Corporation, New York

I. 'Es gingen zwei Gespielen gut' ('Two Comely Maidens'; before 1540)

First sketch on 2 staves, in pencil, on 4 half-sheets of blueprint paper. Text handwritten, partly in pencil and partly in ink. Date of completion: *VI/24/48 Arnold Schoenberg.*

A copy on 4 staves (corresponding to the 4 choral voices) is lacking.

II. 'Der Mai tritt ein mit Freuden' ('Now May Has Come with Gladness'; before 1545)

First draft noted on 2 staves, in pencil, with an initialled flourish at the close. This is on a half-sheet of blueprint paper (oblong format, 43 × 28 cm.). It is recopied on 4 staves, on a double sheet torn in two (both sheets 43 × 28). The text is partly written in ink, partly typed. Date of completion: *June 26, 1948 Arnold Schoenberg.*

III. 'Mein Herz in steten Treuen' ('To Her I Shall Be Faithful'; 15th cent.)

Written in pencil, on 4 staves, on 2 half-sheets (oblong format, 43 × 28 cm.) and 1 whole loose sheet (upright format, 43 × 56 cm.). The text was added by Schoenberg in ink. In accordance with the varying syllable-relationships in the different stanzas, the rhythm is changed from time to time. Also, the sign indicating the principal voice (**H**) has been added later. The first sketch for this chorus exists, too. It is on 2 staves, and has been initialled by the composer.

One and a half pages of the same size contain sketches for the three arrangements, drafts in several voices, some in stretto and double counterpoint ('Mein Herz in steten Treuen') with a countermelody.

(See also the commentary of Schoenberg on his arrangement for voice and piano of the 'Four German Folksongs'; below, under I, B, 'Works without Opus Numbers'.)

DREIMAL TAUSEND JAHRE ('Thrice a Thousand Years'), for mixed chorus a cappella, Op. 50A
(Text by Dagobert D. Runes)
B. Schott's Söhne, Mainz

The manuscript is written in pencil on 3 sheets of 12-lined transparent music paper (upright format, 43 × 56 cm.). No beginning date; date of completion, noted in Schoenberg's handwriting: *Copyright Arnold Schoenberg April 20, 1949.*

With this are 3 sheets (as above, only on paper of 43 × 28 cm.) of sketches. Among other things, we find the first 4 measures in a version which differs from the final one. Following this, with erasures and corrections, is the final version of mm. 1–3. In the middle of the lower margin, a diagonal strip of 20 × 5 cm. has been cut away.

The facsimile of the manuscript was published by the Swedish magazine 'Prisma' (Nr. 4/1949). There, it was still numbered Op. 49B. Originally, Schoenberg published the 'Three Folksongs', Op. 49, without any opus number. When 'Dreimal tausend Jahre' was published in 'Prisma', Schoenberg added the number 49A to the 'Three Folksongs' and gave 'Dreimal tausend Jahre' the number 49B. However, when 'De Profundis' was finished, Schoenberg found that 'Dreimal tausend Jahre' went better with it than with the tonal folksongs, and therefore changed the opus number 49B to 50A. 'De Profundis', accordingly, received the number 50B. Finally, the 'Three Folksongs' were numbered Op. 49 by Schoenberg. The explanation of this numbering is due to Richard Hoffmann, Schoenberg's pupil and his last assistant. It receives its definitive confirmation in Schoenberg's own 'Verzeichnis meiner Werke' ('Catalogue of my Works').

PSALM 130, DE PROFUNDIS, Op. 50B
for six-part mixed chorus a cappella
Israeli Music Publications (Leeds Music Corporation, New York; Chester Ltd., London, etc.)

Title-page (oblong format, 30 × 45 cm.) on blueprint paper. Title printed by Schoenberg himself in India-ink block letters, and signed: *Arnold Schoenberg fecit, 1950*. The title reads:

Psalm 130 / for Mixed Chorus a cappella / (six voices) / by Arnold Schoenberg / opus 50b.

The manuscript consists of 7 loose sheets of blueprint paper (upright format, 43 × 56 cm.) folded in half. The paper is hand-lined (12 lines, as in the String Trio) and the manuscript is written in pencil or crayon. Handwritten note on the first page: *June 20, 1950*; on the last page: *July 2, 1950 Arnold Schoenberg*. The Psalm was composed to the Hebrew text; the Latin and English texts are printed as preface to the published edition.

Six sheets of hand-lined music paper (upright format, 21·5 × 28 cm.) contain pencil sketches. Date of completion: *2. Juli 1950 A. Sch.* With this are 2 sheets of paper bearing the text in Hebrew and English.

History of the work's origin:

Chemjo Vinaver, the editor of the 'Anthology of Jewish Music' (Edward B. Marks Music Corp., New York), asked Schoenberg for a composition for his anthology. He sent the composer the original Hebrew text of the 'De Profundis', and also, at the latter's request, an English translation.

From a letter of Schoenberg to Vinaver, May 29, 1951 (original English):

. . . Should you have already performed it, I would like to know how it came out, that is, how the dramatic character appeared which is produced through the alternation of speaking and singing voices. I want also to know wether as a chorus director, you see great difficulties to perform the piece. There is no objection of mine against using with every voice a wood instrument to keep intonation and rythm in order: because this is always my main demand and I deem it more important than the so-called 'pure' sound of voices.

[Both editions are posthumous. For Schoenberg's expression marks, both should be consulted. That of Israeli Music Publications (1953) uses only treble and bass clefs; Schoenberg's original C clefs are retained in Vinaver's 'Anthology of Jewish Music' (1955).]

MODERNER PSALM, Op. 50C
for speaker, four-part mixed chorus and orchestra (text by composer); unfinished
B. Schott's Söhne, Mainz

The manuscript, written in short-score form, in pencil, extends to m. 86. It consists of 11 loose sheets of thin, hand-lined paper (3 mm. space between lines). Each sheet consists of 2 pasted-together notebook-sheets. The first 3 sheets (oblong format, 40×18 cm., 8-lined) are written on both sides of the page, the remaining 8 (oblong format, 37·5×25 cm., 9-lined) on one side only. In all, there are 15 written and numbered pages (the 13th page is numbered 12a). On p. 12, several clefs and one passage in the orchestral accompaniment (mm. 68–69) are written in ink (traced over?). Likewise, after p. 12a a part of the text is written in ink, as is part of the short score on the last page. The manuscript shows that the composition was begun on *2. Oktober 1950*. The text of the Psalm, which was the first in a series of such texts of religious character written by the composer, was written on *29. September 1950*. Schoenberg called them 'Moderne Psalmen' (see under 'Poems', No. 13).

Rudolf Kolisch transcribed the short score into a full score, and published them both, together with a great part of the existing sketches and all of the psalm texts (see below, 'Poems'). This material was published by Schott's Söhne, Mainz.

Schoenberg's 'Verzeichnis meiner Werke' lists this Psalm as Op. 50C. Therefore, we list it here, even though it is an unfinished work.

ADDENDUM

1. SIX ORCHESTRAL SONGS, Op. 8

See * p. 27, and add:

There is also a manuscript piano reduction (called *Partiturauszug* on the title page). Like all other piano reductions of these songs, it is written in ink on 12-lined music paper (upright format, 26×34·5 cm.).

2. SUITE FOR PIANO, Op. 25

See * p. 46, and add:

A note in blue pencil: *genau beachten*! refers to the directions (written in ordinary lead-pencil) for the printing of the title-page: *alles in einfacher unverzierter 'Romana' nicht zu gross, kleiner als hier vorgezeichnet*. ('Follow directions carefully! Everything in simple, unadorned 'Romana', not too large, smaller than sketched here.')

On the bottom of p. 2, in red ink: *Es ist unangenehm, aus dem Auftrag zum Platzlassen für die beiden andern Sprachen, sowie aus den Klebespuren und dem Buchstabenrest bestätigt zu sehen, dass das Manuskript der Anmerkungen im Verlag vorhanden war. Schönberg*. ('It is unpleasant to have confirmation of the fact that the manuscript of the directions was at the publisher's, in the traces of glue, the remaining letters, and the instructions to leave room for the two other languages.')

B. WORKS WITHOUT OPUS NUMBERS

(a) Original Compositions

GURRELIEDER (Jens Peter Jacobsen), for soli, chorus and orchestra
Universal Edition, Vienna

The manuscript, which differs in some particulars from the final version, presents the first draft of the composition. It is loose in a cover, with the handwritten note (translated): *Gurrelieder 1st draft Parts II and III without final chorus—who has the 1st part?* It consists of 68 pages, numbered in blue pencil, written in ink on paper of from 12 to 28 lines (upright format, 26·5 × 34·5 cm.). There are numerous corrections, compositional changes, additions and completions. Also, there are especially precise indications of instrumentation (added in pencil, probably, in some cases, later than the time of composition). This draft (undated, bearing the title written in pencil at the top of the first page of score) already closely resembles the short-score form which was almost exclusively used by Schoenberg later on. This is particularly clear in the 'Melo-drama'; there, the composer uses 3 to 5 staves for the instrumental voices, which, up to that point, had been written for the most part on 2 staves only.

The manuscript begins with Waldemar's song (Part II) and ends with the first 4 measures of the entrance of the final chorus. The question posed by Schoenberg, 'Who has the first part?' can now be answered; for the apparently missing parts were also found in the legacy. They consist of the first draft of the entire first part and of the final chorus, also written in short-score form, in ink, on 3 staves. Here, too, indications of instrumentation have been written at the same time as the first draft—partly in ink, partly in pencil. Part I is written on 30 sheets of music paper (upright format, 26·5 × 34·5 cm.), 5 of which are used for the 'Song of the Wood-Dove'. There follow 3 pages of Part II, Waldemar's song, which is also in-cluded in the manuscript described above. The final chorus is written on 5 sheets of upright format, 26·5 × 34·5 cm. The page numbered 7 was originally No. 1, as is noted on the upper right-hand corners of the pages. The new numbering (at the bottom of the page) became neces-sary because the introduction was evidently composed later and came before the first (now 7th) page. This page 7 still bears the title of the work and its date: *Gurrelieder von Peter Jens Jacobsen, Begonnen im März 1900.* At the bottom of p. 19: *7./4.900;* on p. 24: *14./4. 900.*

FACSIMILE PLATE VIII

In addition, there are 23 sketch-sheets, including, among other things, parts of the melo-drama. In Schoenberg's regularly used copy of the published piano reduction, the following sentences have been written in ink, undated, on p. 3 (original English): *My consent to a change of ownership must be written by myself or my heirs on this page and signed by myself or by them. Arnold Schoenberg. This score is my property and must not be sold if I do not agree by my signature to it. Arnold Schoenberg.*

The manuscript of the 'Gurrelieder' full score is in the possession of Universal Edition, Vienna. It is bound in yellow wrapping-paper, and consists of 2 volumes, written in ink.

Volume I (Part I) consists of a title-page (music paper) and 48 sheets comprising 95 numbered, written pages (upright format, 36 × 57·5 cm., 48-lined). The last page is blank. Various notes to the engraver are written diagonally across the title-page, in pencils of various colours. Also, there are 3 stamped addresses: *Wien XIII Gloriettegasse, Berlin-Südende*, and *Mödling bei Wien*. The score shows many entries in coloured pencil, made partly by Schoenberg himself, partly by others (conductors?). There are many, often drastic, instrumental retouches! In the seventh and eighth measures after cue No. 27, changes have been pencilled into the English horn and bass clarinet parts. At the bottom of p. 28, a piece of paper with directions to the engraver has been pasted on. On p. 33, 4 measures in the string parts (beginning 1 measure before cue No. 32) have been pasted over with another version. A piece of blue paper pasted on the top of p. 77 contains detailed instructions as to the size of the printed score. Finally, on p. 92, the third measure after cue No. 109 has been cut.—Vol. I is undated throughout.

Volume II (Parts II and III) begins with an unnumbered title-page (*II. Theil*) and contains 43 sheets (pages numbered 96–179). To p. 122 (inclusive), the format is the same as that of the first volume. From p. 123 till the end, paper of upright format (30 × 40 cm.), also 48-lined, is used; it is also enlarged to 36 × 57·5 cm. by the pasting-on of an additional paper margin. As in the first volume, there are also instrumental retouches here. Pp. 177–179 are either entirely or partly pasted over with a new version. After Parts II and III, there are stamped addresses: Wien XIII Gloriettegasse 43. Signed note of completion: *Arnold Schönberg Zehlendorf 7. November 1911.*

[The autograph full score was published in facsimile with copyright date 1912. It does not contain the revisions described above. They were taken up, with many others, in the engraved score of 1920. The cancelled third bar after figure 109, however, does not occur in Berg's vocal score, which appeared contemporaneously with the facsimile.]

LIED DER WALDTAUBE ('Song of the Wood-Dove')
Version for voice and chamber orchestra
Universal Edition, Vienna

Lied der Waldtaube (aus den Gurreliedern), Bearbeitung für Kammerorchester und Gesang (there follows the exact orchestration, with 17 instruments plus percussion) *von Arnold Schönberg*: this is the handwritten title of the manuscript. Under it is a note which we may translate as follows: *prepared in connection with the performance of the Chamber Symphony in Copenhagen, on which occasion, besides the 2nd Quartet, the Song of the Wood-Dove is to be sung by Frau Marya Freund from Paris.*

The further use of this arrangement is permitted exclusively in small halls, in connection with performances of the Chamber Symphony. Mödling 14./XII. 1922 Arnold Schönberg.

The manuscript, written in score-form in ink, consists of 12 sheets of 32-lined music paper (upright format, 34·5 × 41 cm.), which are bound in a thin grey cardboard cover. Note of completion: *Mödling 14. December 1922 Arnold Schönberg.*

I. PUBLISHED WORKS

SUITE FOR STRING ORCHESTRA
G. Schirmer, New York

Suite im alten Stile für Streichorchester von Arnold Schönberg—this is the title (written by the composer in block letters) of the manuscript, which, with 19 related sketch-sheets, is in the possession of Dr. Arthur Wilhelm in Basle. The hand-bound manuscript is written in black India ink on 18-lined music paper (upright format, 26·5 × 33·5 cm.), and consists of 28 sheets comprising 51 written, numbered pages. At the bottom of the title-page is a red-pencilled note (here translated): *The spots on this score are Klemperer's drops of sweat.* (Klemperer had given the world première of the work on May 18, 1935, with the Los Angeles Philharmonic Orchestra.) On the back of the title-page, there is a pencilled note (original English): ⊢⌐ = *Hauptstimme could be remplaced by P(principal part).* An additional pencilled note at the bottom of p. 1 may be translated as follows: *Prefatory note to each part | all directions Italian or English | the engraver must make everything as I give it.* Continuing in red pencil: *The continuous measure-numbers are to be put into all the parts.* The composer's subsequent corrections (cancellation-signs, wrong notes, etc.) and additions (dynamics, phrasing, rests and accents) are in red or violet pencil. On the other hand, the dynamic changes made in ordinary lead pencil from p. 4 onwards were obviously not written by the composer. In fact, they even contradict two of his 'authentic' dynamic markings in violet pencil—a 'fp' in the second half of m. 76 and a 'molto rit.' on p. 27.

On pp. 18, 25 and 33, calico strips, sticking out from the side of the page, have been attached; on each, the name of the movement beginning on that page is written. These are obviously intended to indicate where the page should be turned (e.g., where to turn back for the 'da capo' of the minuet).

On pp. 12, 13, 15, 17 and 29, the following measures have been pasted over with new versions: 145, 149–151, 154 (viola), 176, 190 and 389. P. 37 of the score is pasted over entirely with a new version of mm. 473–488: the same thing has been done with the upper part of p. 38 (mm. 489–491). From time to time, there are erasures in individual measures.

The second movement (Adagio) was completed on *6.XI. 1934*. The note beside this date, *Takt 192 entfällt* ('measure-number 192 is to be dropped'), has to do with the erroneous measure-numbering (later corrected). The Minuet shows *23.X. 34* as its date of completion; the Gavotte, *11.X. 1934*. Beside the latter date is a pencilled note, *5 Minuten 10 Sekunden*. The score, according to a note at the end, was completed on *26.XII. 1934* and is signed *Arnold Schoenberg 5860 Canyon Cove Hollywood*.

The above-mentioned 19 loose sketch-sheets for this work (oblong format, 34·5 × 27 cm., and upright format, 26·5 × 33 cm., 1 sheet 27 × 20·5 cm.) are written partly in pencil, partly in ink, and are affixed to cardboard with paper strips. They are in a home-made cover of thin grey cardboard, with the handwritten title (in pencil) *Suite für Streichorchester*. They include first drafts of large continuous sections of the Suite (Fuga, Gavotte, Andante) as well as rough sketches for these. One sheet, bearing the note *7.9.34*, contains a sketch for the stretto of the fugue in the first movement. The unusually numerous sketches for this work give valuable insights into the technical mastery of the composer.

This Suite is also noteworthy in that it was Schoenberg's first purely tonal composition since the Second String Quartet in F sharp minor—a lapse of 28 years. The stimulations and considerations which led to the composition of the work may be deduced from the following

8. First autograph of the GURRELIEDER.

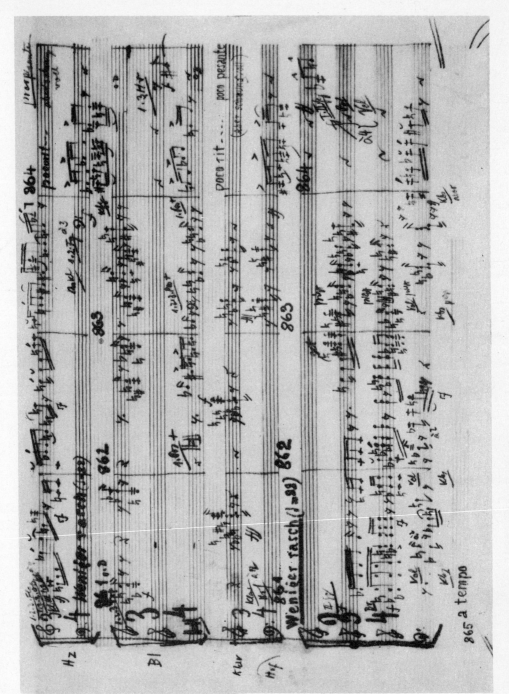

9. A page of short score from Act II of Moses und Aron.

10. Sketch I for Moses und Aron.

11. Sketch II for Moses und Aron.

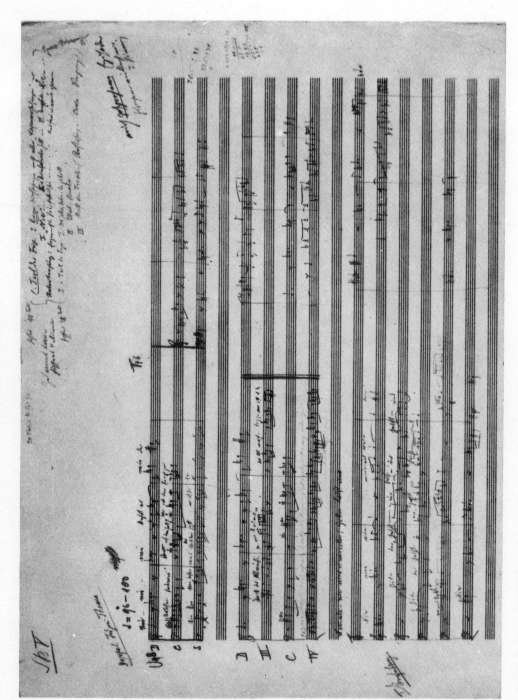

12. Sketch for the Interlude in MOSES UND ARON.

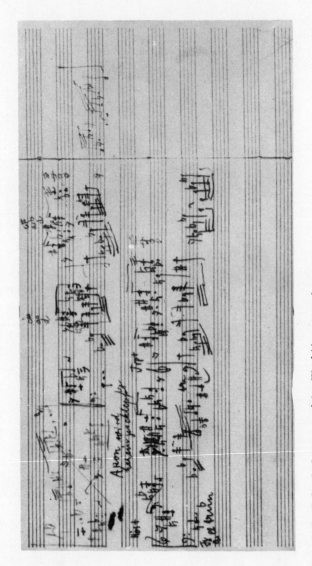

13. Sketch for the beginning of Act III of MOSES UND ARON.

'Sketch of a Foreword to the Suite for String Orchestra, composed for College Orchestras by Arnold Schoenberg' and from a letter to the conductor Fritz Reiner. The foreword (which Schoenberg then did not include in the score after all) reads, in translation, as follows:

The composition of this piece was suggested to me by the favourable impressions and perspectives which Prof. Martin Bernstein, New York University, gave me concerning the ambitions, achievements and successes of American college orchestras. I became convinced that every composer—especially every modern composer, and I above all—should be interested in encouraging such efforts. For here, a new spiritual and intellectual basis can be created for art; here, young people can be given the opportunity of learning about the new fields of expression and the means suitable for these.

Thus, my task was set. This is what I had to achieve.

Without harming the students by a premature dose of 'Atonality Poison', I had to prepare them, using harmony which leads to modern feelings, for modern performance technique. Fingerings, bowings, phrasing, intonation, dynamics, rhythm—all this should be developed without the introduction of insuperable difficulties. But modern intonation, contrapuntal technique and phrase-formation were also to be emphasized, so that the student might gradually come to realize that 'melody' does not consist only of those primitive, unvaried, symmetrical structures which are the delight of mediocrity in all countries and among all peoples. Already here there are higher forms, which belong to a higher order of art not only technically, but also, and especially, spiritually.

In doing this, I was guided not only by my personal knowledge of the stringed instruments, but also by the advice of the one who suggested the work to me and who has practical experience in this field.

With the piece, an analysis (perhaps of some individual sections only?) is included. This, too, has a double purpose. Above all, it should enrich the knowledge of the student players; but it should also be informative to their teacher and conductor. Today, so many call themselves 'conservative' who have nothing to conserve because they possess nothing that is worth conserving or maintaining—not even the capacity to write a fugue like the one in this work. Therefore, they maintain and conserve only their own incapacity and ignorance; they want to protect themselves and others from the possibility that new things should ever be said which would call for at least one prerequisite: technical competence. Therefore, this work should give genuine, real teachers and propagators of culture—genuine and authentic leaders, in other words—an opportunity which they have certainly been wishing for: the chance to educate their students to have the deepest respect for artistic capacity, and to make it clear to them that culture can be maintained only through growth. Like everything that lives, it can live only so long as it grows; as soon as it stops developing, it dies and withers away. Therefore, any technical or spiritual achievement is worth conserving (from the artistic point of view) only because it is preliminary to a new step forward, to new life. Only then—and only therefore—is it worth conserving. Perhaps after the above it is superfluous to mention that this piece represents no repudiation of what I have created up till now.

In a letter to Fritz Reiner (April 24, 1939) Schoenberg recommends to him not only this work but also the Second Chamber Symphony (original letter in English):

Both can only be called a preparatory introduction to my present style of composition. But I believe a start should be made to acquaint the public with my music. P.S. Do not be disappointed if at first glance you see that the themes of the 'Suite' do not have my personal style. You know perhaps that the Work was intended for student orchestra. After all, a considerable number of the themes are worth-wile, and insofar as the others are concerned, they might be considered as one would consider a theme for variation, and the question then is only: what could a composer do with them. And from this viewpoint, I dont think I deserve contempt.

MOSES UND ARON
Opera in Three Acts
B. Schott's Söhne, Mainz

The text, written by the composer, is complete; the music for the first two acts was also completed. The third act, whose text consists of a single lengthy scene, exists musically only in the form of sketches of a few measures.

The manuscript of the score of Acts I and II is loose in a much-damaged thin grey cardboard cover. It consists of 100 sheets of music paper (upright format, 27 × 34·5 cm., 32-lined) comprising 200 numbered pages, of which the last 4 are blank. It is written in ink. Every 10 sheets (5 double sheets) are bound together with white thread.

The beginning of the score is marked on p. 1: *Lugano 17. VII. 1930 17. Juli (Schönberg).* On the last page (196) is written: *Ende des II. Aktes / Barcelona 10./III. 1932 / Arnold Schönberg.*

FACSIMILE PLATE IX

In detail, the score shows the following notations (translated here):

Pages 1–3: in the margins, detailed directions for performance. On p. 1, a slip of paper has been pasted: *RECIT* [in blue pencil; all the rest of this note in ordinary lead pencil] *check through the entire score and, at every necessary spot, indicate by means of the sign* V [a breathing-sign] *where the singer should begin freely after the accompaniment, or, vice versa, the accompaniment after the speaker or singer.*

Page 23 (after the end of the second scene): *22.VIII. 1930.*

Page 29, m. 330: *interrupted 8 days here, continued on 9. IX.*

Page 41, after m. 480: *broke off here, 30.IX. 1930; the next ten measures in the first days of October, 1930, in Meran. Then a break till Berlin!*

Page 42, after m. 483: *continued here in Berlin, January (15.) 1931; but without success!* [illegible word] *continued in Territet, 15./V. 31.*

Page 60: new versions are pasted over m. 685 (chorus), mm. 686–689 (chorus and orchestra), m. 690 through first half of 691 (chorus).

Page 68: mm. 794–795 pasted over with a new version.

Page 85 (bottom): *End of the first act, Territet 14.VII. 1931.*

Page 86: blank.

Page 87: *Interlude, Territet 20./VII. 1931*—date of completion: *25.VII. 1931.*

Page 92: blank.

Page 93: *II. Akt 26./VII. 1931*—date of beginning.

Page 97, after m. 109: pencilled date *28./VII.*

Page 105: the lower half of this page (mm. 194–199) is pasted over with a new version.

Page 136, right-hand margin, after m. 543: *stopped in Montreux, end of September—Barcelona, continued middle of October.*

Page 141, right-hand margin, in pencil: *the* ⌐ . . . ¬ *signs and the directions for staging and playing are to be entered into the score of about the last 50 pages as well as the following ones!*

Page 148, right-hand margin, in pencil: *put in double-bars throughout the entire score to mark the boundaries of important sections (principal tempo, etc.).*

Page 179: the second half of m. 981 is pasted over with a new version; the same happens in Aaron's part on p. 180, m. 986.

The following items also belong to the score:

(*a*) a loose piece of paper, on one side of which is written a detailed listing of the soloists as well as of the proportions and numbers of the chorus.

(*b*) a piece of paper fastened to the first page (12·5 × 19·5 cm.), on which the precise orchestration is noted.

(*c*) 4 sheets (26·5 × 21·5 cm.) comprising 7 pages, closely written in ink and numbered. These are especially important, since they give the most precise indications for *instrumentalists, conductor, notation, dynamics, recitative, singers and singing technique, acting, decorations, painting, lighting, the 'Dances around the Golden Calf', speakers, etc.* Excerpts from these instructions are translated here because they show the clarity and plasticity with which Schoenberg realized the visions of his fantasy, taking full account of the utmost technical and artistic possibilities available to the theatre for this realization.

Excerpts from the instructions:

(Page 1) Recitative (*see remarks in 'Von heute auf morgen'*) *refers especially to the abandonment of beats of equal length. Therefore, indications as to speed may still be used. Here, they should always be noted in the singer's part in small letters and in parentheses, e.g. (not too slowly). The indication 'recitative' then holds till the next regular tempo indication, which will also bear a metronome-mark.*

Singers (*soloists and chorus*) *and speakers: in these parts, certain notes often appear on a beat where, according to the usual declamation, they should not be. However, it is self-evident that such passages should be interpreted according to the requirements of speech-accents rather than according to the conventional accentuation of strong beats (which I consider inartistic, and which I alter as needed with my sign* ▼, *indicating shifting accents).*

(Page 3) Producer, acting, staging: *In several scenes, there must definitely be a change of scenery. These are as follows:* [not filled in] . . . *But I have nothing against it if the stage-director also designs other stagings for other parts of scenes, so long as he does it tactfully, tastefully and moderately. Everything which brings out the idea is good. I do not wish to hinder the director from bringing in a bit more variety where it is necessary. Only, he should consider this: it could be that constant change might, in the end, prove more monotonous than the style which is indicated here.*

In the fifth scene *of Act II, the musical characterization was purposely so planned that the two actors (Moses and Aaron) have much more freedom than usual. However, the musical characterization is fixed enough to distinguish between soft and hard, energetic and tender, defiant and unresisting, excited and quiet. But, in the transition from one mood to another, much is left quite free; and the finer nuances, too, are not so strictly notated. For the task of these two actors can hardly be fulfilled unless they add their own expression to what is written.*

The meeting of Aaron and Moses (Act I, Scene 2) *is to be staged in such a way that the two char-acters ostentatiously talk 'past' each other instead of* to *each other* (*to put it trivially*)*. For instance, Aaron might stand left front and Moses right centre; they should not look at each other.*

The entrance of Moses and Aaron before Act I, Scene 4, must have the effect that is described by the chorus. The approach of both must seem unreal. *Floating, gliding—it must be unclear whether they are walking side by side or who* (*if either one*) *goes first. Their way must seem unusually long.*

Aaron (*Act II, m. 138*): '*He stays upon this height*'—*the singer must make a 'pointing' gesture which indicates not only the mountain but also the* spiritual height. *Therefore, he should not point merely in the direction of the mountain, but, rather, simply* upwards.

'*Dances around the Golden Calf*'—*m. 824: it is by no means my intention that these different rhythms* (*especially in the percussion*) *should fix the parts of the measures during which the 'beating and smashing'* ('*zerschlagen, zertrümmern*') *should regularly be audible or visible. Naturally, the stage-director will have to choose the noisier moments for this sort of thing, and will be careful not to 'let loose' during softer passages, or to permit 'empty' movements on the stage* (*i.e., movements when there is no movement in the music*). *But, although accents and phrases are, in a way, quite irregular to the ear in this passage, they would still be too regular for the eye; if one followed them exactly in the staging, the effect would be too 'marionette-like'. Therefore, the stage-director must find another basis for* '*his irregularity!*'

Chorus, *at text* '*Stay away from us with your God . . .*' ('*Bleib uns fern mit deinem Gott*', *Act I, Scene 4*), *must be constantly in motion. Its position is about as follows:* [drawing]; *in this scene, the chorus is always far to the front of the stage. Moses and Aaron are more in the background, but visible, i.e., standing on a higher level. If Moses and Aaron come nearer to the foreground, they should not come right to the front of the stage at once. They should come further and further forward only when the miracles occur!*

During the third miracle in Act I, the water should be quite clear when it first begins to flow; it should not begin to turn red until one has been able to see that it is water. In any case, the vessel must *be rather large, and Aaron must hold it very high, so that one can see that the water is clear on top, red underneath.*

Singing technique: *with the exception of the* recitative, *the voice is always to be the* melody, *the* principal part. *This applies especially to* arioso *passages in the recitative. In the recitative itself, the tones* (*intervals*) *must be absolutely in tune and must never be altered* (*12-tone row!*) *The rhythm, on the other hand, is relatively free, and is governed by the dramatic expression.*

The melodies *are to be sung beautifully and with good characterization. Of principal importance:* noble tone, *good legato, smooth transitions. The tones should always be held to their* full value: long vowels, short, quick consonants, legato. . . . *But the singer should be careful not to* exaggerate the accentuation *of strong beats.*

Characterization should never take place at the cost of beautiful tone!

DRAFTS AND SKETCHES FOR 'MOSES UND ARON'

The drafts and sketches which were found (mostly notated in pencil, with the exception of a few passages in ink) may be divided into two groups. One includes 9 large sheets of music paper (upright format, 32×42 cm.); the other consists of 16 loose sheets (including some double sheets), mostly of oblong format, 27×35 cm. With the exception of sketches I–V (described below) they belong to Act II. The large sheets include a long continuous portion of this act (mm. 320–666, inclusive); only p. 7 (mm. 544–584) is missing. In addition, we find mm. 702–739, 842–852, 861–873 and 881–936. All of this is notated in short-score form on 5 or 6 staves, with detailed indications of instrumentation. Differences in the measure-numbering in comparison with the printed version (in the present work, the numbering of the final version, piano reduction or full score, is used) may be explained by the alterations which Schoenberg undertook in these first drafts. For instance, m. 666 is numbered 676 in the sketch, etc.

The special value of these 25 sheets is not merely that they make it possible to follow the formation and development of a musical thought, to trace its alterations and their consequences. In addition, they give us the rare opportunity to glance into Schoenberg's compositional workshop, to trace the development of large sections of the form, in a way that is not possible (so far as I know) with any other piece of music. Thus, the omission of certain measures, to be filled in later, or the hasty notation of certain passages in one line only, shows us the speed with which the composer wrote down his musical ideas and conceptions—'as when one writes a letter'. One realizes that details were set aside to be worked out later on, because it was more important to the composer to retain and fix the conception of the greatest possible *Whole*.

After the German edition of this book was in print, 40 more sketch-sheets were found. Of these, 63 pencilled pages (with a very few passages in ink) written on 34 sheets of paper (31 of oblong format, 3 of upright format; all about 35 × 23—or 28—cm.) contain the almost complete first draft of the first act, in part with exact indications of instrumentation. Three additional sheets, written in pencil on both sides of the paper (oblong format, 35 × 28 cm.) are concerned with sketches for the choral interlude. One of these sheets bears the red-pencilled note *Sk. IV₁*. To the second act belong the following pages: a sheet of upright format, 32 × 42 cm., on one side of which the chorus of the four virgins (mm. 780–810) is written in pencil, partly traced over in ink; and two sheets (upright format, 27 × 36 cm.), three pencilled pages of which contain the beginning of Act II (mm. 43–93), while the fourth page bears sketches for the second scene of Act II.

The page with the beginning of the first act bears the same date as the score: *Lugano 17.VII. 1930.*

FACSIMILE PLATES X AND XI

A happy chance has spared for us the very first sketch for the opera: a double sheet of music paper with the note *Berlin 7.V. 30* and, on the other side of the page, *Arbeit angefangen 16./VII. 30, Reihe entworfen und I. Skizze 7. V. 30* ('Work begun July 16, 1930, row drafted and first sketch May 7, 1930'). This sketch, numbered I, begins with m. 8 of the opera, and contains the sketches for 6 different passages in the text (indicated in red pencil, *I₁–I₆*). The same passages are found in Sketch II (*II₁–II₆*), etc. Especially informative is Sketch V, which begins with the note: *Doppel-Fugen-Thema* ♩= *96–100* 'Nie, nie kehrt er wieder' ('Never, never will he return') and, below this, shows the *I. Engführung* (first stretto) of the theme. On the wide upper margin of the sheet, Schoenberg noted the general layout of the double fugue which, in the opera, functions as the interlude between Acts I and II. He wanted a 'total duration at most 4 min., at most 48 measures'. The final version has 42 measures!

I. PUBLISHED WORKS

Below, we translate Schoenberg's following notes on *Thematic Metamorphoses*.

Part 1 of the fugue, 3 short developments . . . (?) . . . all 'transpositions of register' . . .
I. 'Never' . . . II. 'A false God' III. Stretto. 'Never' . . .
Interruption: 'seize them, bind them . . . Into the fire with them'
Part 2 of the fugue I. 'The Gods have taken him'
II. 'Ptah, Bnaha'
III. 'Punish the blasphemer' (liquidation . . . Coda . . . crescendo)
also a spoken episode
perhaps spoken in 2 voices

FACSIMILE PLATE XII

With this is a sketch on a small piece of music paper, bearing the note: *tonale 12 Tonfuge im 8, 10 und 12 f. Kp.* (i.e., with double counterpoint at the octave, tenth, and twelfth).

That Schoenberg, contrary to many opinions, definitely planned to compose the third act is proved by the following items:

(1) An ink sketch on a single sheet of music paper. It consists of 8 measures, the first 4 in 2 voices, the last 4 in 1 voice only. Under this, in pencil, is a note (here translated): *Beginning of Act III | but don't forget: | already here a | five- or six-part passage | should be included.*

(2) A sketchbook bound in red by Schoenberg, presently in the possession of the author (music paper, 12·5 × 10 cm.). The year 1937 and (in block letters) the composer's name and last address in Los Angeles are written in ink on the outer page of the binding. On the second page, the book contains 4 worked-out measures, with indications of instrumentation, bearing the note *Aron wird hereingeschleppt* ('Aaron is dragged in'—beginning of Act III).

FACSIMILE PLATE XIII

It is important that, in the short score on the 9 large sheets which contain continuous sections, Schoenberg added, in ink, quite new directions for staging (of the 'Dance around the Golden Calf') in closest connection with the corresponding passages of the music. This gives an unambiguous picture of the intentions of the composer for the scenic realization of the work.

The following materials are also at hand: a small bound sketchbook (11·5 × 16·5 cm.) with many text-sketches and new versions of entire sections; a detailed table of timings, such as Schoenberg was accustomed to draw up for his other works (especially those of his latest period); 4 strips of music paper with row-forms; a sheet of blueprint paper with a fair copy of mm. 1–12 (inclusive) of Act I, and a sheet of ordinary music paper (32 × 42 cm.) with a fair copy of mm. 143–165 (chorus only, mm. 156–165) of Act II. Of the versions of the text, two pertaining to Act III are especially important. One of these is dated *New York 21.VI. 1934*; the other, *5./V. 1935*.

The legacy also includes the following items:

Compositionsvorlage ('Basis for Composition')—this is the handwritten title of a bound manuscript, one of the 3 versions of the text. It is typed, with many handwritten corrections, additions, and alterations (often pasted over the original).

B, WORKS WITHOUT OPUS NUMBERS

A hand-bound *notebook* (10·5 × 17 cm.) contains notes from the end of September and the beginning of October, 1928. It consists of 24 closely-written pages. Some of this material is also associated with the drama 'Der biblische Weg' ('The Biblical Way', 1926), the ideas of which are connected with those of 'Moses und Aron'. At the end, a folded page (24 × 20·5 cm.) has been bound in. It is headed *Bibelstellen* (Biblical Passages) and contains passages from Isaiah.

A bound *sketchbook* (oblong format, 17·5 × 10 cm.) which accompanies the score consists of 14 sheets, on 13 of which the row and its mirror-forms are written in ink. On the outside page: *Moses und Aron*.

A 32-lined page of music paper (upright format, 32 × 42 cm.), has a short score written on both sides of the page in black ink. The draft begins with Aaron's words, 'Perhaps his God has forsaken him'; 13 measures, on the first page, are complete. On the second page, only the chorus is notated, ending with the words, 'Burn them! Strike them down! Kill them!'

A small bound *sketchbook* (oblong format, 16 × 12 cm.), 8-lined, 56 numbered pages. The first 18 pages contain sketches for Act I; the following 16, sketches for Act II (the Dance); these are written mainly in pencil, partly in ink. There are notes on the row-forms and trans-positions used. Then, on the 2 next-to-last pages (54 and 55) there are further sketches.

From a letter of Schoenberg to Alban Berg, August 8, 1931.

. . . So you, too, have an opera act finished; well, so have I. It is nearly 1000 measures long. But I already have 250 measures of the second act, too; I am just enjoying a little pause for refreshment ('pause' is good; I think that I have worked at least several hours during every day of this 'pause'!), which I am using to work on the second act. I think it's not bad. Strangely, I am working in exactly the same way; the text takes on its final form only while I am composing it—often not till afterwards. This works out unusually well. Naturally—and I am sure you have had the same experience—this is only possible when one has a very precise conception of the whole in advance. The trick is then not only to keep this vision lastingly alive but even to strengthen, enrich and broaden it when one works out the details. One should recommend this procedure to all opera composers. But naturally it wouldn't help much!—I should like to do my best to have the opera finished before I come to Berlin. It is not going as fast as I had hoped at the beginning, when I could reckon with an average of 20 measures a day. I am not anywhere near fulfilling that quota, although I could reckon with finishing 25 measures a day when I was working on my previous opera. [Ed. note: 'Von Heute auf Morgen'] The principal reasons for this difficulty: the text and the choruses. The writing-out of the choral parts is such drudgery and waste of time—why, working out four- to six-part counterpoint is a bagatelle in comparison! Then I am held up still further by the fact that I am writing the full score right from the start; of course, this takes up a lot of time. But at least I have the advantage that when I have composed the last note I shall be entirely finished. I am afraid of just one thing: by then I shall have forgotten everything I wrote. For even now I hardly recognize what I wrote last year. If some sort of unconscious memory were not at work to keep me on the right track in music and text, I have no idea how the whole thing would attain any kind of organic unity.

From a letter to Anton Webern, September 12, 1931.

As far as my work is concerned, unfortunately it is not progressing as rapidly as I expected (probably I expected too much, for, after all, I am writing a full score and really completing the text only now, too!). Up till now I have written about 800 measures and sketched some 300 more. But, besides these, the second act, which I am working on now, will have at least 500 measures more. And, after my present experiences, I hardly dare to estimate the duration of the third act (which, up till now, I had thought would be 20 minutes long at most). I hope that I shall be through with the second act (which I began on July 27) at least in September . . .

. . . .

As I have mentioned, the preparation of the text in 'Moses und Aron' takes a great deal of time. For instance, the exact working-out of the scene 'Dance around the Golden Calf' cost me much time and trouble. I wanted to leave as little as possible to the new tyrants of the theatre, the stage-directors, and to think out the choreography to the best of my ability.

. . . You know that I don't have much use for the dance. In general, its power of expression is on no higher a level than that of the most primitive programme music; and its 'beauty' is odious to me in its petrified mechanics. However, up till now I did succeed in thinking out some movements which at least approach a different sphere of expression from that of the usual ballet hop-skip-and-jumping. I hope that I can make further progress in this direction.

A letter of Schoenberg to Walter Eidlitz, Vienna. (Eidlitz was a writer born in Vienna in 1892):

15. III. 1933

Honoured Herr Eidlitz, I thank you very much for your two books, which pleased me greatly, although my involvement with my own work hinders me to a certain degree from following the course of your ideas completely. Nevertheless, I was able to appreciate the beauty and significance of your thought.

From this mighty subject, I myself selected the following elements for the foreground: the ideas of the Inconceivable God, of the Chosen People, and of the Leader of the People. My Aaron rather resembles your Moses, although I have not developed so many sides of his character and of his human relationships as you have done. My Moses—in appearance, at any rate—rather resembles that of Michelangelo. He is not human at all. However, it is interesting that we treat the theme of the Golden Calf rather similarly. For me, too, it is a sacrifice of the masses who wish to divorce themselves from 'soul-less' belief. Since this scene is associated with the central tenets of my belief, I have gone very far in carrying out its implications. Here, my piece is probably at its most operatic—as, after all, it must be!

My third act, which I have been revising (and in part completely rewriting) for at least the fourth time, is still called 'Aaron's Death'. Here, certain almost irreconcilable contradictions in the Bible have given me the greatest trouble up till now. For, although I do not stick too strictly to the Bible, just at this point it is very difficult to get around the contradictions; in one place it reads, 'Smite the rock', in another, 'Speak . . .'! You have worked with this material for a very long time; can you, perhaps, recommend some literature pertaining to this subject that I might read? Up till now, I have been unable to find a solution myself. And, so far as my drama is concerned, I can work it out even without this solution. But the problem just will not leave me alone!

With cordial greetings, your
Arnold Schönberg

B. WORKS WITHOUT OPUS NUMBERS

(b) Arrangements

CONCERTO FOR STRING QUARTET AND ORCHESTRA
Freely adapted from Handel's Concerto Grosso, Op. 6, No. 7
G. Schirmer, New York

The manuscript fair copy of this work is with the publishers in New York. It is written in India ink on 46 sheets (pages) of yellowish blueprint paper (oblong format, 40×30·5 cm.).

A note, presumably added later, reads *angefangen etwa 20.V. 1933*. However, this beginning-date contradicts the handwritten completion-dates of the movements. (First movement, *10.V. 1933*; second movement, *12.V. 1933*; third movement, undated; fourth movement, signed *Arnold Schönberg, Arcachon, 16.VIII. 1933*.)

Schoenberg made notes for his edition in a photocopy of Handel's score. Also, there are 8 sketch-sheets, mostly for the 'Hornpipe', which Schoenberg altered extensively.

GEORG MATTHIAS MONN,   SYMPHONY IN A MAJOR
'CELLO CONCERTO IN G MINOR
CEMBALO CONCERTO IN D MAJOR
JOHANN CHRISTOPH MANN, DIVERTIMENTO IN D MAJOR

These four works were published, with figured basses realized by Schoenberg, in the 'Denkmäler der Tonkunst in Österreich' (XIX. Jahrgang, Zweiter Teil, 39. Band, 1912). The D major cembalo concerto later served as the basis for Schoenberg's 'Cello Concerto of 1932.

Schoenberg arranged a piano reduction of the G minor 'Cello Concerto, the manuscript of which is with Universal Edition, Vienna, who published it. It consists of 16 loose sheets of music paper (upright format, 26·5×34 cm.) comprising 31 numbered pages written in ink. P. 1 bears the stamped address: Berlin-Südende, Berliner Strasse 17a. There is no date for the beginning of the edition; on the other hand, the ending is signed, but the date under the signature is incomplete (—: 26./ . . .) The following notes have been added in red pencil (here translated):

Page 2: *From time to time I have given the solo part other 'markings' (this refers only to piano, forte and eventually* v, ⌒, *etc.) than those found in the original. I think it would be a good idea to indicate that these markings originate with the editor by placing them in parentheses. Schbg.*

Page 8: *changed from the original, which, both here and in parallel passages, has notes which do not fit the bass. Probably a copyist's error. Schönberg.*

Page 14: *I think this trill is wrong! Schönberg.* (This concerns the trill on f1, second movement, tenth measure after cue No. 6.)

In addition, there are 5 loose sheets of music paper of the same size, written in red ink, and containing supplementary engraving instructions for the score.

Cadenza to G. M. Monn's 'Cello Concerto in G minor

The manuscript of this, found in the legacy, is written on 6 sheets of music paper (upright format, 26×34·5 cm.). On 2 sheets, numbered (1) and (2) in ink, the words *letzter Satz* ('last movement') stand at the beginning of the following cadenza. On p. 4: *2. (kurze) Kadenz zum letzten Satz Seite 90* ('(short) cadenza to the last movement, p. 90'). (The page-number refers to the above-mentioned volume of DTÖ containing Schoenberg's continuo realization.)

Three additional sheets, numbered in pencil (1–3), bear the note, on p. 1: *Seite 64, 2. System nach Takt 1* ('p. 64, second stave after measure 1'). The last of these sheets is blank.

Handwritten note (in pencil) in Schoenberg's hand-bound separate copy (published by Universal Edition) of the concerto, on p. 3, at the beginning of the work (translated): *The bowings and dynamics in the 'cello part are not by me, but by Jeral! They were put into my manuscript behind my back, apparently on purpose!! without asking me and without mentioning it on the copy!* Jeral was a Viennese 'cellist.

In the above-mentioned 'Denkmäler' volume from Schoenberg's library, there is an undated slip of paper between pp. 39–40, bearing a pencilled note (here translated):

Answer to Graf Continuo

    I. Cont. not a question of scholarship, but of 'conception', artistic fantasy.

    II. Adler: just an appoggiatura. All the rest: merely chords, as those without imagination always did it.

    III. Passages: Continuo-accompaniment

binds together (harmonies)
brings ♩♩♩; real voices have a stronger effect.

Octaves

see Bach example from 'Harmonielehre'
Fifths with a sustained tone!
Doubling of the leading-tone, see Labor
    " " " seventh, " "

    Bass from the violin part: simply because the bass goes along with it! I did not know that the bass goes along with it; for only Basso is written there!

    I have orchestrated 7000 pages of scores

N.B.: 'Graf' probably means the music critic Max Graf, who apparently reviewed Schoenberg's realization of the continuo part (where, could not be determined). 'Adler' was Guido Adler, the editor of the 'Denkmäler'. 'Labor' was the Austrian composer, pianist and organist Josef Labor (1842–1924).

CONCERTO FOR VIOLONCELLO AND ORCHESTRA
after a concerto for Cembalo by GEORG MATTHIAS MONN (1717-1750)
G. Schirmer, New York

The handwritten title on the binding and on the first page of the hand-bound manuscript reads as follows: *Pablo Casals gewidmet | Konzert für Violoncell und Orchester (nach dem Concerto per Clavicembalo von Matthias Georg Monn, komp. 1746) | in freier Umgestaltung von | Arnold Schoenberg* ('Dedicated to Pablo Casals | Concerto for violoncello and orchestra (after the concerto for harpsichord by Matthias Georg Monn, composed 1746) | freely adapted by | Arnold Schoenberg').

B. WORKS WITHOUT OPUS NUMBERS

The score is written in ink, on 56 pages of 48-lined music paper (sheets cut in half, oblong format, 29 × 36·5 cm.). The first page bears the date *11. XI. 1932*; the date of completion of the first movement is *11. XII. 1932*. The second movement bears no beginning-date and was obviously written immediately after the first movement; its completion-date is *23./XII. 1932*. At its beginning (p. 24 of the score) there is the note: ♪ *= 80 Adagio* (Monn gives 'Andante') (time-signature 2/4). The beginning and completion-dates of the third movement are as follows: *23.XII. 32; beendet am 4. I. 1933 Arnold Schönberg*. With this are handwritten lists of *errata*.

SKETCHES

There are 16 pages of sketches for this work (mostly in oblong format, 26 × 37 cm., partly written in ink). One bears a stamped date: 16. Dezember 1932.

From a letter of Schoenberg to Pablo Casals (to whom the work was dedicated; see above), February 20, 1933 (translated):

. . . Down to business then: the work bears the title:
Concerto for violoncello and orchestra, after the concerto for clavicembalo and orchestra by G. M. Monn, freely adapted by Arnold Schönberg.
I think it has turned out to be a very brilliant piece. In any event, I have taken a great deal of trouble with the sound, and am well satisfied with it. In certain respects, the piece is less soloistic than a concerto by Monn would be; for very often the function of the 'cello is more like that of a soloist in a piece of chamber music, through whose brilliant playing a very beautiful, interesting sound is produced. Furthermore, my principal concern was to get rid of the deficiencies of the Handel-like style of the original work. Just as Mozart did with Handel's 'Messiah', I have taken away whole handfuls of sequences (rosalias, 'shoemaker's patches') and replaced them with real substance. Then, I tried to combat the other principal fault of the Handel style: the theme is always best at the beginning and becomes weaker and more insignificant as the piece progresses. I think that I have succeeded in bringing the whole piece somewhat nearer to the style of Haydn. As far as harmony is concerned, I often go a bit beyond this style (and often more than a bit). Nowhere, however, does it go essentially further than Brahms; in any event, there are no dissonances which are not to be understood in terms of the older rules of harmony; and: nowhere is it atonal!

FRANZ TUMA: SINFONIA A 4tro, 1st movement (Adagio–Allegro)
> **PARTITA A TRE, C minor:**
>> **First movement (Adagio–Allegro)**
>> **Second movement (Minuet)**
>> **Third movement (Adagio)**
> **PARTITA A TRE, A major**

These works were copied, by another hand, from the 'Denkmäler der Tonkunst in Österreich'. Schoenberg then pencilled in his own realization of the figured bass. With this is a sheet bearing handwritten comments on harmonic and formal problems in connection with the style of the music.

The manuscript is in the possession of the Library of Congress.

I. PUBLISHED WORKS

THREE FOLKSONGS (fifteenth and sixteenth centuries)
    arranged for 4-part mixed chorus a cappella
C. F. Peters, Frankfurt—London—New York

1. 'Es gingen zwei Gespielen gut' ('Two Comely Maidens'; folk tune, before 1540)

2. 'Herzlieblich Lieb, durch Scheiden' ('Beloved Love, Our Parting'; melody, fifteenth century)

3. 'Schein uns, du liebe Sonne' ('Shine Down on Us, Dear Sun'; Antonius Scandellus, 1570 [1517–1580])

The first draft of No. 1 is written mainly in pencil (partly in ink) on 4 16-lined sheets of music paper (oblong format, 26 × 34·5 cm.), using 4 staves. There are many changes. On the backs of the first 3 sheets, and on parts of the front page, there are sketches for this music. In all, there are 55 measures, 54 of which are numbered. The draft is undated.

The other choruses, too, are found in their first draft in 4 staves on 2 pieces of 15-lined music paper (oblong format, 26 × 34·5 cm.). In No. 2, the notes are written in pencil, while the text is written sometimes in pencil, sometimes in ink. At the end of this arrangement is the following note in ink (translated): *I should like to know if this is the original division of the measures. I believe that someone has changed it and that the whole piece should be in 6/4. There are 78 quarter-notes (6 into 78 = 13 measures!). 78 divided by 6 = 13.*

In No. 3, the notes are also written in pencil. The text, in pencil and ink, is put in for two voices only, and only through the first 16 measures. The notes of the middle voices are missing in the second half of the fortieth measure; this spot was marked (presumably at the time of a later proof-reading) with a ? in blue pencil.

FOUR GERMAN FOLKSONGS (fifteenth and sixteenth centuries)
    arranged for voice and piano

C. F. Peters, Frankfurt—London—New York

1. 'Der Mai tritt ein mit Freuden' ('Now May has Come with Gladness'; folk tune, before 1540)

2. 'Es gingen zwei Gespielen gut' ('Two Comely Maidens'; folk tune, before 1540)

3. 'Mein Herz in steten Treuen' ('To Her I Shall Be Faithful'; composer unknown, fifteenth century)

4. 'Mein Herz ist mir gemenget' ('My Heart is in Confusion'; composer unknown, fifteenth century)

The manuscript of the first draft is written in pencil on 3 sides of 5 sheets of music paper (oblong format, 26 × 34·5 cm.). There are several changes and improvements. Note after No. 1: *Schluss 26./I. 1929.* Directly following on the same page, we find No. 3, with this note (translated): *End / I have an idea that this has been differently 'measured' by somebody; then I shall have to have it sent to me again. 27./I. 1929.*

Nineteen years later, Schoenberg arranged the songs Nos. 1–3 for a cappella chorus as Op. 49 (see above). In addition, there is still another, earlier choral version of No. 2, entirely different from that in Op. 49. It was published in the collection of 'Three Folksongs' by C. F. Peters (see previous item).

Origin of the folksong arrangements.

The 'State Commission for the Folksong-Book for Youth' in Berlin had written to Schoenberg on July 14, 1928, requesting him to make such arrangements. As a basis for these, they sent along copies of 'Schein uns, du liebe Sonne' and 'Herzlieblich Lieb, durch Scheiden'; the type of arrangement was left entirely to the discretion of the composer. These two songs were then included in the 'Three Folksongs' (see above). Apparently additional sources were sent to Schoenberg, as appears from a letter which he wrote to Carl Lütge in Berlin on February 4, 1929 (Lütge must have been writing to Schoenberg on behalf of the Commission):

Dear Sir: I am sending you four songs with piano accompaniment by registered mail. Unfortunately, your answer came when I had already nearly finished the work, so that I could no longer make use of the possibilities of dividing the measures differently. However, I have now arranged my version so that it also works for the measure-division which I consider correct—so no harm has been done to the whole. It is rather mysterious to me how the measure-divisions in the sources you sent me came about, for, as far as I am concerned, the original leaps to the eye, not only in the working-out of the motifs but also (and especially!) in consideration of the counterpoint. I saved myself the trouble of copying out the text completely; the engraver can very well use the copy which was sent to me for this purpose.

I still had the copy of one of the pieces which you gave me to use for the choral arrangements. Too bad that I could not get this piece ready to send off to you now—it was almost finished and needed a few more days' work. (It is in variation form, each of the six stanzas being arranged quite differently.)

Another point: since these pieces are in church modes, I did not put modern key-signatures at the beginning. However, I did not strive for pure church modes, but used the play with the various accidentals for purposes of colour only. Nevertheless, I would consider it correct to print the pieces with the old style of indicating the tonality, for both the melody and the harmony can be understood only in this manner. N.B.: I do not consider these songs as folksongs, but as art-songs.

(c) Orchestrations

J. S. BACH: 'SCHMÜCKE DICH, O LIEBE SEELE' ('Deck thyself, O Soul, with Gladness'; chorale prelude)
   orchestrated by Arnold Schönberg
Universal Edition, Vienna

The manuscript of the score is in the possession of the Library of Congress. It consists of 7 sheets (14 numbered pages) of music paper (upright format, 26·5 × 34·5 cm.), written in ink. Begun *Ende April–Mai 1922*, completed *Traunkirchen 24. Juni 1922*.

J. S. BACH: 'KOMM, GOTT, SCHÖPFER, HEILIGER GEIST' ('Come, God, Creator, Holy Ghost'; chorale prelude)
   orchestrated by Arnold Schönberg
Universal Edition, Vienna

The manuscript consists of 4 30-lined sheets of music paper (upright format, 26·5 × 34·5 cm.), bound together with red silk cord and written in ink. Date and place of completion: *Mödling Ende April 1922 Arnold Schönberg.*

I. PUBLISHED WORKS

A letter of Schoenberg to the conductor Fritz Stiedry, July 31, 1930 (translated):

Dear Dr. Stiedry,

I believe that I have already put down an explanation of my Bach orchestrations for myself, in my 'little manuscripts'. However, I gladly take advantage of the opportunity to do so once more.

I. Bach himself prepared orchestrations and arrangements of others' works: Vivaldi!

II. With the exception of the keyboard works (which Riemann believes—I disagree!—were meant to have their two-part counterpoint filled out with harmony), you cannot perform Bach without interpretation; you have to realize the continuo! *We do not know how far artists of Bach's time, with imagination and contrapuntal skill, may have gone with this; our only yardstick is what such artists of today can do!*

III. What the Bach organ was like, we barely know!

IV. How it was played, we do not know at all!

V. If we assume that the organ of today has, at least in some particulars, developed from the spirit of the Bach organ, the tremendous multiplication of registers cannot be entirely contradictory to this spirit. In that case, the organist who exploits his instrument not only in pleno, *but also in a* differenti-ated *manner, must* use *all registers and change them frequently.*

VI. Then you have a choice: do you prefer an interpretation by Straube or Ramin or any other organist to an arrangement by me?

VII. Our 'sound-requirements' do not aim at 'tasteful' colours. Rather, the purpose of the colours is to make the individual lines clearer, and that is very important in the contrapuntal web! Whether the Bach organ could achieve this, we do not know. Today's organists cannot; *this I know (and it is one of my points of departure!).*

VIII. Our modern conception of music demanded clarification of the motivic *procedures in both horizontal and vertical dimensions. That is, we do not find it sufficient to rely on the immanent effect of a contrapuntal structure that is taken for granted, but we want to be aware of this counterpoint in the form of motivic relationships. Homophony has taught us to follow these in the top voice; the inter-mediate phase of the 'polyphonic homophony' of Mendelssohn, Wagner and Brahms has taught us to follow several voices in this manner. Our powers of comprehension will not be satisfied today if we do not apply the same yardstick to Bach. A 'pleasant' effect originating in an ensemble of skilfully con-structed parts is no longer sufficient for us. We need transparency, that we may see clearly!*

All that is impossible without phrasing. However, phrasing is not to be used 'emotionally' as in the age of pathos. Rather, it must

1. *distribute the stresses correctly in the line*
2. *sometimes reveal, sometimes conceal the motivic work*
3. *take care that all voices are well-balanced dynamically, to achieve transparency in the total sound.*

And much, much more!

I think that, in these circumstances, transcription is not a right, but a duty.

With most cordial greetings, your

Arnold Schönberg

B. WORKS WITHOUT OPUS NUMBERS

J. S. BACH: PRELUDE AND FUGUE IN E FLAT MAJOR FOR ORGAN
arranged for large orchestra by Arnold Schönberg
Universal Edition, Vienna

The title-page of the manuscript bears the German title (*Präludium und Fuge in Es-dur für Orgel, für grosses Orchester gesetzt von Arnold Schönberg*) written in pencil, in block letters. In the lower left-hand corner, there is a note by Schoenberg's son-in-law Felix Greissle (translated): 'All entries in coloured pencil were made during the proof-reading.' These pertain to indications of principal and subordinate voices, dynamics, clefs, wrong notes, phrasing, etc. In the lower right-hand corner is the stamped address: Charlottenburg, Nussbaumallee 17. Two typed sheets lying in the manuscript give the orchestration, as well as other prefatory notes such as are found in all similar orchestral scores of Schoenberg.

The manuscript, which is in the possession of Universal Edition, Vienna, is bound, and contains 26 pages of 32-lined music paper (upright format, 34·5 × 42·5 cm.). It is written in pencil. Pages and measures are numbered continuously. P. 1 bears, at the upper right, the note *1/V. 28*. Note and signature on the last page: *angefangen: 1. Mai 1928 | beendet: 11. Oktober 1928 Arnold Schönberg* (stamped address underneath). At the bottom of this page are handwritten notes concerning the notation of transposing instruments, as well as directions for the engraver.

Pages 29–32 are blank, showing merely the numbered bar-lines from 180 through 204. The following note is written in red pencil diagonally across p. 29 (translated): *Measures 7 through 31 are to be written into measures 180 through 204.* A footnote on p. 33, where the fugue begins, tells us, *In the entire fugue, the theme is not to be brought out more than is required by the prescribed dynamics. On the other hand, it should stand out somewhat if played as indicated.*

JOHANNES BRAHMS: PIANO QUARTET IN G MINOR, Op. 25
arranged for orchestra by Arnold Schönberg
G. Schirmer, New York

The manuscript is in the possession of the publishers. It consists of 45 loose, numbered pages of yellowish blueprint paper (oblong format, 40 × 30 cm.) written in India ink. It shows the following dates:

> Beginning of the work: *May 2, 1937*
> End of the first movement: *Friday July 16, 1937*
> End of the third movement: *August 22, 1937*
> End of the last movement : *September 19, 1937 Arnold Schoenberg* (the corner with the second half of the signature is torn off).

The instrumentation involved no tampering whatsoever with the composition itself. Schoenberg jokingly called his version of the work 'Brahms's *Fifth*.'

From a letter of Schoenberg to Alfred V. Frankenstein, San Francisco Chronicle, March 18, 1939 (original English):

Here a few remarks about the 'Brahms'.

I. PUBLISHED WORKS

My reasons:

1. I like this piece.

2. It is seldom played.

3. It is always very badly played, because, the better the pianist, the louder he plays and you hear nothing from the strings. I wanted once to hear every thing, and this I acchieved.

My intentions:

1. To remain strictly in the style of Brahms and not to go farther then he himself would have gone if he lived today.

2. To watch carefully all these laws to which Brahms obeyed and not to violate such, which are only known to musicians educated in his environment.

How I did it:

I am for almost 50 years very thoroughly acquainted with Brahms style and his principles. I have analyzed many of his works for myself and with my pupils. I have played as violist and cellist this work and many others numerous times: I therefore knew how it should sound. I had only to transpose this sound to the orchestra and this is in fact what I did.

Of course, there were heavy problems. Brahms likes very low Basses, for which the orchestra possesses only a small number of instruments. He likes a full accompaniment with broken chord figures, often in different rhythms. And most of these figures can not easily be changed, because generally they have a structural meaning in his style. I think I resolved this problems, but this merit of mine will not mean very much to our present day musicians because they do not know about them and if you tell them there are such, they do not care. But to me it means something.

CARL LÖWE: 'DER NÖCK' ('The Water-Sprite')
orchestrated by Arnold Schönberg
Universal Edition, Vienna

The manuscript of the score (originally bound) is in the possession of Universal Edition. It consists of 20 sheets of music paper (upright format, 26·5 × 34 cm.), some of which are loose. Thirty-four pages are numbered and written in ink. No date is given.

In several passages of the score, sections which are repeated are written in pencil. P. 29 is blank, and bears a red-pencilled note: *come sopra Takt 1–26 von Seite 1–6.* Underneath, in ink: *Text siehe Seite 36 'da tönt des Nöcken Harfenschall'—Seite 38, 4. Zeile Takt 1 inclusive* ('for text see p. 36 "there sound the water-sprite's harp-tones"—p. 38, line 4, measure 1, inclusive').

JOHANN STRAUSS: EMPEROR WALTZ
for flute, clarinet, string quartet and piano
B. Schotts Söhne, Mainz

The manuscript, written in ink, comprises 12 loose sheets of music paper (oblong format, 27 × 35 cm., 22-lined). Pp. 1–23 are numbered and written on, while the last page is blank. Signature at the end: *Arnold Schönberg 1./4. 1925.* Title at the top of the first page of the score: *Kaiser Walzer von Johann Strauss.* The first 6 measures of the piano part show erasures and

14. Conclusion of the cabaret song GALATHEA (Wedekind).

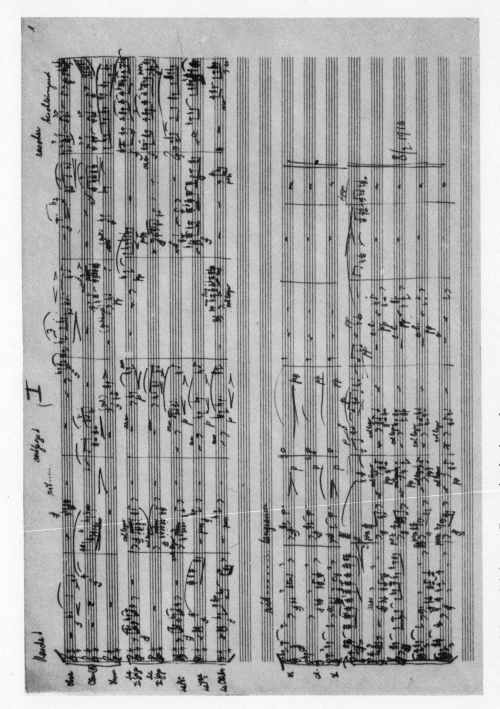

15. No. I of the untitled three small pieces for chamber orchestra.

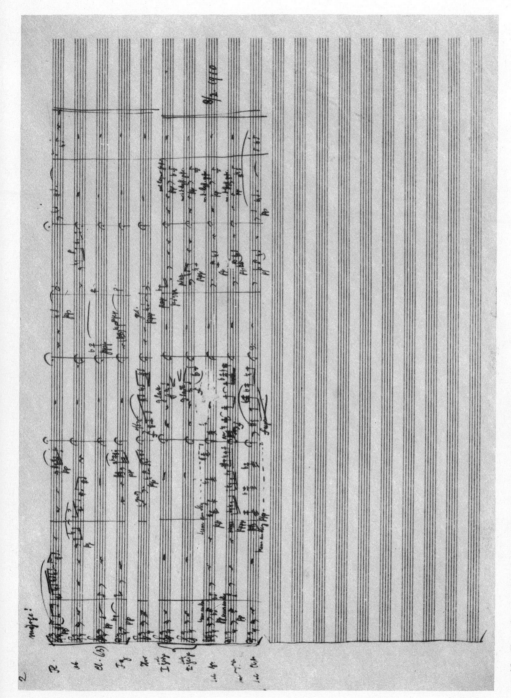

16. No. II of the untitled three small pieces for chamber orchestra.

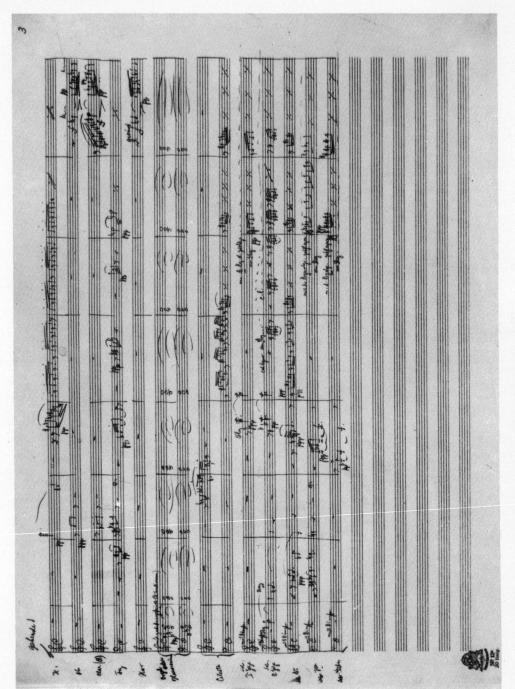

17. No. III (unfinished) of the untitled three small pieces for chamber orchestra.

subsequent alterations. A few pencilled additions have to do with dynamic and technical directions for performance; there are also several directions to the copyist for the extraction of the parts.

Schoenberg made this arrangement (which changes the composition not at all) for a tour of the 'Pierrot' ensemble which he directed in Spain. The instrumental makeup of that group was, of course, the basis for this instrumentation.

[(d) Piano reductions

ALEXANDER VON ZEMLINSKY: SAREMA

Schoenberg wrote the libretto for this opera, basing it on Rudolf von Gottschall's dramatic poem 'Die Rose vom Kaukasus', and arranged the vocal score in 1897. It was published two years later by Berté & Co., Vienna.

G. A. ROSSINI: THE BARBER OF SEVILLE

Arrangement of the overture and fifteen numbers for piano, 4 hands, by Arnold Schoenberg. Published by Universal Edition, Vienna, 1903.]

II. UNPUBLISHED WORKS

A. COMPLETED WORKS

(a) Piano music

1. SIX PIECES FOR PIANO FOUR HANDS

Photocopy of the manuscript, with handwritten date of completion: *Wien, im Oktober 1894*. Aside from the title-page, only three pieces—Andantino in C♯ minor, Andante grazioso in E major, and Presto in A minor—were photocopied.

2. ALLA MARCIA

Twenty-two measures (E flat major) on a sheet of music paper (upright format, $25 \times 31 \cdot 5$ cm.), written in pencil (not all parts filled in). On a second sheet, partly in ink, partly in pencil (continuation or completion), the entire composition. Undated.

(b) Songs

Here, we have not attempted to list the material in chronological order. Some of the songs are undated, while others are arranged in folders or envelopes on which, in some cases, the period when they were written is noted.

1. IN HELLEN TRÄUMEN HAB ICH DICH OFT GESEHEN ('In Bright Dreams I Oft Have Seen Thee')

This song, composed in the summer of 1893, is probably the earliest of Schoenberg's songs to have been preserved. It was found in the possession of D. J. Bach, London.

2. ELEVEN SONGS

Only the end of the final song is missing. These undated songs (probably composed before 1896) are written continuously on several double sheets (upright format, $26 \cdot 5 \times 34 \cdot 5$ cm.) in ink. They are in an envelope labelled *Erste Lieder* ('First Songs').

3. LIED DER SCHNITTERIN ('Song of the Reaper Girl': Ludwig Pfau)

4. WANDERLIED ('Wandering Song': O Beta; unfinished)

Both these songs are written in ink on a double sheet (upright format, $26 \cdot 5 \times 34 \cdot 5$ cm.); they are undated.

5. MÄDCHENFRÜHLING ('Maiden's Spring': Richard Dehmel; dated *15./9. 97*)

A. COMPLETED WORKS

6. NICHT DOCH! ('But No!': Richard Dehmel; undated)

These songs, too, are written on a double sheet of the same format as Nos. 3 and 4 (unless otherwise specified, all the following song manuscripts have the same format, also). The second song is incomplete, but is found in a complete form on a separate double sheet.

7. GRUSS IN DIE FERNE (' Greetings to Afar'; Hermann Lingg)

Two manuscripts of this song exist. One is undated, while the other bears the following note at the end: *Arnold Schönberg 19. August 1900, auf Bestellung des Herrn Redlich 'angefertigt'.* ('Prepared at the order of Mr. Redlich.')

8. ECLOGE (poet unnamed) and

9. WALDESNACHT ('Forest Night': Paul Heyse)

Each of these songs is written in ink on 3 sheets of music paper (upright format, 25 × 33 cm.); both are undated.

In a cardboard folder with the inscription *Alte unveröffentlichte Lieder und Brettelsachen* ('Old unpublished songs and "Brettl" pieces') were found the next two songs:

10. MANNESBANGEN ('Man's Fears': Richard Dehmel)

Written in ink, on a single sheet of music paper; undated.

11. (Untitled), a verse by Hugo v. Hofmannsthal, with the note (translated) (*less to be sung than to be declaimed, in a descriptive manner, as if reading from an old picture*). The manuscript is written in ink on 3 sheets, and is dated *2./4.99 Arnold Schönberg.*

12. 'DEINEM BLICK MICH ZU BEQUEMEN' ('To Grow Accustomed to Thy Gaze': Goethe, West-Östlicher Divan)

The manuscript is written in ink on a double sheet (upright format, 26 × 34· 5 cm.). Note at the end: *Berlin 3. Jänner 1903.*

13. AM STRANDE ('On the Beach': Rainer Maria Rilke)

Both a first draft and a fair copy of this manuscript exist. The former is written in pencil on a sheet of music paper (oblong format, 14· 5 × 36· 5 cm.). Date: *8./2. 1909.* The fair copy is in ink on a double sheet (upright format, 26· 5 × 34· 5 cm.). Alongside the title is the following undated note, in pencil (translated): *This song was written before the 'George-Lieder'. At the same time as opus 14: 'In diesen Wintertagen' and 'Ich darf nicht dankend'. Could have been published, though. I did not bring it out because of the text.* At the end, next to the stamped address (Arnold Schönberg, Berlin-Zehlendorf-Wannseebahn, Machnowerchaussee, Villa Lepcke), there is a note to indicate that this stamp was added later.

BRETTELLIEDER

These 'Brettl Songs', with the exception of the one to a text by Schikaneder, were composed in 1901, in Berlin, for Ernst von Wolzogen's 'Bunte Bühne' ('Überbrettl'). This was a literary cabaret modelled on the 'Grand Guignol'. Among others, von Levetzow collaborated in it; Schoenberg was musical adviser and director.

1. 'Galathea' (Frank Wedekind). Signed *Schönberg 2./9. 1901*. Written in ink on a double sheet (upright format, 26·5 × 34·5 cm.; all other 'Brettllieder' also written in this format).

FACSIMILE PLATE XIV

2. 'Gigerlette' (O. J. Bierbaum), also signed, but undated. See below, 'Mahnung'.

3. 'Der genügsame Liebhaber' ('The Satisfied Lover': Hugo Salus), written on a double sheet, in ink. Date, unsigned: *22./4. 1901*.

4. 'Einfältiges Lied' ('Simple Song': Hugo Salus), in ink, on a double sheet; signed *22./4. 1901 Fr. Schönberg*. Here, Schoenberg signed his Lutheran baptismal name, Franz. There is still another copy of this song, signed but undated.

5. 'Nachtwandler' ('Sleepwalker': Gustav Falke), for a singer accompanied by piccolo, snare-drum, trumpet and piano. The manuscript is in score-form, written in ink on 2 double sheets. Signed *30./4. 1901 Schönberg*.

6. 'Jedem das Seine' ('To Each His Own': Colly). Manuscript in ink, on 2 double sheets. Note at end: *Ende Juni 1901 Schönberg*.

7. 'Mahnung' ('Warning': Gustav Hochstetter), written on 2 double sheets, in ink, along with 'Galathea' and 'Gigerlette'. Closing signature: *Schönberg Juli 1901*.

8. 'Seit ich so viele Weiber sah' ('So many women I have seen', from Schikaneder's 'Mirror of Arcadia'), Slow Waltz. The manuscript, written in ink on a double sheet, is signed, undated, and stamped: Direktion Jung-Wiener Theater 'zum lieben Augustin'.

(c) Chamber music

1. PRESTO for string quartet (string orchestra?)

The undated manuscript is bound and written in ink on 20 pages (upright format, 25 × 32·5 cm.). It probably stems from Schoenberg's very earliest period.

2. GAVOTTE AND MUSETTE for string orchestra (in olden style)

The manuscript consists of 3 sheets of music paper (26·5 × 34·5 cm.), and is written in ink. Date of beginning: *22./3. 97*.

3. STRING QUARTET IN D MAJOR

The original manuscript is in the possession of the Library of Congress. It comprises 13 sheets of music paper (24 numbered pages; oblong format, 34·5 × 26·5 cm.), is written in ink, and bears no dates. The Quartet consists of 4 movements—Allº molto, Intermezzo, Andante

18. Canon for the Jubilee of the Concertgebouw, Amsterdam.

19. Canon (No. 17).

(Theme and Variations), and a Finale, *alla breve*, without tempo indications. It may be considered as the close of Schoenberg's first period of development, in which he followed Viennese classical models, above all Brahms. A photocopy of the original, consisting of 24 sheets, is found in the legacy. Schoenberg told his wife that the work was written in 1897.

4. (Untitled) LITTLE PIECES FOR CHAMBER ORCHESTRA

This manuscript includes the scores of two finished pieces and one beginning, for a number of solo instruments. It is written in ink, on 2 double sheets (oblong format, 26·5 × 34·5 cm.).

The first piece (rapid ♩), comprising 12 measures, is for oboe, clarinet, horn and solo string quintet. Date: *8./2. 1910.*

The second piece (moderate ♩), comprising 7 measures, is for flute, oboe, clarinet, bassoon, horn and solo string quintet. It, too, is dated *8./2. 1910.*

The manuscript of the beginning of the third piece (quickly moving ♩) breaks off with the eighth measure. Orchestration: flute, oboe, clarinet, bassoon, horn, organ or harmonium, celesta and solo string quintet.

These pieces were composed after the 'Five Orchestral Pieces', Op. 16, 'Erwartung', Op. 17, and the 'George-Lieder', Op. 15. Far more characteristically than the later 'Six Little Piano Pieces', Op. 19, they document the aphoristic mode of expression which Schoenberg initiated at this time.

FACSIMILE PLATES XV–XVII

(d) Canons

Of the numerous canons found in the legacy, most come from the years between 1922 and 1949. Three, composed to proverbs of Goethe, come from the year 1905, and are in the second large sketchbook. Only 5 canons are undated.

All of these canons are tonal, and follow the rules of strict counterpoint. (In this connection, we may also refer to the canons published in the appendix to the 'Three Satires', Op. 28, of which the same is true.)

The canons composed for special occasions were, in some instances, published in special commemorative volumes or in music magazines (e.g., the canon for the jubilee of the Concertgebouw in Amsterdam, or the one for the Genossenschaft Deutscher Tonsetzer ('Association of German Composers'). Schoenberg planned to bring out an edition of most of his canons; this can clearly be seen from the fair copies on blueprint paper, which may be considered his personal selection for this proposed work.

Many of the texts are written after the manner of the 'riddle canons' of the old Netherlands masters; the devices of these composers were brilliantly revived by Schoenberg. That such works were not merely manifestations of masterly handwork, but also real compositions, is proved by the following passage from his essay 'Heart and Brain in Music':

> *There are times when I am unable to write a single example of simple counterpoint in two voices, such as I ask sophomores to do in my classes. And, in order to write a good example of this sort, I must receive the co-operation of inspiration. I am in this respect much weaker than some of my pupils who write good or poor counterpoint without any kind of inspiration.* ('Style and Idea,' p. 170.)

II. UNPUBLISHED WORKS

A chronological listing of the canons now follows:

1. *Eyn doppelt Spiegel und Schlüssel-Canon for vier Stimen gesetzet auf niederlandsche Art* (4-voiced mirror- and clef-canon in Netherlands style)—this is the title (written in Gothic characters, highly ornamental, in black and red ink) of a canon written in ink on a single sheet of music paper (26·5×22·5 cm.). Signed: *Arnold Schönberg Mödling 16./II. 1922*. The name is also written in mirror-writing.

2. A 4-voiced perpetual canon (in 3/2) of 10 measures, written in pencil on a single sheet of music paper (oblong format, 25·5×34·5 cm.), in threefold diminution ($\circ$, $\downarrow$·, $\downarrow$, $\downarrow$). Signed: *20./IV. 1926 Schönberg*. On the back of the sheet, there is a 3-voiced canon (3/2), also in diminution; it breaks off after 17 measures.

3. Four-voiced canon of 9 measures; mm. 4–9 are set as an endless canon to the text *für Erwin Stein zu Weihnachten 1926* ('for Erwin Stein for Christmas 1926'). Written in pencil on paper of oblong format (29×34·5 cm.).

4. Manuscript fair copy of a 4-voiced canon for a jubilee of the Concertgebouw, Amsterdam. Written on a sheet of music paper (oblong format, 20·5×25·5 cm.) in ink. This is notated as a riddle-canon for 4 voices in 4 keys, with a fifth freely accompanying voice (bass). The 4 voices are in A major, E flat major, C major, and G major respectively; these keys stand for the initials of the names Arnold, Schönberg (S=Es=E flat), Concert, and Gebouw. The dedication may be translated: *For truly Netherlandish arts the undersigned can thank you only with imitated ones: Arnold Schönberg—Berlin, March 1928.*

FACSIMILE PLATE XVIII

With this is the first draft in 5-voiced score, done in pencil on one leaf of a double sheet (oblong format, 27×34 cm.). Note (translated): *Finished in an hour / March 7, 1928*. Underneath is the notation as a riddle-canon, in 1 voice.—In addition, there are 2 sketch-sheets with various drafts, among others a sketch with the beginning of an 'Agnus Dei' by Josquin.

5. Manuscript fair copy of a 3-voiced, 8-measure canon, notated in ink as a riddle-canon in 1 voice, on a sheet of music paper (upright format, 26·5×35·5 cm.); it has a free 2-voiced accompaniment (bass). The 3 voices are notated in G, D and E flat major (for Genossenschaft Deutscher TonSetzer). Signature: *8. IV. 1928 Arnold Schönberg.*

Below this is the resolution of the riddle-canon in score-form. In addition, we have the manuscript of the first draft, written mostly in pencil on a strip of music paper (12×34·5 cm.); the lower of the 2 accompanying voices is written in ink, as is the signed date (*8.IV. 1928 Arnold Schönberg*). On the reverse side of the strip is the sketch of an unfinished 4-voiced crab-canon (6 measures) in the keys D, F, E flat and A major.

6. Two-voiced mirror-canon (A major) of 14 measures in the outer voices (ink), together with two free middle voices (pencil), on 20-lined music paper (oblong format, 35×27 cm.). On the reverse side of the page is a pencil sketch for the canon. Date: *1.4. 1931 Arnold Schönberg.*

7. A 4-voiced mirror-canon (A major), 10 measures long, is notated in pencil and ink on a cut-off sheet of music paper (upright format, 23×35 cm.). Written below it (translated): *sick two days, can write nothing better today. 15./XII. 31 Arnold Schönberg.*

8. Two-voiced mirror-canon of 8 measures; the second voice sings in doubled note-values (augmentation). It is notated in India ink on a sheet of blueprint paper (oblong format, 18·5 × 27·5 cm.). First, it is written as a 1-voiced riddle-canon, set to the words (translated): *Mirror thyself in thy own work; thou shalt be doubly rewarded for what thou gavest simply; there shall reflect back upon thee what thou gavest sincerely, directly. Slowly open the depths, quickly come then the heights.* Underneath this is the resolution of the canon, followed by the dedication (translated): *To Hermann Abraham, a philanthropist who introduced schoolchildren's lunches, wartime canteens and children's rest homes, for his 85th birthday, December 1931 Arnold Schönberg.*

With this is a sheet of music paper bearing a sketch and first draft in pencil, as well as a copy and draft of the text in ink. On the reverse side is a copy (in ink) of canon No. 7.—In addition, there is a fair copy in ink on a sheet of music paper (upright format, 24·5 × 32 cm., 12-lined) that contains 3 canons. The first is a 2-part mirror-canon of 10 measures, for string quartet. Simultaneously with the two violins, the viola and 'cello play the same two parts in crab-form.—There follow the copies of canon No. 9 (see below), canon No. 7 (see above), the canon dedicated to Hermann Abraham, and the beginning of mirror-canon No. 6.

9. A 4-part double canon of 8 measures, written in ink across the inner pages of a double sheet (upright format, 26·5 × 34 cm.). Superscription (translated): *Double canon at the lower fifth and in mirror form for Carl Moll, on 27. XII. 32 Arnold Schönberg.* (Carl Moll was a Viennese painter, stepfather of Alma Mahler.) With this is a draft noted on a memorandum-sheet, at the top of which Schoenberg made note of his *mysteriously unsuccessful attempt to thank Meister Carl Moll for a splendid gift.* In the margin is still another note (translated): *Attempt, with mysterious if unsuitable means (a double canon lasts better, but gives less than it promises) to thank Meister Carl Moll for the splendid picture. Solution follows.*—In addition, there is a sketch for the canon dated *17.XII. 1932.*

The fair copy of this canon is on a sheet of white blueprint paper (upright format, 28 × 38·5 cm., 20-lined); directly following it on the same page is the fair copy of the 3-voiced canon dedicated to Dr. D. J. Bach on his 50th birthday (cf. No. 13).

10. Two 3-voiced canons (the alto doubly augmented, the soprano quadruply), a 4-voiced mirror-canon of 10 measures, and a 4-voiced perpetual canon of 15 measures (the repetition beginning in m. 4)—these are found on 3 single sheets of music paper stapled together with wire clamps (sheet 1, 34 × 32 cm., 27-lined; the others 34 × 26 cm., 16-lined). None has a text; the manuscript is written partly in ink, partly in pencil. All 4 canons are signed with the note: *Berlin 14. IV. 33.*

The two 3-voiced canons were later (1943) provided with texts by Schoenberg, and dedicated to his friend, the American musicologist Carl Engel, for the latter's 60th birthday. (Engel was, among other things, director of the Music Division of the Library of Congress, and later held a leading position with G. Schirmer, New York.) One of these canons is written as a riddle-canon in a single line, with the afterword (in English): *In the 8th and 15th, or in the prime, if tolerance is granted for a few passing $^6_4$-chords (and for my poor english too).* This canon has 17 measures, while the second has 13. This latter canon is also notated in 1 voice, in 3 clefs, and, like the first canon, in double and quadruple augmentation. With this are 7 sketch-sheets, a fair copy of both canons with their solutions on 3 sheets of music paper (upright format, 27 × 35 cm., 12-lined), and 3 sheets of photocopies (19 × 37 cm.) with the handwritten text.

There is a separate blueprint fair copy (oblong format, 23 × 30 cm., 12-lined) of the 10-measure 4-voiced mirror-canon. Of the 15-measure 4-voiced perpetual canon, there are also the following copies: (*a*) a fair copy on the first page of an otherwise blank double sheet (upright format, 26·5 × 34·5 cm., 16-lined), together with the 20-measure 4-voiced mirror-canon listed under No. 11; (*b*) a fair copy on transparent paper (upright format, 28 × 33 cm., 16-lined), together with a 3-voiced perpetual canon of 6 measures (No. 23).

11. The first draft of a 20-measure, 4-voiced mirror-canon is on one side of a sheet of music paper (oblong format, 27 × 21 cm., 12-lined), written in pencil; only the clefs are traced over in ink. Date, unsigned: *10. XII. 33*. The fair copy of this is notated on the first page of the same double sheet that also contains canon No. 10 (see above). Under this is a note in blue pencil (translated): *I hope that all these canons are not as ghastly as these two, but I fear so. It is unbelievably difficult to achieve even this much. Sch.*

12. Two 4-voiced, perpetual riddle-canons of 8 measures each, and a 3-voiced one of the same kind, 6 measures long: see No. 1 above and No. 23. All these are written, in a first fair copy, in ink on both sides of a 16-lined sheet of music paper (oblong format, 26 × 20 cm.). Each canon is written in one voice, and its solution follows.

Above the first canon (translated): *If none of the four singers has forgotten his clef, it should fit together. But the people do not seem to be properly together. For at every moment one is singing twice as fast or twice or four times as slow. How they get together is a riddle!* Date: *12.III. 1934.* Unsigned.

Above the second canon stands the following saying (translated): *Always the same old thing; only if you don't try to be different from the start will it sound different in the end.* At the end of the third, untexted, 3-voiced riddle-canon: *10./III. 34.*

To this set of canons belong the following copies: (*a*) a blueprint fair copy of the two 4-voiced canons, written in 1 line with text and in score, in India ink, on a sheet of blueprint paper (upright format, 30·5 × 43·5 cm., 24-lined); (*b*) a blueprint fair copy of all 3 canons on 2 staves (treble and bass clefs), done in India ink (corrections in red pencil) on 2 transparent sheets (upright format, 24 × 30·5 cm., 10-lined); (*c*) a pencil copy of the second canon on a sheet of music paper (upright format, 20·5 × 27 cm.).

13. Three-voiced canon, text by the composer, 21 measures, for the 60th (?) birthday of Dr. David J. Bach (music editor of Vienna's 'Arbeiterzeitung', and director of the Social-Democratic Arts Bureau; founder of the Vienna Workers' Symphony Concerts, the direction of which he later turned over to Anton Webern).

First draft, in ink, on 1 page of a double sheet (upright format, 27 × 37 cm., 24-lined). Superscription: *für Dr. Bach.* Text added under music, also written separately in the margin, with the postscript (translated): *Text written 24.III. 1926 | obviously intended for choruses| Arnold Schoenberg.* Signed: *Arnold Schoenberg Chautauqua 30./VII. 1934.*—Also, 2 sketch-sheets and a slip of paper with text and the date *24.III. 1926*, as well as 2 photocopies of a fair copy (evidently that sent to Dr. Bach) with the following dedication (translated): *Dear friend, it is easy to reckon that our 70th, or at least our 80th birthdays, will turn out better. And we shall try to live that long! To my dear friend Dr. David J. Bach, his Arnold Schoenberg.*

14. Four-voiced perpetual canon of 16 measures; 4 measures introduction, 4 measures coda. It is notated on a sheet of music paper (upright format, 20 × 27 cm., 12-lined) in ink, with text added under the lines of music; it is also found on a sheet of blueprint paper (upright format,

20. a-c. Evolution of a melody.

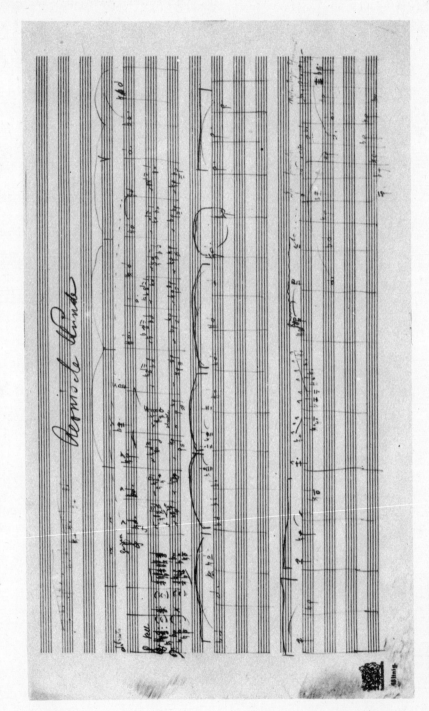

21. Sketch for a symphony.

A. COMPLETED WORKS

28·5 × 42·5 cm., 16-lined) in India ink. Both sheets unsigned, but dated *1. IX. 1934.* Intended for Dr. Rudolph Ganz, with a humorous text (translated): *It is too stupid, it is a pity, that I cannot come to you in Chicago*, etc.

15. Four-voiced counterpoint, sketched in mirror-form, with stretti and imitations in the first 2 measures (for text, see below). The 12 measures are written in pencil on 2 staves on 1 side of a sheet of music paper (oblong format, 24·5 × 15·5 cm., 10-lined). The text, written underneath, reads as follows (translated): *One may think what one likes about Schoenberg*; next to this, in English: *Credit may sometimes be based on a statement like that. Creed and credit.* The sheet is headed: *für Frau Charlotte Dieterle 15./XI. 1935.* Unsigned.

16. A 4-voiced mirror-canon of 10 measures, written in ink on a sheet of music paper (upright format, 20 × 27 cm., 12-lined) and signed *Arnold Schönberg 22./I. 1936.* Underneath, in pencil: *poor.* The canon is also written in India ink on a sheet of blueprint paper (upright format, 28 × 38 cm., 24-lined), together with the canon mentioned under No. 7, and with the one dedicated to Hermann Abraham (No. 8).

17. A particularly skilful 4-voiced double canon of 16 measures; in each voice-pair, one voice brings the diminution of the other. Written in India ink on a sheet of blueprint paper (upright format, 24 × 32 cm., 13-lined). Undated, but with copyright notice for 1938, and signature. No sketches.

FACSIMILE PLATE XIX

18. A 4-voiced perpetual canon of 12 measures, notated in 1 voice (with underlying text), with entrances marked. Written in India ink on a sheet of blueprint paper (oblong format, 19·5 × 22·5 cm., 8-lined). Heading: *Canon for Mr. Saunders Christmas 1939.* The underlying text (in English) is at once a dedication and an expression of thanks: *Mister Saunders, I owe you thanks for at least four years. Let me do it in four voices so that ev'ry one of them counts for one year. Merry Christmas four times, listen how they sing it! Also merry Christmas to Missis Saunders.*

19. Four-voiced mirror-canon of 10 measures. Once as a sketch, in pencil, on a sheet of music paper (upright format, 22 × 28 cm., 13-lined); then as a fair copy, in India ink, on a sheet of blueprint paper (oblong format, 22·5 × 19·5 cm., 8-lined). Signed and dated *VI./7.1943.*

20. A 3-voiced canon for 4 sopranos, 8 measures on blueprint paper (oblong format, 23 × 28 cm., 7-lined), in India ink. Sketches for this on the back of a letter from the conductor Artur Rodzinski, who asked Schoenberg for a musical birthday wish for his newborn son. The underlying text (English and German) reads: *I am almost sure, when your nurse will change your diapers, she will not sing you one of my George-Songs, nor of my Second String Quartett; but perhaps she stills you: Sleep, Richard, sleep! Dein Vater hat dich lieb!*

21. Four-voiced endless canon (4/2 time) of 8½ measures; each voice is played backwards after each 2½ measures, then turns around again, etc. The fair copy is written in India ink on a sheet of blueprint paper (upright format, 21 × 29·5 cm., 16-lined). Heading: *Thomas Mann, 6. Juni 1945.* Below this (translated): *Probably to show you in a special way how I value you, I made it especially hard for myself in this canon—in fact, almost impossible. It sounds impossible, too, and I hope you will not want to hear it (wherefore I notated it in the 'old' clefs).*

II. UNPUBLISHED WORKS

It is not without (honest) egotism that I wish we may remain good contemporaries of one another for many years. Most cordially, your Arnold Schoenberg.

With this are 8 larger and smaller sketch-sheets; one bears a first draft (in pencil) on 2 staves.

22. Four-voiced canon of 15 measures; first draft, in pencil, on 2 staves (no clefs, but treble and bass clefs are obviously meant); notated on a hand-lined strip of paper (oblong format, 43×9 cm., 5 mm. space between lines). The underlying text is also found on a separate sheet of paper. It may be translated thus: *Centre of gravity of its own solar system circled by shining satellites—so thy life appears to thy admirer.* Signed: *Arnold Schoenberg 1.VIII. 49.*

23. A 3-voiced perpetual canon of 6 measures (see also No. 1 above and No. 12) with entrances at the half-measure; notated in 1 voice, solution underneath. Written in India ink on a sheet of blueprint paper (upright format, 28×33 cm., 16-lined); on the same sheet, following, is the canon described above under No. 10.

24. A 3-voiced mirror-canon, 7 measures (outer voices in half-notes throughout, middle voice in quarters); in pencil, on a half-sheet of paper ($26 \cdot 5 \times 18$ cm.), undated and unsigned.— A 2-voiced canon of 4 measures; text (translated): *Where are the pictures, here is the autograph.* Written in ink on a sheet of music paper, 26×20 cm. Undated.

25. Three canons on Goethe proverbs (from Sketchbook II; see below)

(1) 'Wenn der schwer Gedrückte klagt' ('When the sorely pressed complains'); 16-measure perpetual 4-voiced canon.

(2) 'O dass der Sinnen doch so viele sind' ('Oh that our senses are so numerous!'); 4-voiced, perpetual double canon of 35 measures, in quadruple counterpoint.

(3) 'Gutes tu' ('Do good'); 4-voiced perpetual canon of 21 measures; of the coda (after the double bar) there are only 2 unfinished measures.

These 3 canons are undated, but must have been written in the middle of 1905, as they are found on the first page of the sketchbook begun in April, 1905.

B. UNFINISHED WORKS (INCLUDING BEGINNINGS)

(a) Piano and organ music

1. PIANO PIECE

In an envelope labelled *Erste Lieder* (see above, II. A, (*b*)) was also found a piano piece of 46 measures, written on 2 pages (upright format, 26·5 × 34·5 cm.) in ink. At the beginning is the date: *vom 25. oder 26. December 1900*. The manuscript breaks off with the following note (translated): *In February 1901 | continuation follows . . . If I only knew how the continuation will be! I have been wrong about it twice already. Now I do not dare either to hope or to fear.—Will a continuation follow? . . . Arnold Schönberg.*

2. SCHERZO for piano

Seventy-nine measures. Undated, in any case before 1910.

3. PIANO PIECE

Seventy-six measures. Undated, in any case before 1910.

4. PIANO PIECE

Sketched in ink on a double sheet (oblong format, 27 × 34 cm.). It is of march-like character, in F major, and has 26 measures. Below is a revised version, with continuations. At the upper right, in red pencil, is a note: *1926 oder 1927 Sch.*

5. PIANO PIECE

The manuscript, written in ink on a double sheet (upright format, 26·5 × 34 cm.), breaks off after 35 measures. Date: *21.II. 31.* Also 2 sketch-sheets.

6. PIANO PIECE

Twenty-five measures, in pencil, on a sheet of music paper (oblong format, 25·5 × 34·5 cm.). Date: *25./VII. 31.*

7. PHANTASIA FOR PIANO to four hands (N.B.: Schoenberg's English title)

Date noted at beginning: *27. I. 37.* This manuscript contains the first 24 measures of a movement headed *Poco allegro*. The draft begins on the inside page of the first of 7 sheets of music paper (upright format, 27 × 34 cm.), which are bound together with gummed tape. The first of these sheets is 24-lined, while the others are 12-lined. Also, there is a sheet of music paper, trimmed at the lower edge (30·5 × 24 cm.), with the row-forms.

There is no visible connection with the piece for two pianos begun in 1941 (see below, No. 9).

8. Beginning of a PIANO PIECE

On a piece of blueprint paper (upright format, 24×30·5 cm.), in India ink; 23 measures, of which 1–3 and 6–9 are complete. Undated (probably around 1941).

9. 12 measures of a COMPOSITION FOR TWO PIANOS

According to a handwritten note on the manuscript, it was begun on *January 21, 1941.* It is headed *Poco sostenuto* ♩=84 and is written on a page of blueprint paper with pre-printed lines (upright format, 28×38 cm.).

10. SONATA FOR ORGAN (Schoenberg's English title)

Manuscript on 4 loose sheets of blueprint paper (20-lined), 50 measures, *Molto moderato* (♩=96).

On the first page, a handwritten note: *August 7, 1941.* Mostly notated on 2 or 3 staves in black India ink; obviously a fair copy.

(b) *Songs*

1. IM REICH DER LIEBE ('In the Land of Love': Richard Dehmel)

Undated; in any case before 1910.

2. AUF DEN KNIEN ('On My Knees': Karl v. Levetzow)

Undated; in any case before 1910.

3. IN LANGEN JAHREN BÜSSEN WIR ('In Years So Long We Must Atone': J. P. Jacobsen)

Undated; in any case before 1910.

4. GETHSEMANE (Richard Dehmel) for male voice and orchestra

The manuscript is written in ink, on 2 double sheets (upright format, 26·5×34·5 cm.). It includes a prelude of 37 measures, notated as a short score (with occasional indications of instrumentation) on 2 staves; then, 50 measures with voice part. Note: *angefangen 11.5.99.*

5. DUET (soprano and tenor): 'WIE KOMMT ES DASS DU TRAURIG BIST' ('Wherefore are you so sorrowful?' from 'Des Knaben Wunderhorn')

Dated *Berlin 19./3. 1903.*

6. NÄCHTLICHER WEG ('Road at Night': Wilhelm Scholz)

This is found on p. 22 of the sketchbook begun in April, 1906. The 46 measures of the voice part are complete; however, only the first 12 measures have piano accompaniment.

22. Sketch for a symphony.

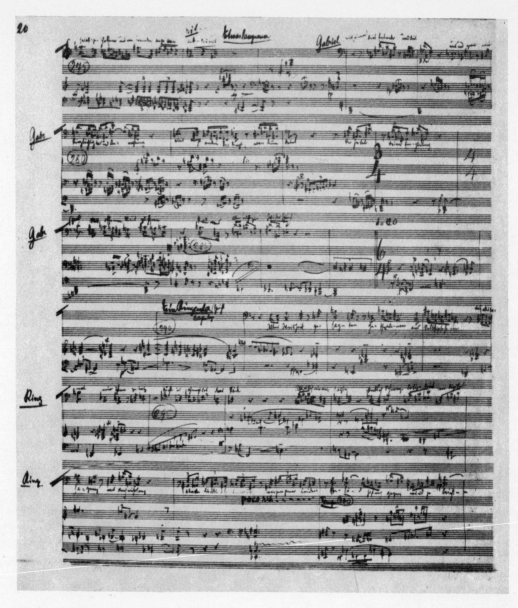

23. A page of short score from the JAKOBSLEITER.

B. UNFINISHED WORKS (INCLUDING BEGINNINGS)

7. FRIEDENSABEND ('Peaceful Evening': Stefan George)

The manuscript is written in pencil on the first 2 pages of a double sheet (29 × 37 cm.). The voice part is complete; the piano accompaniment is not always completely carried out, but is sketched till the end of the song.

On the fourth page, there is an early draft (8 measures, completely differing from the final form) of the seventh song from Op. 15.

8. JEDUCH (Hermann Löns)

Manuscript written in ink on 4 pages of 2 double sheets (upright format, 26·5 × 34·5 cm.). Undated. The extremely expanded tonality (E-flat minor) suggests that the work was written between 1906 and 1910.

(c) Chamber music

1. TOTER WINKEL ('Dead Corner': Gustav Falke) for first and second violins, violas and 'celli

The manuscript is written in ink on a double sheet (upright format, 26·5 × 34·5 cm.); undated. 35 measures.

2. STRING QUARTET IN C MAJOR

A manuscript of 51 measures, undated, written in pencil on 2 loose sheets (upright format, 26·5 × 34·5 cm.).

3. From FRUCHTLESE ('Harvest of Fruit': Rabindranath Tagore, LXXXIII, I.). For voice (tenor), clarinet, horn, violin, viola, piano and harmonium

Only 11 measures of manuscript, written in ink on a sheet of paper (oblong format, 29·5 × 38 cm.).

This manuscript was found in a folder marked *Anfänge* ('Beginnings'). In addition, it contains a number of loose sheets of varying format. On these, sometimes in ink and sometimes in pencil, are written a few measures each of various compositions, without any headings and often without dates. Among other things, there are 9 measures of a piano piece (*9.III. 1918*); Goethe proverbs as 4-voiced canons for mixed chorus; 10 measures of score (in ink) dated *20.7. 1914*, for flute, oboe, clarinet, bassoon, horn and piano.

4. Sixteen measures ('Anmutig bewegt' ('With pleasant motion')) of a STRING QUARTET IN F MAJOR

Undated.

5. EIN HARFENKLANG ('The Sound of the Harp': Gustav Falke) for women's voices, string quartet and harp

Undated.

II. UNPUBLISHED WORKS

6. Twenty-six measures of a STRING QUARTET IN D MINOR ('Nicht rasch' ('Not fast'))

Undated.

7. Beginning of a STRING QUARTET (D minor; 'Langsam' ('Slow'))

Undated. 48 measures.

8. Manuscript of a STRING QUARTET (expanded tonality)

Seventy-nine measures, written in ink on 2 double sheets (oblong format, 27 × 33·5 cm.). Undated.

9. SCHERZO (with Trio) for string quartet

This composition is in F major (trio in A minor) and is headed *II. Satz*. This, together with the numbering of the pages from 17 to 24 (they are of upright format, 26·5 × 34·5 cm.), suggests that the other parts of the manuscript were lost. The manuscript is written in ink. Date of beginning: *27./7. 1897*; date of completion: *27./8. 97*.

10. The beginning of an ALLEGRO FOR CLARINET AND STRING QUARTET (D minor)

Written in ink on a double sheet (upright format, 26 × 34 cm.); 28 measures; undated.

11. EIN STELLDICHEIN ('A Rendezvous': Richard Dehmel) for oboe, clarinet, violin, 'cello and piano

The manuscript of this chamber-music work (without voice) comprises 90 measures and is written in ink on 4 loose double sheets (upright format, 26·5 × 34·5 cm.), in score-form. It is in C minor (*Sehr langsam* ('Very slow')) and breaks off after the double bar of m. 90, immediately before the beginning of a new section for which Schoenberg noted only the tempo-indication (*Sehr rasch, heftig* ('Very fast, vigorously')), the time-signature (C) and the key-signature (5 flats). This fragment is undated.

The continuation (incomplete) of this work was found in Sketchbook II (begun in April, 1905), on pp. 73–77 and 84–86. Dated *21.X.05*.

12. Beginning of a CHAMBER SYMPHONY (C major)

Setting for solo instruments: flute, oboe, English horn, clarinet, bass clarinet, bassoon, two horns, string quintet. Manuscript of 22 measures (*Langsam* ('Slow'), C) notated in ink, on a double sheet (upright format, 26·5 × 34·5 cm.). Undated.

13. SEPTET for 2 violins, 2 violas, 2 'celli and double bass

This is the heading (translated) for a 25-measure fragment, written in ink on a double sheet (oblong format, 20 × 36·5 cm.). Date: *13.III. 1918*. Also, a pencil sketch on a single sheet.

B. UNFINISHED WORKS (INCLUDING BEGINNINGS)

14. CHAMBER MUSIC for clarinet, horn, bassoon, violin, viola, 'cello

The manuscript, untitled, is written in ink on a double sheet (upright format, 27 × 35·5 cm.). It consists of a single thematic idea, comprising 5 measures of antecedent and (in one line only) 5 measures of consequent. Dating from 1920 (?).

15. BEGINNINGS OF STRING QUARTETS

(*a*) Manuscript on a sheet of music paper (upright format, 26·5 × 34·5 cm.); contains 12 measures, dated *6./III. 1926*. Also, 2 sheets of music paper of the same format, with sketches and the row. All this is written in ink.

(*b*) From the same year (dated *14./9. 1926*) come 4 sheets of music paper (2 of oblong format, 29 × 34·5 cm., 2 of upright format, 27 × 34(35·5) cm.), written in ink and pencil. Here, too, only a few measures are notated. A sheet of paper bears the complete row-chart, but the row is entirely different from that of (*a*).

(*c*) The manuscript shows the first 13 measures completely carried out; 24 more are merely sketched in the principal voice (first violin). The close shows a clear cadence, and is marked with a double bar. In pencil, on a single sheet (oblong format, 26·5 × 34·5 cm.), undated.

16. Sketch of a MELODY (Adagio)

There is no indication for what purpose, or for what instruments, this melody was intended. Consisting of 13 measures, it is already fully formed; it is notated on 3 sheets of hand-lined paper (3 mm. distance between lines, upright format, 21·5 × 27·5 cm.). The crossed-out sketch is written in ink; the 2 other pages are written in pencil.

These sketches are very revealing of Schoenberg's method of composition. From them, one sees that he never constructed the row first, but that the musical inspiration was always primary; the 'construction' came afterwards. From the inspiration, the basic row was then derived. The first idea, on a separate sheet, is already very like the final version in terms of its extent and form. It is crossed out. The explanation for this is found on the second sheet. The row, derived from the original inspiration, shows traces of alterations of individual tones. In this altered form, the inversion of the first six tones a fifth lower contains the last six tones of the basic set in a different order (a procedure always used by Schoenberg in order to avoid octave-doublings). This form is now the basis for the entire work—in this instance, the final version of the melody as it is found on the third page (headed *Adagio*).

FACSIMILE PLATE XX (*a*)–(*c*)

17. Beginning of an untitled COMPOSITION FOR VOICE, 'CELLO AND PIANO

(*a*) On a sheet of 7-lined transparent paper (3 mm. space between lines) is written (partly in pencil, partly in ink) the beginning of a 'cello melody (15 measures), one part only, in an extremely virtuoso style. Above this is written *Introduction*.

(*b*) A fair copy, notated in black ink, on a sheet of transparent paper (upright format, 43 × 56 cm.), in 4 staves (*Voice, Cello, Piano*) includes 3 measures of introduction for 'cello and piano; there then begins an *Andante gracioso* (4/8) of which only the above-mentioned 'cello part exists.

Also we find, cut off the sheet mentioned under heading (*a*), the right half of the 2 upper staves, on which the 12-tone row is notated with its inversion. A white sheet of paper (typed carbon copy) bears an English text of humorous character, with various changes in ink made by Schoenberg's own hand.

18. Sketches for a STRING QUARTET

In the folder with the manuscript of the chorus 'Dreimal Tausend Jahre', Op. 50A, were found sketches for 4 movements of a string quartet. The beginnings of each of these movements are notated, in pencil, on 4 separate pages of white paper with holes in the margins (upright format, 20 × 26·5 cm.)—6 staves, 5 mm. space between lines. Three sheets bear the date *June 1, 1949*; the sheet with the beginning of the fourth movement, on the other hand, is dated *June 1, 1948*. However, this is obviously a mistake; 1949 must be meant, especially since the last movement is involved.

Sheet 1: I. ♩=76—11 measures, 2/2 time, completely worked out on 2 staves.

Sheet 2: II. Allo molto ♩.=92—11 measures, 6/8 time, notated in 4 voices on 1 staff.

Sheet 3: III. Largo ♩.=40—6 measures, 6/4 time; the melody in the first violin is accompanied, in the first 2 measures, by chords in the other instruments. This page is written on 4 staves.

Sheet 4: IV. Moderato ♩=80—29 measures of a single complete idea in the first violin, 2/4 time. On an additional sheet of transparent music paper (oblong format, 43 × 28 cm.), the first 12 measures are carried out in 4 voices on 2 staves. In addition, there is a second identical sheet on which several row-forms of the work are sketched.

(*d*) Orchestral works, instrumental concerti

1. SERENADE for small orchestra

The composition was begun *1./9. 96*. The manuscript is written in ink on 9 double sheets (upright format, 26·5 × 34·5 cm.). The first movement, *Andante moderato*, was completed on *3./9. 1896*. The Scherzo was begun on *30./11. 96* and remained unfinished, as did the (undated) Finale.

2. FRÜHLINGS TOD ('The Death of Spring', after Lenau), for large orchestra

There are 15 pages of this score (upright and oblong format, 26·5 × 34·5 cm.). The manuscript of the composition, which is notated in ink on 2 staves (with indications of instrumentation for large orchestra) breaks off at m. 254, dated *20./7. 98*.

3. Beginning of a SYMPHONY in G minor

The manuscript is notated as a short score, in ink, on 2 double sheets (upright format, 26·5 × 34·5 cm.). There are 73 measures of introduction ('Nicht rasch' ('Not fast')), plus 6 measures of the following *Allegro*. Begun *12./2. 1900*.

24. From the sketchbook of the film music for THE GOOD EARTH (Pearl S. Buck).

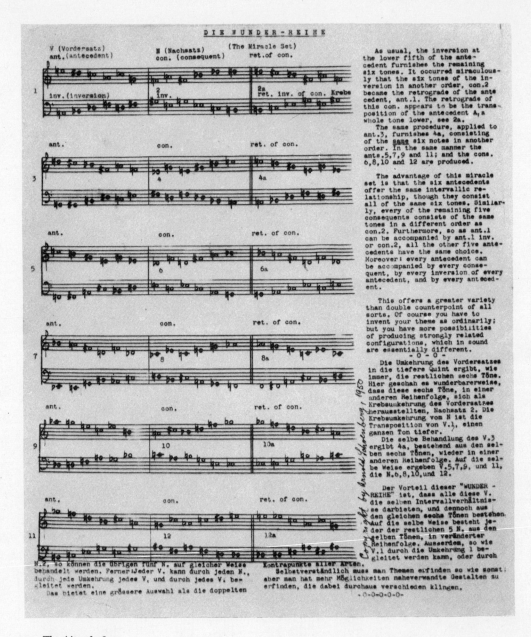

DIE WUNDER-REIHE
(The Miracle Set)

As usual, the inversion at the lower fifth of the antecedent furnishes the remaining six tones. It occurred miraculously that the six tones of the inversion in another order, con.2 became the retrograde of the antecedent, ant.1. The retrograde of this con. appears to be the transposition of the antecedent A, a whole tone lower, see 2a.

The same procedure, applied to ant.3, furnishes 4a, consisting of the same six notes in another order. In the same manner the ants.5,7,9 and 11; and the cons. 6,8,10 and 12 are produced.

The advantage of this miracle set is that the six antecedents offer the same intervallic relationship, though they consist all of the same six tones. Similarly, every of the remaining five consequents consists of the same tones in a different order as con.2. Furthermore, so as ant.1 can be accompanied by ant.1 inv. or con.2, all the other five antecedents have the same choice. Moreover: every antecedent can be accompanied by every consequent, by every inversion of every antecedent, and by every antecedent.

This offers a greater variety than double counterpoint of all sorts. Of course you have to invent your theme as ordinarily; but you have more possibilities of producing strongly related configurations, which in sound are essentially different.

Die Umkehrung des Vordersatzes in die tiefere Quint ergibt, wie immer, die restlichen sechs Töne. Hier geschah es wunderbarerweise, dass diese sechs Töne, in einer anderen Reihenfolge, sich als Krebsumkehrung des Vordersatzes herausstellten, Nachsatz 2. Die Krebsumkehrung vom N ist die Transposition von V.1, einen ganzen Ton tiefer.

Die selbe Behandlung des V.3 ergibt 4a, bestehend aus den selben sechs Tönen, wieder in einer anderen Reihenfolge. Auf die selbe Weise ergeben V.5,7,9, und 11, die N.6,8,10,und 12.

Der Vorteil dieser "WUNDER-REIHE" ist, dass alle diese V. die selben Intervallverhältnisse darbieten, und dennoch aus den gleichen sechs Tönen bestehen. Auf die selbe Weise besteht jeder der restlichen 5 N. aus den selben Tönen, in veränderter Reihenfolge. Ausserdem, so wie V.1 durch die Umkehrung 1 begleitet werden kann, oder durch

N.2, so können die übrigen fünf N. auf gleicher Weise behandelt werden. Ferner:Jeder V. kann durch jeden N., durch jede Umkehrung jedes V, und durch jedes V. begleitet werden.
Das bietet eine grössere Auswahl als die doppelten Kontrapunkte aller Arten.
Selbstverständlich muss man Themen erfinden so wie sonst; aber man hat mehr Möglichkeiten naheverwandte Gestalten zu erfinden, die dabei durchaus verschieden klingen.
-0-0-0-0-

25. The Miracle Set.

B. UNFINISHED WORKS (INCLUDING BEGINNINGS)

4. Beginning of an ORCHESTRA PIECE (untitled), Andante poco Adagio

The manuscript is notated in ink on 2 double sheets (upright format, 26·5 × 34·5 cm.). Undated.

5. Beginning of an OPERA 'UND PIPPA TANZT' ('And Pippa Dances': Gerhart Hauptmann)

The manuscript is notated in ink on 3 double sheets (upright format, 26·5 × 34·5 cm.). Superscription: *I. Akt.* An introduction of 36 measures (very freely treated B♭ minor) is followed by a 31-measure recitative between 'Director' and 'Wende'; all of this is written in short-score form. The work is undated, but, to judge from its harmonic style, might have been written about 1908.

6. Beginnings and sketches of a PASSACAGLIA for orchestra

The manuscript is written in ink on a double sheet (oblong format, 26·5 × 34·5 cm.). The score breaks off after the tenth measure; this fragment has an introductory character. Date: *5./III. 1920.* Apparently at a later time Schoenberg took up the composition once more. On two loose sheets of music paper (oblong format, 25·5 × 34·5 cm.), we find, among other things, the 10-measure passacaglia theme in pencil, as well as 2 identical row-charts. A comparison with the draft of 1920 shows that this was already 12-tone.

7. Beginnings of TWO VIOLIN CONCERTI

(*a*) Manuscript of No. 1: Concerto for violin, with accompaniment of piano, 3 clarinets, 1 trumpet, 1 horn, 1 trombone, violin, viola, 'cello, and double-bass. This consists of a pencil sketch of 19 measures, written on a sheet of music paper (oblong format, 25·5 × 35·5 cm.). With this is a sheet bearing the row of the concerto. Date: *14./XI. 1927.*

(*b*) The manuscript of the other concerto is written on a double sheet (upright format, 26·5 × 34 cm.), in ink. Mm. 1–16 are written in ink, mm. 17–43 (where the manuscript ends) in pencil. The accompaniment is written as a short score on 2 staves; although no indications of instrumentation are given, it is evidently not conceived for piano. With this are a row-chart and a sketch-sheet bearing the note (translated): *begun Cannes 2. I. 1927, then became ill; then to London!;* at m. 17 in the manuscript: *continued here, Berlin, 5./II. 1928.*

8. Beginning of a PIECE (Concerto?) FOR PIANO AND ORCHESTRA

Drafts and sketches on 3 loose sheets of music paper, in ink and pencil. Date: *März 1933.*

9. MARCIA (Allegro) for string orchestra (divided into obbligato and tutti groups)

Manuscript on a sheet of blueprint paper (upright format, 28 × 38 cm.), written in India ink. Undated, but with note: *tried to begin May 1.*

10. Sketches for a SYMPHONY IN FOUR MOVEMENTS

Written in pencil and ink on 7 loose sheets of music paper (oblong format, 25·5 × 34·5 cm.). These sketches, which are in the possession of Winfried Zillig, contain the beginnings and thematic concepts of the 4 movements (about 30–50 measures of each) in short-score form, on 3 or 4 staves, with exact indications of instrumentation and of the row as well as hints of a programme (see below). The orchestration is listed on the sketch for the first movement, which also bears a slip of paper with a sort of philosophical programme for the 4 movements (here given in Schoenberg's original German and English): *1. Predominance (superiority) provokes envie* / *2. (a) What they think about us,* / *(b) what we think about them—(a)* and *(b)* bracketed together, with the word *Scherzo* alongside— / *(c) conclusion* / *3. The sacred feasts and costumes— Die heiligen Feste und Gebräuche* / *4. The day will come.* The numbering corresponds to the 4 movements of the work. The sketches are dated: *I./7. 37, 9. 2. 37* and *10. 2. 37.*—The work was obviously intended as a musical apologia for Judaism.

11. Beginning of a COMPOSITION FOR LARGE ORCHESTRA (triple woodwind, etc.)

Largo ♩= 50. The manuscript is written in India ink on a sheet of blueprint paper (upright format, 24× 30·5 cm.). It contains 23 measures, of which 1–10 and 17–19 inclusive are completely carried out. Date: *May 24, 1941.*

12. Beginning of a WORK FOR ORCHESTRA

Date on one of the 3½ pages of short score: *November 22, 1946*; on another: *October 26, 46.*

Written in pencil on 1 page (upright format, 43× 56 cm., 5 mm. space between lines. There are 28 numbered measures: *Introduction Adagio* ♩= 58. This is obviously a sketch for a larger work (triple woodwind).

Also, there is a row–chart, written partly in pencil and partly in India ink (upright format, 43× 56 cm.), as well as sketches for an additional theme. A characteristic of the first half of the row is that it consists of three tritones connected by half-steps (C♯–G–F♯–C–B–F).

13. Beginning of a WORK FOR ORCHESTRA

The manuscript consists of 2 hand-lined sheets (upright format, 43·5× 56 cm.); 5 mm. space between lines. On these, in black crayon, are written 25 measures of a completely worked-out orchestral movement, with precise indications of dynamics and instrumentation (Lento, ♩=48). Also on the same sheet are sketches, a row–chart and a small piece of paper bearing the following tempo-indications (original English):

Adagio ♩= 40 (*instead of 48*)
♩= 48 (*instead of 63*)
Finale ♩= 72 (*instead of:*

Thus, Schoenberg must have had a rather extensive work in mind. The first page shows the beginning-date: *April 15, 1948.*

14. FANFARE for brasses

On a hand-lined sheet of music paper (upright format, 23× 30 cm.), three motives or phrases from Part III of the 'Gurrelieder' have been orchestrated for brass and organized

B. UNFINISHED WORKS (INCLUDING BEGINNINGS)

into 26 (numbered) measures. The conductor Leopold Stokowski had asked Schoenberg, in 1945, for an opening fanfare for the summer concerts in Hollywood Bowl (a huge open-air amphitheatre). Schoenberg answered in the affirmative, as we see from the following letter (original English) of June 2, 1945:

Before I write score I want to tell you what I plan. There are two possibilities:

(I) In the 'Tanz um das Goldene Kalb' (a ballet scene of half an hour duration) there are two or three fanfares, but they are too short. I mention them because they are of my latest (12-tone) style.

(II) and this I have already sketched: using three motifs from Gurrelieder. I would end with the C-major of the sunrise, which does not fit to the hour of the concert, but to the mood.

On August 31, 1945, Schoenberg's assistant at that time, Leonard Stein, sent three pages of the fanfare to Stokowski, expressing Schoenberg's regret that, because of his eye trouble, he could not finish it. This must have been a photocopy.

The manuscript at hand contains 31 measures written in pencil on 3 loose sheets of blue-print paper (upright format, 26·5 × 34 cm.). No date. Heading: *To my friend Leopold Stokowski Fanfare for a Bowl Concert on motifs of Die Gurrelieder by Arnold Schoenberg.*

(e) Choral works, oratorios

1. DARTHULA'S GRABGESANG ('Darthula's Grave-Song': Goethe, after Ossian)

The manuscript is notated in score-form, in ink, on 3 double sheets (upright format, 26·5 × 34·5 cm.); 65 measures. Beginning date: *Berlin 18./4. 1903.* In addition, 6 sketch-sheets.

2. SYMPHONY for soli, mixed chorus and orchestra

This is the plan for a large-scale symphony with which Schoenberg was occupied between 1912 and 1914. There are 16 loose sheets of sketches and drafts (mostly oblong format, 20 × 36·5 cm.; some double sheets), mostly written in pencil (some in ink).

Also, Sketchbook IV, pp. 1–5, contains material for this Symphony.

One sheet bears the following plan for the entire work (translated):

1. Movement: Change of Life (looking backward, looking to the future; gloomy, defiant, with-drawn. All motives that may later become important are in the

2. Movement: (Scherzo) The Joy of Life Part I Scherzo with 2 Trios, Part II.

Part I

Reprise of the whole with voice

(a)	Dehmel 'Schöne wilde Welt' ('Beautiful Wild World')				p. 10: Freudenruf '(Joyous Cry')
(b)	,,	,,	,,	,,	p. 70: Götterhochzeit ('Wedding of the Gods')
(c)	,,	,,	,,	,,	p. 117: Aeonische Stunde ('Hour of Aeons')

3. Movement ('Allegretto') Der bürgerliche Gott ('The Bourgeois God'): Dehmel Cantata (Schöne wilde Welt, Oratorium Natale) ' Schöpfungsfeier' ('Festival of Creation') p. 61

 Orchestra: all flutes, clarinets, violas and harps.

 4. Movement 'Interlude' (1) Unsatisfied. The Bourgeois God does not suffice
      (2) Tagore Nr. 86 Death of the Servant
            Nr. 88 Divinity of the Ruined Temple
    (solo vocal quartet!!) Nr. 92 I know, a day will come

 5. Movement: Psalm: on Biblical words Nr. 100 I dive into the depths of the sea
  (N.B.: the above notes on the fourth and fifth movements were crossed out in the MS.)

Part II

 4. Death–Dance of Principles (basic ideas)

  1. Burial 2. Funeral Oration (quasi) short sketch in between
         Tagore Nr. 88
  events at rest, with offstage orchestra; from 'Joyous Cry'

  3. Dance of Death
  Close: Prayer   *Isaiah 58 p. 711*
                  66 „ 718
               Jeremiah 7 „ 726
                  17 „ 737

 V. The faith of the 'disillusioned one'; the union of objective, sceptical consciousness of reality with faith. In the simple is concealed the mystical.

 On a large double sheet, Schoenberg cited or copied the above-mentioned Bible passages, as well as others (*St. Paul to the Romans*, 22nd Psalm, 88th Psalm).

 In addition, we find a sheet torn out of a book: 'Five Poems of Death', by Rabindranath Tagore. Several passages have been marked in red. The text 'Death-Dance of Principles' is by Schoenberg himself; it was published in his 'Texte' (Universal Edition, Vienna).

 Among the sketches is found a sheet with the heading: *3. Satz Kinder Gavotte* ('*Deine Kinder sehn den Himmel gerne*': 'Your children long to see Heaven'). Following this is a duet, designated '*Mutterseele und Vaterseele*' ('Mother Soul and Father Soul'). These words are found in the oratorio text which Dehmel sent to Schoenberg in December, 1912, at the composer's request. (See below, excerpts from the exchange of letters in December, 1912.) Another sketch-sheet (vocal line only, 76 measures) is headed *Aeonische Stunde*.

FACSIMILE PLATE XXI

 On two double sheets of 60-lined music paper cut in half crosswise (36·5 × 36·5 cm.) there is a 102-measure draft headed: *II. Satz Presto ♩ mehr als 200*. This metronomic indication was later crossed out and replaced by *♩=ca. 84–90*. Date of the beginning of the draft: *27./5. 1914*.

FACSIMILE PLATE XXII

 In other sketches, too, we find beginnings of this Scherzo with the note: *Scherzo; Einleitung zu Dehmel 'Freudenruf' Seite 10* ('Scherzo; introduction to Dehmel, "Joyous Cry," p. 10').

B. UNFINISHED WORKS (INCLUDING BEGINNINGS)

The 12-tone idea of this *Presto* movement recurs in most of the other sketches (also in the vocal ones). This is the 'Scherzo of a Symphony' of which Schoenberg spoke in a letter of June 3, 1937, to Nicolas Slonimsky, an American musicologist. He points out that this Scherzo is based on a 12-tone theme, and, therefore, represents the first step in the development of the method of composition with 12 tones. The last part of the symphony was used in the 'Jakobsleiter'. Schoenberg wrote its text himself, obviously because the combination of texts by different authors (as listed above) did not lead to satisfactory results. Perhaps a small number of the sketches (in which the 3 mirror-forms of the 12-tone set are also found) come from a later period.

In addition, a sheet of music paper (oblong format, 29 × 37 cm.) headed *Seraphita* belongs to this symphony. 10 measures of orchestra and a recitative above bass voices (singing *ppp* and without text) are written in ink. Date: *27./12. 1912*.

From a letter of Schoenberg to Dehmel, *13.XII. 1912:*

> . . . *for a long time I have been wanting to write an oratorio on the following theme: how the man of today, who has passed through materialism, socialism, and anarchy, who was an atheist, but has still preserved a remnant of ancient beliefs (in the form of superstition)—how this modern man struggles with God (see also 'Jakob ringt' by Strindberg) and finally arrives at the point of finding God and becoming religious. How to learn to pray! This change should not be caused by any actions, by blows of fate, or by a love-affair. Or, at least, such things should be merely hinted at, kept in the background as motivations. And above all: the text must mirror the speech, thought and expression of the man of today; it should deal with the problems which press upon us. For those who struggle with God in the Bible also express themselves as men of their time, speak of their own concerns and remain at their own social and spiritual level. Therefore, they are artistically strong, but cannot be put into music by a composer of today who fulfils his obligations.*
>
> *At first I had intended to write this myself. Now, I do not trust my own capacity to do so. Then I thought of arranging Strindberg's 'Jakob ringt' ('Jacob struggles') for my purpose. Finally, I decided to begin with positive religiosity, and I plan to rework the final chapter ('Journey to Heaven') of Balzac's 'Seraphita'. But I could not get rid of the idea of 'The Prayer of the Man of Today'; and I often thought: If only Dehmel . . .!*

Blankenese b/Hamburg, 15.12.12.

Honoured Herr Schönberg!

Your letter brought me great joy, perhaps the greatest that an artist may know, for it is the only proof of our spiritual creative power that we stimulate other spirits to creation. But now your request: I am powerless before it. For such a motivation cannot be planned; it must come of itself, as light streams from one star to another. I, at least, cannot write to order (to put it crudely). Several times I have tried it with the best will in the world, but I always felt myself so closely supervised by someone else's will that my soul could not give of its inmost self. As Goethe says, one *can* command the Muse, but one can do so successfully only when she appears on the parade-ground of her own free will! And, miraculously—perhaps she has already appeared and has fulfilled your desire before we knew anything about it. Last year I also wrote an oratorio which is rooted in, and culminates in, that new belief in God at which you have finally arrived. True, it does not present the struggle for God, but the triumphant 'rest in God', which exalts us above human life-and-death struggles. I enclose the poem herewith. You will feel that I could have said 'God' instead of 'Father-Spirit', and 'Humanity' instead of 'Mother-Soul'; but I did not want to designate a new world of feeling with old terminology. I should be happy if this poetic prayer 'happened' to harmonize with your musical longings (i.e., if this occurred with an inevitability which we do not understand). When I wrote it, I always kept hearing music between the lines; therefore, it must probably be suitable for symphonic working-out—musical preludes, interludes, repetitions by the chorus of lines sung by the individual voices, etc. This would probably bring out the underlying mood of *striving* more vividly, too.

I believe that with such orchestral insertions, the text is long enough for an evening-long work; the texts of Bach's oratorios are not any longer.

Most expectantly,

Your Dehmel

(The text included with the letter bears the title '*Schöpfungsfeier*' ('Festival of Creation'), *Oratorium natale*.)

Sunday, 29.12.12.

Dear Herr Schönberg!

We certainly gave each other a real New Year's treat! And I believe that my text for the oratorio corresponds to your idea even more closely than I thought. When I wrote to you that I could also have written 'Humanity' instead of 'Mother-Soul', that was still not profound enough. I probably meant what the mystics of the Middle Ages meant by Nature—which is the world of confused instincts, again and again put in order by the God-Spirit. In the work of art, too, this mystic wedding of Mother-Soul and Father-Spirit is consummated; and therefore the symbolic meaning of his sensual images always becomes clear to the artist only afterwards.

And now I shall confess to you that you read me strangely aright when you told me I would still write something descriptive of a struggle for God. For 20 years I have been thinking about a theme to which this idea is basic; however, this is not an oratorio, but a heroic drama —Saul, Jonathan, David—but removed from the Biblical realm into a mystical sphere. I do not yet know whether I shall even give the characters names. I have put aside my sketches again and again because I did not feel ready for this subject; perhaps your prophecy will now spur me on to dare a completion in the New Year.

With all good wishes for us both,

Your Dehmel

3. DIE JAKOBSLEITER ('Jacob's Ladder'): Oratorio for soli, mixed chorus and orchestra

The manuscript is notated on several staves in the form of a short score, in ink, on 22 loose sheets of music paper (32-lined, upright format, 36·5 × 37·5 cm.); it has 38 numbered pages. On the 39th page, there is merely an incomplete measure 686 (1st violin only); with this, the composition breaks off. On the other hand, the text, written by the composer, is complete (see Arnold Schönberg, 'Texte', Universal Edition, Vienna). Approximately in the middle of the drama, a 'Great Symphonic Interlude' was planned; in the short score, this begins in m. 610 and is worked out through m. 685. Except for 2 passages of 12 and 16 measures, in which the accompaniment to the principal choral voices is lacking (see below), the composition of the 685 measures of the short score is almost complete, although the usually very detailed indications of instrumentation are missing in a number of places.

The single pages of short score contain the following notes:

Page 1, top: *angefangen am 19./VI. 1917*. On the right margin, the stamped address (added later) of Schoenberg's last home in Los Angeles.

The last 6 measures on this page (from m. 19) are crossed out with broad strokes in ink. The following 8 measures, which filled all of p. 2, have been pasted over with a new sheet of music paper, on which the originally crossed-out 14 measures, now in an entirely new version, have been reduced to 10 measures, which fill the new page 2. (The pasted-on sheet had become loose.)

Page 9, upper left-hand side: the first $1\frac{1}{2}$ measures pasted over with a new version.

Page 10: pencilled note *noch unausgeführt!* ('not carried out yet!') in orchestral part of mm. 113–114, only partially worked-out here.

Pages 11–12: again, a pencilled note *Begleitung noch auszuführen!* ('accompaniment still to be carried out!'). The complete choral parts are present, mm. 115–124 inclusive.

Pages 13–14: here, too, the pencilled note *noch ausführen!!* refers to the orchestral accompaniment of the complete choral setting, mm. 142–157 inclusive.

Page 25, bottom right: pencilled note (translated): *the following passage 'dotted' but then the preceding must also be sung dotted.* This is followed by 2 other words that are hard to read (perhaps *Anmerkung dazu?*). The note meant to be dotted is a high A flat in the part of the bass singer (The Chosen One) in m. 412.

Page 35: a blue slip of paper, pasted in the upper right-hand margin, contains the following directions (here translated) which foreshadow the electro-acoustic developments of later decades. The text (translated) follows:

In this interlude are used several offstage orchestras, choruses, etc. ($H_1 H_2 \ldots F_1 F_2 \ldots CH_1 CH_2$, etc.), some of which are merely to be placed at a higher elevation, others at a distance.

1. *The conductor has to accompany offstage music wherever it occurs, to accommodate himself to it, to find his way to such an elastic tempo (without consideration of principal and subordinate voices, for purely acoustical reasons) that he can easily achieve this accommodation.*

2. *In the offstage orchestras, it will be permissible to have the more slowly-moving harmonies— and eventually even single subordinate voices and the like—played by organs or harmoniums (the latter either with the manuals in the orchestra or set up at a distance from the stage). However, the principal voice should always be played by the instruments indicated in the score.*

3. *The offstage orchestras must not be too far away; the impression of distance is sufficient. For example, H_1 should be 1–2 metres above the highest point of the regular orchestra, preferably opposite the conductor. H_2 is not as high as H_1, and nearer (considerably nearer than H_1)— preferably, for example, to the right of the conductor. F_2 is further away than F_1.*

Page 35, in the right-hand margin, bears the following pencilled notation (translated): *The notation of 4-part rhythms with the help of ♩. (dotted) values is practical. However, there is this against it: the dot, unlike the tied note, does not stand for an absolute value which our senses can comprehend, but rather for a conventional one.*

Page 36 contains the following (translated) explanation of the special notation for the offstage music: *This way of notation means that the offstage music in question is not supposed to begin on definite beats, but should be played in a floating rhythm outside the regular measure. The dotted lines show between what beats (of the rit. . . .) the distant sounds are to be divided.*

The location of relatively independent sounding groups in various points of space, as demanded here, foreshadows the newest acoustical tendencies. It represents an entirely new method of contrasting, or setting against one another in quasi-contrapuntal fashion, a number of sources of musical sound, whose relationships to one another are 'elastic' (see 1, above), and which are constantly exchanging musical functions (as carriers of principal or subordinate voices, harmonies, etc.).

Page 38: m. 667 bears the pencilled note: *noch unausgeführt, Klavier allein?* ('not carried out yet, piano alone?'). M. 680 shows a 'cello part added in pencil, with the notation *siehe Sk 132*. This is a reference to the large Sketchbook IV, which contains only material pertinent to the 'Jakobsleiter'. Other sketch-material was not found in the legacy.

Besides the large manuscript in short-score form, the legacy contains the following pertinent items:

1. Six loose sheets of short score, written in India ink and pencil on transparent blueprint paper (upright format, 30 × 46 cm.). On these, we find the first 44 measures in the new version which Schoenberg was planning (involving, above all, a reduction of the orchestra). Date at the upper right of the first page: *October 21, 1944*; above the seventh measure: *December 3, 44*. The spoken parts are now notated on 1 line each, rather than on 5-lined staves.

2. Enlarged photocopies (upright format, 61·5 × 68·5 cm.) of pages 6–39 of the short-score manuscript, with the exception of the missing p. 10 (mm. 105–114). These photocopies, which begin with m. 58 and end with m. 686, include, on the first pages, subsequently inserted additions to the indications for instrumentation, done by hand in ink. Schoenberg had sent these photocopies to Karl Rankl in London, to aid him in preparing the score (see letter of Schoenberg translated below).

3. Notes on the acoustics of the offstage orchestras planned for in the score, and on their placement, dated 1926 and 1944.

4. Photocopies of the 6 short-score pages mentioned under heading 1 above, as well as of pp. 3, 17, 29 and 36 (these last are probably proofs).

5. The large Sketchbook IV (see below).

FACSIMILE PLATE XXIII

Notes on the Origin of the Work

The first draft of the text of the 'Jakobsleiter' is dated *18. Januar 1915*. At that time, Schoenberg intended it for the fourth movement of an oratorio which he had already been working at between 1912 and 1914. (See above, II, B (e) 2; also below, 'Writings', II, A, 'Poems and Texts'.) When the composer, after a two years' interruption for military service, took up the work once more, he evidently decided to give up the original conception of the oratorio, with its lack of textual unity. The version of the 'Jakobsleiter' text found in a fair copy dated *26. Mai 1917* now becomes the sole basis for the composition, which was begun shortly thereafter. From outward appearances (one kind of music paper, character of handwriting) it is to be assumed that, so far as it exists, it was written down fairly continuously, without any considerable interruptions. From a number of remarks of Schoenberg (especially after 1945) we know that he intended to complete the composition of the work. Two weeks before his death, in a letter dated *27. Juni 1951,* he wrote to his former pupil Karl Rankl in London (letter translated):

Dear friend,

   It is possible that I must come to accept the fact that I am no longer in a position to compose 'Die Jakobsleiter' to the end. In this case, I hope still to be able to write a close to the first part. But in no case can I still write the score.

   Now I want to ask you if you would be ready, if necessary, to prepare such a score. Many and often very extensive indications as to my plans for orchestration are to be found in the manuscript. It would then be a matter of interpreting and completing these indications with the necessary discretion, so that this section can be performed effectively.

   I know that Scherchen could do this also, but I feel that you know 'Erwartung', 'Die glückliche Hand' and 'Von Heute auf Morgen' very well, and that you are better acquainted with my orchestral style than anyone else.

   I should be very happy if you would take this over, since I shall unfortunately have to leave so many of my works behind as fragments. When shall I receive your opera?

   With many cordial greetings, your

Arnold Schönberg

   When Karl Rankl returned this commission to Mrs. Gertrud Schoenberg after the composer's death, she entrusted Winfried Zillig with the preparation of the score.

4. 'ISRAEL EXISTS AGAIN' for mixed chorus and orchestra

   Text (English) handwritten by the composer. Date and signature: *June 10, 1949 Arnold Schoenberg.* The first, typed draft of the text is dated *8. Juni 1949* and reads as follows:

Israel exists again	Abraham saw him.
It has always existed,	Jakob saw him.
though invisibly.	But Moses
And since the beginning of time,	saw he was *our* God
since the creation of the world	and we *His* elected people:
we have always seen the Lord,	elected to testify
and have never ceased to see him.	that there is only one eternal God.
Adam saw him.	Israel has returned
Noah saw him.	and will see the Lord again.

The composition comprises 55 measures. The manuscript, notated on 3 staves, is written in short-score form on 3 sheets of blueprint paper (5 mm. space between lines), and, on the first page, bears the following note: *May 18, 1949. Largo ♩= 56.* The first 33 measures are played by the orchestra alone; its makeup is noted in the composer's handwriting, in the right-hand margin, as follows: *Cl. pic. i Cl., BsCl, Trp, Hrn, Trmb, Vi I II, Va, Vcl Cbs, Piano, Perc.* The composition breaks off with the word 'Invisibly'.

The first draft is written as a short score on 2 staves. It is on a page of blueprint paper, with 12 hand-drawn staves, and extends through m. 54. Before the tempo-indication *Largo*, the word *Andante* is also written. In the first 33 measures, this draft corresponds exactly to the final version; in the following choral section, however, the 2 versions differ, although they start with the same musical idea.

In addition, there are 3 little sketches. One of these, done on staves hastily drawn on the back of a letter to Schoenberg from the Jewish War Veterans of the United States of America (March 9, 1949) and dated *III/15 / 1949*, is obviously the first idea for the work.

The second sketch includes 11 measures of music for the following words (sung): 'we have always seen the Lord, Adam saw him,' etc.; (spoken) 'Since the beginning of the creation of the world'.

The third sketch includes only 2 measures for orchestra. In addition, there is a chart of the row-forms used.

(f) Arrangements (beginnings)

a. Arrangements of own works

1. CHAMBER SYMPHONY IN E MAJOR for piano, 2 violins, viola and 'cello

Manuscript of only 13 measures, written in ink on a double sheet (oblong format, 26·5 × 34·5 cm.). Date: *13./2. 1907.*

2. Manuscript of a STRING QUARTET after the Wind Quintet, Op. 26; Op. 26a

Date and place of beginning: *Venedig, 3.IX. 1925*. Fifteen measures of the 1st movement, in ink, on a double sheet (upright format, 27 × 35 cm.).

3. VARIATIONS FOR ORGAN, Op. 40B. Version for 2 pianos

Manuscript on 2 loose sheets of blueprint paper (upright format, 27·5 × 33·5 cm.), written in India ink. Only from m. 1 to the middle of m. 22. Undated.

b. Arrangements of others' works

1. SONATA A VIOLA DA GAMBA E CEMBALO OBBLIGATO di Johann Sebastian Bach

arranged for Violoncello and Orchestra by Arnold Schoenberg, January 3, 1939

The work did not get past the first 5 measures. The score is written in India ink on 2 sheets of transparent music paper (23 × 33 and 28 × 38 cm.).

2. Chorale 'WACHET AUF RUFT UNS DIE STIMME' ('Awake, a voice is calling us') from the cantata of the same name by Johann Sebastian Bach, for large orchestra

Manuscript on 2 sheets of music paper (upright format, 27 × 34 cm.). The score, written in ink, breaks off after the first 8 measures. Undated.

C. MISCELLANEOUS

(mostly compositions and orchestrations for special occasions)

1. WALTZ for string orchestra

The unfinished composition is written in ink on 5 sheets of music paper (oblong format, 25·5×32·5 cm. and upright format, 26·5×32·5 cm.). Undated; from all appearances, an early work.

2. LIED DER WALKÜRE ('Song of the Valkyrie': F. Dahn) by Heinrich van Eyken Verlag Dreililien, Berlin, Copyright 1901

The printed copy bears the following handwritten note on the first page: *Instrumentiert über Verlangen des Dreililien-Verlages! Arnold Schönberg* ('Orchestrated at the request of the 'Dreililien Verlag'). The whereabouts of the manuscript is unknown.

During his first stay in Berlin (1901–1903), Schoenberg had to earn a living for himself and his family by working with Ernst von Wolzogen's 'Bunte Bühne' as well as by orchestrating operettas and similar works. From this period come the orchestrations of 'Mädchenreigen' (see below) and 'Lied der Walküre'.

3. MÄDCHENREIGEN ('Maidens' Dance') for 3 women's voices with piano accompaniment, by Bogumil Zepler. Orchestrated by Arnold Schoenberg

The manuscript of the score, which consists of 16 sheets of music paper (26·5×34·5 cm.), comprising 31 numbered pages, is in the possession of the Library of Congress. It is written in ink and signed: *21./4. 1902 Arnold Schönberg*.

4. MOTIFS SUNG BY NIGHTINGALES

Noted *8./5. 1912*. Handwritten notes between the motifs (translated): *Even higher tones occur. Some, I could not determine at all! Much higher than piccolo. C frequently occurs. The principal tones come from the chord B flat–D–F–A flat (C occurs once). The accessory tones have not been notated exactly. Instead, I have written down those notes as appoggiaturas which seem to me nearest to the sound of the trill or passage. The rhythms are fairly exact. Mostly in common time.*

5. DER DEUTSCHE MICHEL*; A War-Song by O. Kernstock

This work, for male chorus, is found in an ink manuscript on 2 double sheets (upright format, 26·5×34·5 cm.). With this were found the 4 handwritten choral parts of the a cappella work. Undated; this must be an occasional composition from the time of Schoenberg's military service in World War I. The same is true of the next work:

---

* TRANSLATOR'S NOTE: 'German Michael' is the 'common man' of the German peasantry with his traditional qualities of stubbornness and determination.

II. UNPUBLISHED WORKS

6. March, DIE EISERNE BRIGADE ('The Iron Brigade')

The cardboard cover of this piece bears the following notation, in green pencil: *Die eiserne Brigade, Marsch von Arnold Schönberg in Bruck 1916 für den Einjährigen-Kameradschaftsabend.* (Bruck an der Leitha was the site of the military training camp for the Viennese regiment 'Hoch- und Deutschmeister' which Schoenberg had joined; the march was written for a festive evening of the one-year volunteers.) The copy of the score is written in ink, for piano and string quartet, on 3 bound double sheets; the parts are also in existence. Handwritten note in green pencil on the title-page (translated): *Original manuscript given in 1916 to Dr. Kusmitsch, first lieutenant in Bruck a/L., magistrate in Budapest (who did not know how to value it).*

7. BEGINNINGS OF THE ORCHESTRATIONS OF

(*a*) 'Austrian Grenadiers' March' by Neipperg (11 measures)

(*b*) 'Imperial Grenadiers' March' (30 measures)

8. CHRISTMAS MUSIC for 2 violins, 'cello, piano and harmonium

This (tonal) composition was apparently intended for a domestic Christmas celebration; it is dated, at the close, *Weihnachten 1921 Arnold Schönberg.* We have both the complete first draft, written in pencil, on a single sheet (36·5 × 37·5 cm.) and a double sheet (26·5 × 34·5 cm.), and the fair copy (through m. 76 only) in ink on 2 double sheets (upright format, 26·5 × 34·5 cm.). Date of completion of first draft: *23./XII. 1921.* There is also a handwritten piano part (Schoenberg played the 'cello, while the daughter of his first marriage, Gertrud, played the piano).

9. ORCHESTRATIONS of

(*a*) 'Ständchen' ('Serenade') (Schubert) for clarinet, bassoon, mandolin, guitar and string quartet. Written in ink on a double sheet (upright format, 27 × 35·5 cm.). Undated. Also handwritten parts.

(*b*) 'Der Lindenbaum' ('The Linden Tree') (Schubert): manuscript of a score for large orchestra; in ink, on music paper as in (*a*). Only 20 measures.

(*c*) 'Santa Lucia' and 2 smaller pieces for violin, viola, 'cello, mandolin, guitar and clarinet. Manuscript as in (*a*); also some of the handwritten parts.

During his summer vacation in Traunkirchen (1921) Schoenberg had his students do orchestration exercises for combinations in which they could then play as well. He participated (on the 'cello) in the performance of these, as well as orchestrating (*a*) and (*c*).

10. 'GERPA' (unfinished)
Theme and variations for horn, piano, first violin, second violin, harmonium

The manuscript (first draft), written in ink on a double sheet (upright format, 26·5 × 34·5 cm.), breaks off in the fourth variation, as does the fair copy (in ink, on 2 double sheets, format as above). The note *begonnen anfangs November 1922* confirms the supposition that this work was intended as a kind of tonal 'Hausmusik' for Schoenberg's son Georg (by his first marriage) who was studying horn at the Vienna Academy of Music during this period.

C. MISCELLANEOUS

11. JOHANN STRAUSS: LAGUNENWALZER, Op. 411; ROSEN AUS DEM SÜDEN, Op. 388. Arrangements for chamber orchestra by Arnold Schoenberg

The arrangements of the two waltzes—as well as that of the 'Treasure Waltz' from 'The Gypsy Baron' made by Anton Webern and that of 'Wine, Women and Song' by Alban Berg—were done for a special concert of the 'Verein für musikalische Privataufführungen in Wien' ('Society for Private Musical Performances in Vienna') (founded and organized by Schoenberg). This concert was intended to raise money for the Society, not only through the sale of tickets but also through the auction of the original manuscripts following the concert. The instrumental combination (piano, harmonium and string quartet) was the usual one for the salon orchestras of those days; Schoenberg chose it on purpose to show that one could easily avoid the thick, vulgar sound with which that combination was all too often afflicted. The performers were: Eduard Steuermann, piano; Alban Berg, harmonium; Rudolf Kolisch or Arnold Schoenberg, first violin; Karl Rankl, second violin; Othmar Steinbauer, viola; Anton Webern, 'cello.

Copies were made of the two auctioned manuscripts. Their whereabouts is not known, but it is my recollection that Artur Prager, treasurer of the Society, bought them at the time. The copy of the 'Lagoon Waltz' has been preserved. That of 'Roses from the South' was destroyed in the war; however, the score could be reconstructed from the remaining parts (some copied in Schoenberg's and Berg's handwritings). Only the harmonium part is missing (or, rather, only its first few measures exist).

12. FERRUCCIO BUSONI, BERCEUSE ÉLÉGIAQUE
arranged for flute, clarinet, harmonium, piano and string quartet by Arnold Schoenberg

Intended for a performance of the 'Verein für musikalische Privataufführungen' (see above). The original manuscript was probably lost; a copy is in the possession of the author.

[13. HEINRICH SCHENKER, 4 SYRISCHE TÄNZE
orchestrated by Arnold Schoenberg

Conducted by Busoni in a concert in the Beethoven Saal, Berlin, on November 5, 1903. Schenker wrote the dances for piano duet, in which form they were published by Weinberger, Leipzig, in 1899.]

III. SKETCHBOOKS

Five large sketchbooks, which Schoenberg left behind besides a number of smaller ones, contain an unusual quantity of valuable material—especially the first drafts, generally complete, of several of his works.

SKETCHBOOK I

includes the period from *März 1904* to *20. April 1905*. It consists of 60 numbered pages (oblong format, 14·5 × 34·5 cm.), and is bound in a heavy yellow cover with the inscription *Skizzen*. Its contents consist chiefly of drafts of the First String Quartet in D minor, Op. 7, and of some of the Orchestral Songs, Op. 8.

SKETCHBOOK II

was begun in *April 1905* and consists of 116 numbered pages (oblong format, 19·5 × 36 cm.). On the first page is the stamped address Berlin W 50 Nürnbergerplatz 3, and the handwritten note *1933 Sch*. It contains, principally, the first draft of most of Op. 7 (see above), the Songs, Op. 6, and much of the First Chamber Symphony, Op. 9. Also, there are several canons on proverbs of Goethe, beginnings of songs to texts by Hölderlin, and the second part of the chamber-music work 'Ein Stelldichein' after Richard Dehmel (see above, II, B (*c*), No. 11).

SKETCHBOOK III

was begun in *April 1906*. It is in a black cover with the inscription *Skizzen*, and consists of 175 numbered pages (oblong format, 19 × 36·5 cm.) which have been written on up to p. 132; between pp. 139 and 156, 8 leaves have been cut out. This sketchbook contains several beginnings of songs to verses by Dehmel and C. F. Meyer, sketches for a chorus 'Des Friedens Ende' ('The End of Peace') (Gottfried Keller), 50 measures of 'Kennst du das Land, wo die Zitronen blühn' ('Know'st thou the land where the citrons bloom?'), 4 pages (42–45) of sketches for an opera based on Gerhart Hauptmann's 'Und Pippa tanzt' ('And Pippa dances'). However, its most important contents are the following first drafts: songs, Op. 12 and Op. 14 (pp. 58, 71, 103); Second String Quartet in F♯ minor, Op. 10 (begun on p. 57, *9./3. 1907*; end of the second movement, *27./7. 1908*); First and Second Chamber Symphonies. On pp. 76 ff., we find a continuation of the last-named work, dated *8./7. 1907*; on p. 116: *Fortsetzung der II. Kammersinfonie angefangen am 23./11. 1911* ('Continuation of the Second Chamber Symphony begun on Nov. 23, 1911') (to m. 257); on p. 118: *Fortsetzung begonnen am 6./XII. 1916* ('Continuation begun on Dec. 6, 1916'). A slip of paper pasted to p. 119 contains the beginning of a text for the Second Chamber Symphony (recitation) with the title ' *Wendepunkt*' ('Turning Point'), *Orchesterwerk von Arnold Schönberg*. Beginning of the text for recitation: *Auf diesem Weg weiterzugehn war nicht möglich* ('To continue further along this road was impossible'), etc.—Also, this sketchbook contains the continuation of this composition which Schoenberg resumed in America.

III. SKETCHBOOKS

SKETCHBOOK IV

was begun, according to a note on the title-page, in *Mai 1915*; p. 1 shows the exact date, *4. Mai 1915*. On the upper left-hand side of the dark-blue linen cover, we find the word *Skizzen* written in white Gothic letters. This sketchbook consists of 90 sheets of music paper (oblong format, 19·5 × 37·5 cm.); pp. 1–139 are numbered continuously, while thereafter pp. 141 and 161, only, are numbered. Most of this material is written in pencil; some passages, however, are written in ink, and on pp. 133–134 we also find writing in red and green pencil. The following pages are blank: 6–19 (inclusive), 113, 114, 118, 119, 129, 130, 135–140, 142 to end of book.

Although, from p. 20 onwards, the book contains only sketches and longer drafts for 'Die Jakobsleiter', the sketches on pp. 1–5 inclusive belong to the Symphony for soli, chorus and orchestra (see above, II, B (*e*) 2). They begin with the already-mentioned 12-tone row, and a note in red pencil on p. 3 points out motivic connections and related successions of tones in the musical ideas written down there. This may be considered a first step towards serial composition and its procedures. Between pp. 10 and 11, 3 pieces of white paper have been pasted in; the first 3 sides of these contain the orchestration of the symphony, as well as 2 sketches of the placement of the orchestra on the stage.

On p. 20 begins the group of pages (109 in all) devoted to sketches for 'Die Jakobsleiter'. These comprise not only sketches and drafts (among others, the first continuous concept of mm. 337–564) for the first half of the work as later found in the fragmentary short score, but also larger and smaller sections of the second half. For example, there are the closing chorus (pp. 112 and 117, the latter dated *Juni 1921* and *18. April 1922*), the beginning of Gabriel's great song (p. 59 of the printed text, pp. 97–98 of the sketchbook), the chorus of the Lost Ones and Demons (p. 58 of text-book, pp. 101, 102, 127 and 128 of sketchbook) and many more.

The sketches contained in this book were, according to the date on p. 21, begun on *30./I. 1917*. Other dates and notations are found as follows:

Page 28: *angefangen anfangs Juni 1917 Sch.* ('started beginning of June, 1917 . . .')
Page 78: *2./9. 1917*
Page 86: *2.I. 18*
Page 92: *8.I. 18*
Page 96: *einrücken zum Militär!! 19./9. 1917* ('enlist in the army ! ! . . .'). On the same page: *30.XI. 1917.*

(Schoenberg was drafted into the army once more in 1917, after his first discharge; as we shall see below, he was discharged again on December 7, 1917. The seeming contradiction between succession of dates and of page numbers—e.g., on pp. 86 and 96—is explained by the fact that the various sketches were often not continued on the proper, next-following page.)

Page 97: *wieder enthoben 7./12. 1917* ('discharged again . . .').
Page 103: *4. 1. 18.* Beginning of the composition of the interlude.
Page 117: *Juni 1921* and *18. April 1922.* Closing chorus.
Page 121: *9./III. 1918 Streich Septett.* Interlude.
Page 124: *Juli 1922.* Interlude.

Between pp. 30 and 31 are pasted:

(*a*) Three pieces of paper, on the first 2 pages of which are written the exact specifications for soloists, speakers and orchestra, for the sections of the chorus and its placement on the stage, etc. The third page, dated *Juni 1921*, shows the placement of the (now much reduced) orchestra; the fourth page bears explanations which pertain to the meaning of the dotted bar-lines (elimination of heavily accented beats in favour of longer phrases) and to the musical structure of the interlude (*Bau des Zwischenspiels*).

(*b*) A brown envelope which contains the detailed composition of the chorus (i.e., number of singers to be used in each section), a table (accurate to seconds) of the timings of the individual parts of the work up to m. 567, and a *plan for the organization of rehearsals*.

All of these directions (that is, for the number of performers) are superseded by those of *April 1922* (see also the signed note on p. 112) which are found on a piece of paper pasted in between pp. 50–51. They call for a 75-piece orchestra, a principal chorus (120), chorus below the stage (40) and chorus above the stage (20). In this connection, see also the revision of mm. 1–44 (1944) discussed above, section II, B (*e*) ('Die Jakobsleiter').

The following items are also pasted in:

Page 107, margin: a sheet of white paper with explanations for conductors.

Between pp. 116 and 117: a sheet of music paper with sketches for the final chorus.

Page 108, margin: a sheet of blue paper with directions for the effect of the offstage orchestras in the interlude.

SKETCHBOOK V

consists of 200 numbered pages (oblong format, 25·5 × 34 cm.) bound in a heavy cover that has been pasted over with brightly patterned cloth. On the outer cover is the figure 1922; on the first page is the inscription: *Mit Gott 3. Juni 1922* ('With God . . .').

After p. 180, there are 13 sheets of music paper (oblong format, 26·5 × 34·5 cm.) laid in loosely. These pages are numbered with Roman numerals; they bear (written sometimes on one side of the page, sometimes on both) the final movement (Gigue) of Op. 29, beginning with m. 23.

At the very beginning of the book we find not only the fourth of the 5 Piano Pieces, Op. 23, but also the third and fifth pieces, which are missing among the other manuscripts. The essential content of the sketchbook is (following the page-numbers) as follows:

Page

2–3 Piano piece Op. 23, No. 3. Begun: *Mödling, 6. Februar 1923*; completed: *9.II. 1923 Sch.*

4 *am 10/II 1923 Fortsetzung des Klavierstückes Serie I No 4, begonnen am 20/7 1920 | beendet am 13/II 1923* ('Continuation of the piano piece, Series I, No. 4; begun on July 20, 1920, completed on February 13, 1923').

5–7 Waltz, Op. 23, No. 5; completed *17/II 1923.*

8–9 Op. 25, Intermezzo: *Fortsetzung des Klavierstückes II Serie 2, begonnen 25/VII 21, fortgesetzt 19.II. 1923, beendet 23./II. Arnold Schönberg* ('Continuation of the piano piece, Series II, No. 2; begun July 25, 1921, continued February 19, 1923, finished February 23 . . .')

8 Above the Intermezzo is notated, on 1 line, a beginning of the Minuet, Op. 25, which is quite different from the final form.

III. SKETCHBOOKS

III. SKETCHBOOKS

Page

113   Final movement: *beendet 26/VII 1924 4 Uhr nachm. Arnold Schönberg* ('finished July 26, 1924, at 4 p.m.')

114–118 Sketches for the Suite, Op. 29, dated *28/X 1924*. On p. 118 is pasted a small typed piece of paper:

         1. (Satz) 6/8 leicht, elegant, flott, Bluff ('light, elegant, gay, bluffing')

         2. Jo-Jo Foxtrott

         3. Fl. Kschw. Walzer

         4. AS Adagio

         5. JbeB Muartsch Var

         6. Film Dva

         7. Tenn Ski

119   Beginning of the second movement, Op. 29 (*Tanzschritte*): *17/7 1925*

144   End of the second movement: *13/6 1925* (either the beginning date or the ending date must be a mistake!)

145   Op. 29, *Ouvertüre: 17/6 1925*. From p. 147, the row-forms being used are put in with coloured pencil. Marginal note (translated): *I must often note down the rows, because my 'correctors' often force me to 'improvements' when they can no longer discover the* [illegible word] *row!'*

156   After this page, 6 loose sheets of music paper have been laid in. On the first sheet are sketches; on the second, the continuation of the Overture. (M. 137.) The movement is completed on the last page of these laid-in sheets: *15/IV 1926* [??]

157   Theme with Variations, Op. 29: *19.VII. 25*

176   End of variation movement: *15/VIII 1925 Arnold Schönberg*

177   Gigue (Op. 29), date of completion: *1. Mai 1926 Arnold Schönberg*

180   After this page, 13 sheets of music paper with the Finale of Op. 29 (from m. 23 onwards) have been laid in (see description above, first paragraph concerning Sketchbook V). Also, there is a row-chart pasted on cardboard (16 × 20) as well as a row-chart for the Wind Quintet (32 × 40·5).

Pages 181–200 are blank.

*

Besides these 5 large sketchbooks, the legacy also contains 11 small ones in notebook format. Two of them, 1 begun in 1915 and the other in 1917 (formats 17 × 10 cm. and 11 × 6·5 cm.), contain, on 2 and 13 pages respectively, sketches from 'Die Jakobsleiter' only. Another, begun at Christmas, 1900 (format 7 × 12 cm.), contains, among other material, sketches for the 'Brettellieder' and for a string quartet. Two notebooks pertain exclusively to the film 'The Good Earth' (after the novel of Pearl Buck) for which Schoenberg was to write the music for a fee of $50,000. He declined because the M-G-M film company wanted to reserve the right to make changes in his work. The sketches, in a tonal idiom, depict scenes of nature, crowd scenes, and individual characters in the drama, Gertrud Schoenberg states that they were written down shortly after the composer's refusal to write the score—simply out of interest in the task of solving such an artistic problem.

FACSIMILE PLATE XXIV

WRITINGS

I. THEORETICAL WORKS

A. TEXTBOOKS

(a) Completed works

1. HARMONIELEHRE
Universal Edition, Vienna
THEORY OF HARMONY, translated by Robert D. W. Adams (abbreviated edition)
Philosophical Library, New York

The first draft of the 'Harmonielehre' comprises 294 pages, partly handwritten, partly typed, and extends up to and including the chapter on 'Fourth-Chords'. The title-page, the dedication to Gustav Mahler, the foreword and the table of contents are written in pencil on 7 sheets of paper. Undated, but completed in 1911.

The manuscript of the enlarged edition of 1921 uses the first printed edition as a basis.

On the title-page of a leather-backed bound copy, we find the following handwritten inscription (here translated) intended for Schoenberg's wife, Gertrud:

[Harmonielehre], *my dearest, we shall not need. I wrote this one because I never studied any, and you want to read it, although it will not tell you anything you do not know. 'One learns only what one knows anyway,' I once said. Therefore, the chapter on 'Measure and Harmony' is very brief here. Measure is the disposition to harmony, and the study of harmony is the study of form. Its deepest meaning is revealed only to the one who does not ask about it. This one knows the answer before the question. Your Arnold. 25.VIII. 1924.*

Another copy has a note on the title-page: *Handexemplar mit Fehlervormerkungen März 1922 Schönberg* ('Personal copy with indications of errors . . .'). This copy contains corrections of printer's errors, stylistic improvements, small additions and omissions. The latter apply to lines 180–181, p. 474. These are crossed out in red and marked with a sign of omission, dated *29./V. 1923*. In the margin of this page is the following note in ink (here translated): *I have been punished for this attack in ways that I know about and that were to be expected. But I wanted to take it out long ago. For the attack is uglier than I realized at that time, and is unfair. For it is not at all impossible to compose in this manner. But more important is what comes out; and only this is to be judged; not how it was done. If what comes out is good, then it must have been done correctly, as well.* [This pertains to an attack on Felix von Weingartner.]

2. MODELS FOR BEGINNERS IN COMPOSITION
G. Schirmer, New York

The book is based on Schoenberg's experiences while teaching at the University of California at Los Angeles, and on the materials which he prepared for his elementary composition classes there. The manuscript of the second version consists of 16 typed pages and all the music examples (carbon copies). It bears the date of completion: *Arnold Schoenberg, Sept 12, 1942*.

There is also Schoenberg's personal copy of the printed edition *with corrections and remarks for a new edition* (these words written in red pencil). The following notes are also written in red pencil on the inside back cover:

> *add (1) advice how to insert harmonies between II., III. etc and other degrees*
> (2) *one or 2 simpler menuets*
> „ „ „ *simpler scherzi*
> (3) *motives and phrases for (a) menuettos (b) scherzis*

Below this, in green pencil: *take them partly from ex. for UCLA, perhaps also other characters: Gavotte, March, Andante gracioso etc. see syllabus*; there is also a 4-measure music example in E minor.

3. STRUCTURAL FUNCTIONS OF HARMONY
Williams and Norgate, London; W. W. Norton, New York

DIE FORMBILDENDEN TENDENZEN DER HARMONIE
(translated from the English by Erwin Stein)
B. Schotts Söhne, Mainz

The manuscript consists of 84 typed pages with many handwritten alterations and additions. Undated. Completed 1946.

4. FUNDAMENTALS OF MUSICAL COMPOSITION
Not published in English

GRUNDLAGEN DER MUSIKALISCHEN KOMPOSITION
translated by Rudolf Kolisch
Not published.

The fair copy (typed) used as a basis for the translation comprises 205 pages. The beginning date is given as 1937, the date of completion as 1948.

The first draft consists of over 150 pages (some typed on both sides of the page). They show many cuts, changes and additions (in ink or pencil) as well as many music examples. No date is given.

Also, there is a typed fair copy of 166 pages, with few corrections; in addition, there is a typed manuscript 'Melody and Theme: Melodious and Unmelodious' with the handwritten note: *A chapter from Fundamentals of musical composition by Arnold Schoenberg*. At the end of these 14 typed pages: *Copyright by Arnold Schoenberg Los Angeles 1940*.

To this work there also belong the contents of 5 folders (files containing loose sheets of paper, 21·5×28 cm.). Two of them contain, on 23 sheets of music paper in each folder (21·5×28 or about 25×35 cm.), music examples Nos. 117–184 (incomplete) and Nos. 77–97; there are many cuts, corrections, and changes. Two folders contain the much-corrected, typed text (pp. 3–88 and 81–161); many pages have been replaced by others from a new version of the text, while others show cuts, corrections, etc. The fifth folder contains unrelated pages

A. TEXTBOOKS

(170 is the highest page-number) but also larger continuous sections (pp. 162–170; Scherzo), a list of chapters, etc.

(b) Unfinished works

On four widely separated occasions, Schoenberg took up the idea of a counterpoint textbook: in 1911 (immediately after the 'Harmonielehre'), 1926, 1936 and 1942. The final form of the work was to comprise 3 volumes; however, only the first (up to 4-voiced simple counterpoint) was completed. There are, in addition, many 2- to 4-voiced fugues and chorale preludes, without explanatory text.

1a, 1911: DAS KOMPONIEREN MIT SELBSTÄNDIGEN STIMMEN
Kritik der alten Kontrapunkt-Lehrmethode und Aufstellung einer neuen.
('Composing with Independent Voices: critique of the old method of teaching counterpoint and establishment of a new one.')

The manuscript bearing the above title is in the possession of Universal Edition, Vienna. It consists of 12 pages (written in pencil, on one side of the page only; 21·5 × 34 cm.), with the title-page unnumbered. On this page, there is written above the title: *Inhaltsangabe und Disposition Seite 1–7 ferner (Seite I–IV) Inhaltsangaben des ersten, kritischen Theils* (in other words, a summary of the contents); at the lower right Schoenberg signed his name and dated the manuscript *29./6. 1911*.

The beginning of the introduction may be translated as follows: *Purpose of art. Proof of absolute purposelessness of art in terms of what is usually understood as purpose. Only purpose of art (which is, however, achieved unconsciously) expression of personality; then, further, expression of humanity.* In the legacy was found a carbon copy of this manuscript, together with an additional page headed *Instrumentationslehre (Setzkunst)* ('Study of Instrumentation (The Art of Arranging)'), the contents of which are not directly related to the manuscript. Five additional pages contain:

(a) *Unrecht eines Künstlers* ('An Artist's Wrongs': fragment);

(b) *Zusammenhang* ('Unity': 2 pages of a copy, numbered 3 and 4);

(c) *Gesetze, Regeln, Lehrsätze, Definitionen* ('Laws, Rules, Principles of instruction, Definitions').

1b, 1926: DIE LEHRE VOM KONTRAPUNKT ('The Theory of Counterpoint')

This *second* fragment, found in the legacy, was begun on *29.X. 1926* and consists of 18 numbered pages written in ink (21 × 34 cm.) with 3 pages of music examples.

1c, 1936: Untitled

The *third* textbook, begun in November 1936, also remained unfinished. It consists of 58 typed pages, including a foreword for pupils (additional prefaces for teachers and composers were planned). With this are 16 pages of music examples, partly copied by another hand, partly photocopies of the examples which Schoenberg used in teaching at the University of California at Los Angeles. These were also used by Schoenberg in his textbook begun in 1942.

I. THEORETICAL WORKS

In the first draft of this third concept, the first 19 pages are written in ink, while the remainder is typed. Note at the beginning: *begonnen Mitte November 1936* ('begun in mid-November, 1936').

1d, 1942: Untitled

The *fourth* and final version of the counterpoint textbook consists of 2 handwritten and 2 typed volumes (in letter-files).

Of the handwritten volumes (in ink), the first is designated as *Volume I Handwritten text, begun November 25, 1942*. It contains 35 pages with music examples. The second book, headed *Handwritten Bk II*, contains 22 pages.

The first of the 2 typed volumes is designated *Master Copy Book I, begun April 17, 1943*. It contains 2 pencilled pages (the foreword) and 67 numbered, typed pages, additions and corrections to which have been made in pencil. To this belong numerous music examples, partly written in pencil, partly in the form of photocopies. The second typed volume comprises numbered pages 58–118.

In a fifth folder, entitled *Examples Book I*, are found over 100 handwritten and photocopied examples.

Finally, the legacy contains a manuscript written in ink on 9 bound sheets of notebook-paper (together with a fair typed copy of 4 blueprint sheets) entitled *Contrapuntal Composition. This article belongs to my book on counterpoint, and if I am in the position to finish the book, it will be reprinted there*. A tenth sheet, belonging with this material, contains the beginning (17 handwritten lines) of an additional, untitled article: *I know of course, that this is not the first ars nova—history repeats itself*. The sheets bear the stamp of Schoenberg's last address in Los Angeles.

From a letter to Josef Rufer, June 25, 1946 (translated):

> *As far as my precarious health permits, I am working on two books: Structural functions of harmony will, I hope, be ready in 6–8 weeks, Musical Composition may take a few months more. I have begun a third book in 3 volumes: I. Preliminary Exercises, II. Contrapuntal Composition, III. Counterpoint in Homophonic Music. I could finish the first volume in two months; the second would probably take a half-year, the third at least a year. But where should I find the time for this, when I would [need] another quarter of a year for 'Moses und Aron' (the opera) and a year for the oratorio 'Die Jakobsleiter'?*

A letter to Miss Clara Silvers, written on October 4, 1948, indicates that the second volume was also to deal with multiple counterpoint, while the third was to discuss counterpoint in homophonic compositions of the last 200 years.

2. ZUSAMMENHANG, KONTRAPUNKT, INSTRUMENTATION, FORMENLEHRE ('Unity, Counterpoint, Instrumentation, Study of Form')

This is the heading of one of 2 notebooks which contain detailed, connected observations on and formulations of these four concepts. As may be seen from the notes, each one of them was to be extensively treated in a separate book. The 2 notebooks were written (in pencil) between 11. and 23. April 1917. One of them contains, besides 14 pages headed 'Instrumentationslehre', 25 pages of continuous sections on the study of form and on the concept of coherence. In addition, on $4\frac{1}{2}$ pages, there is an essay *Verstehen=Erkennen der Ähnlichkeit* ('understanding = recognition of similarities'). A copy of pp. 3 and 4 of this is found with the work 'Das Komponieren mit selbständigen Stimmen' (see above, (b)). The remaining pages of this copy are bound with 'Der musikalische Gedanke, seine Darstellung und Durchführung' (see below, 3a).—The second notebook contains 38 pages with a detailed index.

It was because of the realization that the preservation of musical coherence is necessary for reasons of form and comprehensibility, and that this coherence had been endangered by the abandonment of tonality, that Schoenberg discovered and developed his method of composition with 12 tones related only to one another. At about the same time he began to concern himself with the concept of the 'Musical Idea', which we must henceforth consider as the Archimedean point of his attitudes towards music in general and of his musical and theoretical creation.

3a. DER MUSIKALISCHE GEDANKE, SEINE DARSTELLUNG UND DURCHFÜHRUNG ('The Musical Idea: Its Presentation and Development')

This is the inscription on the thin yellow cardboard cover holding 2 manuscripts (21 × 34 cm.). These contain:

(a) On 9 pages, written in ink and dated *6.VII. 1925*, a very precisely formulated presentation of the above-mentioned subject. This is summed up in a series of paragraphs and short chapters (I–VII, breaking off in the midst of the final chapter).

(b) In the following separate manuscript (also written on 9 pages of the same format, in pencil; undated, presumably from the same period), the same theme is treated once more from a special viewpoint. *The task of the present study is to find the rules of form which govern musical works by raising the question of coherence.* Here, too, as in manuscript (a), Schoenberg preserved the division into chapters and paragraphs. This study breaks off with p. 9; there, a pasted-on piece of paper bears the following notes (translated): *7.IV. 1929 | The question as to what a musical idea is has never been answered up till now—if, indeed, it has ever been asked.* Undated: 8 crossed-out lines with the postscript *I thought that I would be able to state this clearly today, I had it so clearly in mind. But I must still wait. Perhaps, though, I shall come to it yet.*—The third note, in blue pencil, reads (translated): *I have dealt with all these questions much better later on. 1940 Sch.*

3b. DER MUSIKALISCHE GEDANKE UND SEINE DARSTELLUNG ('The Musical Idea and its Presentation')

The manuscript is typed on paper of 21 × 34 cm. Several additions were pencilled in the margins. It is divided into 2 sections of 7½ and 1½ pages respectively. It is undated, but is obviously one of the latest versions.

3c. DER MUSIKALISCHE GEDANKE UND DIE LOGIK, TECHNIK UND KUNST SEINER DARSTELLUNG ('The Musical Idea and the Logic, Technique and Art of its Presentation')

The manuscript of this large-scale work is found in 3 small volumes, containing loose numbered sheets (14 × 21) lying as if in a folder. In addition, a fourth, somewhat larger book of this sort contains *Notenbeispiele und Analysen für Ged. etc.* ('Music examples and analyses for

"Idea", etc.')—about 20 sheets of music paper. However, only the material on the first page seems immediately related to the subject of the 'Musical Idea'. The volume entitled *II. Gedanke und Darstellung* (title written on the black binding) contains 3 loose sheets, not in any special order; one of these contains a series of keywords, another a discussion of rhythm arranged according to keywords. There is also a specially bound alphabetical index of keywords (beginning of June 1934). Nothing else has been written in this volume.—Of the 2 other volumes, the one entitled *I. Gedanke und Darstellung*, with 199 pages, is by far the more extensive. These notes were written, according to the dates in the manuscript, in June and July, 1934. They contain a great many related discussions of such subjects as these: rhythm, theme, motif, variation, basic figure, figure and phrase, sentence, development section, laws of comprehensibility, laws of coherence, cadence-formation, methods of connection, tendency of the smallest notes, introduction, preludes and interludes, sound as a formative element, etc. etc., all with music examples included. This material is supplemented by the notes and music examples of the other volume, entitled *Gedanke* (on the cover), and dating from September-October 1936. The volume contains, on 16 clearly-written pages, *Konstruktionelle Funktion der Harmonie* ('Structural Function of Harmony') (the first 2 pages: *Gedanke*); these are followed by 11 pages of *Prinzipien des Aufbaus* ('Principles of Construction'). With this are several pages of music examples.

4a. INSTRUMENTATIONSLEHRE

A folder of heavy brown cardboard (upright format, 30 × 41·5 cm.), with the handwritten inscription (in green pencil, copying-pencil and charcoal) here translated: *pedagogic examples for practice as instrumentation assignments, an incomplete but good attempt / Stein and Polnauer made these reductions for me.* (Erwin Stein and Josef Polnauer were two of Schoenberg's earliest pupils.)

Loose sheets:

(*a*) Examples written by Schoenberg himself in the form of piano reductions, taken from the following works: Wagner, 'Rheingold', 'Siegfried' (Act II), 'Tristan' (Act III); Beethoven, Violin Concerto (two movements).

(*b*) Two handwritten lists of the additionally planned piano reductions (Stein's and Polnauer's are also preserved; see above). The first list is as follows: *Schubert Es dur Trio, Scherzo; Beethoven Streichquartett opus 18 Allo I; Beethoven, Streichquartett opus 95 Scherzo; Wagner, Walküre; Brahms, Klavierquartett Andante; Streichquartett Intermezzo Scherzo; Streichsextett Scherzo; Klarinettenquintett Adagio; Mozart Streichquartett Menuett.*

The other list contains, like the first, additional precise examples as well as names of the composers whose works should be included: Haydn, Schubert, Mozart, Schumann, Dvořák, Bruckner, Debussy, Wolf, Bartók, Pfitzner, Schoenberg, Reger, Busoni.

This plan for a textbook of instrumentation must have originated about 1920. At that time, Schoenberg tried to realize it as follows: each of his pupils was to attend a performance of an opera or of a symphonic work which was to be heard in Vienna at that time, and was to follow it with a piano score, paying special attention to some particular passage which he had selected in advance. Then the pupil would try to orchestrate the passage in question from the piano reduction, writing down what he thought he had heard. Subsequent comparisons with the original score would show how well the pupil had been able to reproduce the tone-colours he had heard. This was a preparation for writing down the tone-colours which he himself would invent and hear with his inner ear. For Schoenberg taught that a good composer does not 'orchestrate', but invents the instrumental sound just as he invents rhythm, melody or harmony.

At that time, Schoenberg gave up the attempt after a short period. However, a slip of paper found in the legacy shows (as does the work 'Orchestration' resumed in 1949) that Schoenberg had taken up this mode of instruction again in the University of California at Los Angeles, only now under more favourable conditions (using gramophone records). The paper reads as follows: *Examination Oct. 19, 1943 | 1 to 5—Orchestration—given a 4hd piano score and a record—orchestrate about 24 meas—Mahler Schbg—secure music paper with inst. on the margin.*

4b. ORCHESTRATION

Photocopy of 19 typed pages and a letter, written at Schoenberg's request by his assistant Richard Hoffmann on June 1, 1949. In this, composers are asked to make a selection of 8–16 measures from those of their works for which records and scores (or piano scores) are available. The 19 pages contain an explanation of Schoenberg's method of teaching, together with a list of the classical and modern composers to be considered in this work. There are already 35 sheets of transparent music paper (27×38 cm.), with 90 examples as a basis, and a list of further examples to be prepared.

Also: 14 pages (handwritten in pencil) of 'Instrumentationslehre' written *18–21.IV. 1917*; an additional 7 pages of notes (concerning order of materials) *Instrumentation, Satz- und Setzkunst, 16.4. 1917.*

Finally: *Aufgaben zur Instrumentation* ('Exercises in Instrumentation') (handwritten in pencil), on 24 pages of a notebook, including 3 pages of foreword; 1917 (according to Schoenberg's own list of 'Unfinished Theoretical Works').

In a file-folder are found 23 typed blueprint pages of text for this book on orchestration; also, there are countless notes, both loose and in little notebooks. A foreword of one page, dated *3. Januar 1949* and obviously (from its wording) dictated to a typist, explains the principal features of Schoenberg's method to teachers and students.

5. THEORY OF PERFORMANCE

Of this planned textbook, there exist 12 handwritten pages (8 of them continuous) and 2 typed ones, as well as several pages in a little notebook. All this is undated, but, to judge by the handwriting, it comes from Schoenberg's last years.

B. APPENDIX TO 'THEORETICAL WORKS'

According to the procedure followed thus far in this book, (quotation, at appropriate points, of important, largely unfamiliar statements of Schoenberg regarding his own works), I have assembled, in this section, a selection from the composer's many commentaries, letters, essays and notes. This material contains the thoughts of Schoenberg on general and particular problems of theory and practice (especially those having to do with composing). These thought-processes illuminate and complete our picture of Schoenberg the composer and thinker, in essential ways.

No. 1. Note (on 'Darstellung des Gedankens')

Scholarship is concerned with presenting its ideas exhaustively and in such a way that no question remains unanswered. Art, on the other hand, contents itself with a many-sided presentation in which the idea appears unambiguously without having to be directly stated as such. Thus, a window remains open through which—from the viewpoint of knowledge—surmise may enter.

In counterpoint it is not so much a matter of the combination itself (that is, it is not an end in itself) as of such a many-sided presentation of the idea. The theme is so constructed that it already contains within itself these many figures through which the many-sided presentation of the idea is made possible.

No. 2

Barcelona 17.IV. 1932
Bajada de Briz 14

Mr. Edgar Prinzhorn
Cuxhaven, Friedrichstr. 13

Honoured Sir,

With the exception of the 'Harmonielehre', in the field of theory I have published, up till now, only essays of a rather polemic character. For nearly twenty years I have been collecting material, ideas and sketches, for an all-inclusive textbook of composition. When I shall finish it, I do not know. In any case: I have published nothing about 'composition with twelve tones related only to one another' and do not wish to do so until the principal part of my theory is ready: the 'Study of Musical Logic'. For I believe that meaningful advantage can be derived from this art of composition when it is based on knowledge and realization that comes from musical logic; and that is also the reason why I do not teach my students 'twelve-tone composition', but 'composition', in the sense of musical logic; the rest will then come, sooner or later, by itself.

The second version of my 'Harmonielehre' (1921) comes from a period during which I had already made considerable progress along the road to musical logic. Therefore, you will find many such viewpoints expressed there. But of course I have come a long way further in the following ten years.

B. APPENDIX TO 'THEORETICAL WORKS'

As far as the question of a new manner of counterpoint is concerned, I can only refer you to my compositions published since about 1921. I do not know, as yet, the theoretical basis for these; on the purely compositional side, I must depend entirely on feeling, sense of form, and musical instinct.

I hope that you are able to derive at least some profit from the little that I was able to tell you.

With highest regards

Arnold Schönberg

No. 3

From a letter (original English) to Arthur W. Locke, Tucson, Arizona, May 25, 1938:

My dear Mr. Locke:

I dont know, wether my fourth quartet has already been published. I[t] would be wise, if you write to G. Schirmer, 3 East, 43rd Street New York City and ask them to send you a copy. I can lend you a score of the third quartett and also the records of both, 3rd and 4th.

Now one word about your intention to analize these pieces as regards to the use of the basic set of twelve tones. I have to tell you frankly: I could not do this. It would mean that I myself had to work days to find out, how the twelve tones have been used and there are enough places where it will be almost impossible to find the solution. I myself consider this question as unimportant and have always told my pupils the same. I can show you a great number of examples, which explain the idea of this manner of composition, but instead of the merely mechanical application I can inform you about the compositional and esthetic advantage of it. You will accordingly realise why I call it a 'method' and why I consider the term 'system' as incorrect. Of course, you will then understand the technic by which this method is applied. I will give you a general aspect of the possibilities of the application and illustrate as much as possible by examples. And I expect you will acknowledge, that these works are principally works of musical imagination and not, as many suppose, mathematical constructions. I do not know wether under these circumstances you will find that the projected conferences will be profitable enough for you, but, I assume I am not too immodeste contending that, according to my experiences of almost forty years, nobody left me without having got something.

No. 4

From a letter to Rudolf Kolisch, July 27, 1932:

. . . You deduced the row of my string quartet correctly (except for one small point; in the second consequent, the 6th tone is c♯, the 7th g♯). That must have been a great deal of work and I do not think that I would have had the patience to do it. Do you really think that there is any use in knowing this? I cannot quite imagine why. I am convinced that, for a composer who is not yet very familiar with the use of rows, such analysis can offer some suggestions as to how to proceed, and that it can provide some purely technical hints as to the possibilities of derivation from the rows. But the aesthetic qualities cannot be deduced from all this (or, at least, they would appear to be merely a side-issue in this sort of analysis). I cannot warn often enough against the over-valuation of these analyses, since they lead only to what I have always fought against—the recognition of how the piece is made; whereas I have always helped my students to recognize—what it is! I have tried and tried to make that comprehensible to Wiesengrund and also to Berg and Webern. But they do not believe me. I cannot

say it often enough: my works are twelve-tone compositions, not twelve-tone compositions. Here again I am confused with Hauer, to whom composition is only of secondary importance.

Of course I know and never forget that when you are carrying on such investigations you never stop experiencing what first brought you into relationship with this music: its spiritual, sonorous and musical substance. Nonetheless, I cannot do otherwise than speak out against such analysis, as I have always done (e.g., in the 'Harmonielehre'). I consider the only real analysis to be one which brings out the idea and shows its presentation and carrying-out. Naturally one should also not overlook the artistic finesses!

You will be surprised that I go into so much detail about this. But, although I am not ashamed of a sound constructive basis for a composition even when I have put it there deliberately (in other words, when it is less good than if it were an instinctive result and a product of the subconscious), I do not want to be regarded as a constructor because of my few little row-combinations, for that would not be enough of an achievement on my part. I think that I should accomplish more to deserve that title; in any case I am of the opinion that I am able to fulfil extensive demands made on me by those who have a right to do so.

No. 5. Note (original English)

Leverkühn's 12-Tone Gulash

Leverkühn is one of those amateurs who believe composing with 12 tones means nothing else but always using the basic set or its inversions. In fact, the meaning of this rule should be expressed in another manner. It should be: None of the twelve tones must appear without the order of the basic set or its derivatives. But to think that obeyance to this rule produces a composition, is as childish or amateurish or laymanish as to suppose avoidance of other forbiddings suffices to create music. For instance avoidance of parallel fifths or octaves. These rules are only restrictive. You must be able to produce music in spite of those severe restrictions.

N.B.: Leverkühn is, of course, the principal character in Thomas Mann's controversial novel 'Doktor Faustus'. His use (or misuse) of the 12-tone method was the subject of a lengthy controversy between Mann and Schoenberg.

No. 6

Mr. Joseph Yasser
7, West, 83th Street
New York City   *10. Juni 1934*

Most honoured Herr Yasser,

I am very glad that you write German so well and that therefore I do not have to answer you in my awkward English.

First, I should like to thank you for your friendly appreciation of my article. I must say at once that this lecture is deliberately in a popular style. For I gave it in Berlin before a rather large audience to whom such considerations were, after all, new. Perhaps you will then grant that I did not use the chart of the overtone-series in a strictly scholarly or theoretical sense, but simply as a little illustration of my assertion that the connection of tones is based on their relationship and that the chromatic scale, too, appears to be justified by natural conditions. Far be it from me to argue that your assertion does not conform more closely to the demands of scholarship. But my only concern is to show that the chromatic scale was stimulated by relationships in those overtones which the ear perceives unclearly (!) —just as, for instance, a painter is stimulated by a model to make a picture, a free representation, while, on the other hand, the photographer reproduces his original as accurately as his lens allows him to do (he can then correct its errors through 'mood-lighting') and the scholar must make an effort to tell the unvarnished truth even if the error would be more beautiful, more pleasant or more useful. I believe that this is one of the differences between art and scholarship.

As far as your example under Point 3, taken from my piano pieces, is concerned, I believe that this problem is more likely to come up on stringed or wind instruments than on the piano with its tempered intonation. Furthermore, I always requested tempered intonation from string players with whom I worked (you will note from this that I have concerned myself with these questions, and perhaps you do not know that Hauer, whose theory of atonal music was published by Universal Edition, maintains the same standpoint). In any case, a listener can expect, from the piano, only those tones which can mean, for instance, either c sharp or d flat. Certainly one of the difficulties of my music is that an ear trained on classical music will ask, when it hears a tone c sharp, whether it should not be a d flat, whereas in reality it is nothing else than the exactly measured half step between d and c, without any relationship to harmonic questions. And I think that a listener who 'combines other tones in his ear' than those which I wrote is insufficiently prepared. For to be musical means to have an ear in the musical sense, not in the natural sense. A musical ear must have assimilated the tempered scale. And a singer who produces natural pitches is unmusical, just as someone who acts 'natural' on the street may be immoral.

By this, I do not mean to say anything against your theory, which I do not know well enough to say 'yes' or 'no' to. But I merely want to emphasize the viewpoint of a composer (who has nothing to do with other kinds of scholarship) on the theory of composition.

Finally, two more small corrections. The question in your first paragraph (lines 6–9) was really answered in my 'Harmonielehre,' where I once compared hand-signalling, electric telegraphy and wireless telegraphy, with results that I have also illustrated by means of another example: just as phonetic writing must be superior to syllable writing or picture-writing (no matter how artfully constructed these may be), even so, a tonally unlimited music is naturally predestined to higher development through the richness of its combinations, ideas and tone-pictures. But, as always in art, everything depends, not on the material, but on the genius.—My second comment has to do with your question as to why I consider the number of consonances to be limited. Above all, here I meant the word 'consonances' in the older sense and that is, of course, limited. But you do not know that the first edition of my 'Harmonielehre' (1911) already contains the following sentence:' . . . the difference between dissonances and consonances is a gradual one . . . and: dissonances are the more remote consonances. . . .' I believe that all of this is in the chapter 'Consonance and Dissonance'.

I thank you very much for your extremely interesting letter. It is by no means ruled out that viewpoints like yours, strange though they may be to me today, might become very serviceable to me at a certain stage of my theoretical presentations.

With highest regards, your

Arnold Schönberg

(There follow these music examples: Op. 30, mm. 23–28 / Op. 11, No. 1, mm. 1–5 / No. 2, top of p. 11 / 'Moses und Aron', 8 measures.

I. THEORETICAL WORKS

From the above examples (chosen at random) you will see that small intervals are just as important a part of my method of melodic construction as are the unusually large ones. This is a circumstance that my students already discovered many years ago. They also noted that large intervals were present in my music long before I entered my so-called 'atonal' period (e.g., the end of the Adagio of my Chamber Symphony). If I were to try to find an explanation for the use of both the small and the large intervals, I should say that they have in common the quality of being unused, unhackneyed. *Naturally, one's imagination most easily finds novelty in previously unused material. But then, how to make music with it is something which could not be taught.*

No. 7. Exchange of letters between Arnold Schoenberg and Dr. Max Unger

Your Excellency:

I take the liberty of sending you some questions in connection with a musicological work on absolute pitch; in view of the importance of the matter I should be most grateful to you for painstaking answers.

1. Do you have absolute pitch? If so, always or only sometimes? If the latter, under what conditions?

2. Did you possess your sense of pitch in your youth or have you attained it or improved it with practice?

3. Do you imagine colours with individual tones or keys, or does imagining colours help you to fix these? If so, which colours?

4. What advantages or disadvantages do you ascribe to absolute pitch?

5. Are you of the opinion that absolute pitch is an indispensable prerequisite of musical talent, or do you know important musicians of the past or present who did not possess it, and do you know persons who possess it without being at all, or particularly, musical?

In this connection, may I be permitted to observe that masters like Weber, Schumann, Wagner, Mottl and others have been said *not* to have had absolute pitch. (Therefore, I should appreciate your kindness in answering these questions as far as possible even if you do not have it yourself.)

7.* Do you believe in special characteristics of special tones? What do you consider to be the special sound–characteristics of individual tones and keys?

8. Any special observations.

With special thanks for your friendly interest, and with highest regards

Leipzig, end of February 1923   Dr. Max Unger

Arnold Schönberg
Mödling bei Wien
Bernhardgasse 6   *3. März 1923*

    Dr. Max Unger, Leipzig, Dresdnerstrasse 28. II.
    Honoured Herr Doktor! before I answer your questions, I must remark that I am

    I. *unsure whether you mean the same thing by the expression 'absolutes Tonbewusstsein' that is commonly called 'absolutes Gehör'; and that I*

    * TRANSLATOR'S NOTE: Paragraph 6 would appear to be missing from the text of this letter.

144

II. envisage the latter as a complex which (generally speaking) consists of the capacities of

(a) *Perceiving*
(b) *Noticing*
(c) *Recognizing again*
(d) *Reproducing*
(e) *Imagining the tones and their relationships.*

These capacities are applied to the perception of

1. *Pitches*
2. *Successions of tones*
3. *Combinations of tones*
4. *Effects of pitches and their interconnections (feeling for function: tonality, etc.).*

Please do not consider me too presumptuous if I give an opinion of my own with respect to this scientific question, when I do not even know whether this opinion is new or is already familiar. I had to mention it simply because I formed my judgments on the basis of this opinion and, if I did not include it here, many of the answers which I shall give to your questions might seem confused.

Now to your questions.

I. I do have absolute pitch; it is quite good and dependable; it fails me sometimes, mainly when I am overtired or when this sense has been dulled by overstimulation.

II. Evidently I possessed it (without knowing it) from my childhood. When I was about 9 years old, I heard that Mozart had composed without the aid of an instrument; I then tried the same thing and was immediately successful. I was brought to an awareness of my pitch-sense only much later; at first, it was not so keen, but then developed along with my other musical qualities without the use of any special exercises. The more chords, tone-colours, etc., I became precisely familiar with in practice, the greater became my capacities of recognizing, remembering, etc.

III. No, neither the one nor the other.

IV. No special advantages or disadvantages. Since orchestra players nearly always have it, they consider musicians who do not have it as inadequate. And since they do not like their superior, the conductor (especially if he is a composer too), they may pay particularly hostile attention to him in an effort to find fault. This may be the source of the statements about Weber, Wagner and others, who were probably insufficiently experienced and calm (or indifferent) to make an impression on the musicians when correcting them in rehearsal. Also, someone who has too much imagination hears principally what he sings himself or imagines to himself, and does not pay attention to what is being played.

V. I believe that I recognize individual pitches more securely than chords and mixtures of sound. Like every other sense, hearing is also subject to gross deceptions. Naturally, it is easier to recognize one tone than many; therefore, in that case, the possibility of error is not so great.

VI. That tonal memory is more than a symptom of musicality may be realised when we try to imagine a musician who lacked all of these capabilities completely. Now, to what extent may they be lacking? Are they not necessary (up to a point, at least) to the sense of form as well? But I do not believe that these capabilities are ever entirely lacking. In extreme cases it may be that a person has only limited control over his capabilities—just as an asthmatic can breathe, but not always just when he wants to. That all of this is not just a simple matter of 'yes' or 'no', but that the most various forms of deficiency may occur—this I can prove with many examples. For instance, I know a composer whose memory for imaginary tones is greater than for those he actually hears. He cannot identify pitches and chords that are played for him. However, at an orchestral rehearsal, when he can see in the score what the chord or the tone ought to be, he hears every mistake at once. On the other hand, I have often known people with splendid absolute pitch who were inferior in the hearing of errors (this also applies to score-reading and the control of what is audible) to persons who have specific experience in the analysis of orchestral sound. Again, it once happened that I was right in contradiction to ten musicians, at least three of whom have a better pitch-sense than I. I maintained that I had heard a wrong note; but questioning revealed that no one had played it. I named the note; finally, I had everybody play his part individually for me (they were all enjoying it and smiling in a rather superior fashion)—then it came out that, in the harmonium, the note which I had named was sounding, softly but unmistakably, with another note; a mechanical fault in the instrument.—Now, since one must also have good rhythm, a sense for sound and form, a good memory and much more besides to be musical in our sense (one must also include the ability to play a piece of music so that it makes sense!) it is certainly possible that there are people who possess absolute pitch and yet are quite unmusical or at most slightly musical. At the moment, I cannot think of any such person, but I certainly must have met many of them.

VII. I believe in characteristics of specific tones. However. as these are related to the number of vibrations in the tone—which is, unfortunately, not a constant factor in the practical experience of a musician—the musician will probably not be able to derive much benefit from this. At least, I cannot cite any observations of my own on this point.

I hope these answers help you. I am happy to send them to you, all the more so as this subject interests me very much but I shall probably not be able to find the time to deal with it more thoroughly myself. As you see, I have directed all my answers to the question of 'absolute pitch' so that my own views on the place of this topic will not be too intrusive. With highest regards—

Arnold Schönberg

I know your nice Reger biography, the quiet tone of which is very sympathetic.

No. 8. From a letter to Hans Rosbaud, 12.5.47

Dear friend,

I received the programme of your performance of my 'Chamber Symphony' several days ago, and today your very dear letter came. It had already occurred to me that you might have made as excellent an analysis of the 'Chamber Symphony' as you had already done of the 'Variations'. I consider this present analysis even more important than its predecessor, for the understanding of my music still suffers from the fact that most musicians do not regard me as a normal, common or garden variety of composer who presents his more or less good and new themes and melodies in a not too inadequate musical language—but as a modern, dissonant, twelve-tone experimenter.

I, however, wish nothing so much as to be considered a better sort of Tchaikovsky—for heaven's sake, a little better, but that is all. Or, at most, that my melodies may be remembered and whistled.

I think that if this experiment of yours were repeated often enough the success of my music would be considerably more 'satisfying'—more satisfying to me, at any rate, since I do not want to be interesting. Perhaps this tells you how and why I value your achievement so highly.

B. APPENDIX TO 'THEORETICAL WORKS'

No. 9. From an article 'National Music'

. . . While Debussy did succeed in rousing the Romance and Slavic peoples to oppose Wagner, he was unable to free himself from Wagner's influence; his most interesting discoveries can be used only within the framework of Wagnerian form and organization. Also, it should not be overlooked that much of the harmony used by him was also discovered independently in Germany. No wonder; for it was a logical consequence of Wagnerian harmony, a further step along the road pointed out by Wagner.

It is amazing that the following fact was never noticed—although a thousand circumstances point to it, although the fight against German music during the war was mainly directed against my music, and although (as someone said recently on the radio without knowing what he was talking about) my art has no following abroad today (although previously they stole everything but my bones, or tried to)— it is amazing, I say, that no one has yet noticed that, in my music, which originated on German soil uninfluenced by foreign elements, there is to be found an art which, as it most effectively opposes the fight for hegemony waged by the Romance and Slavic nations, has stemmed completely from the traditions of German music.

That no one has yet noted this is due not only to the difficulty of my music but even more to the laziness and presumptuousness of my critics. For it is plainly to be seen.

But I shall say it myself, for once.

My teachers were, in the first place, Bach and Mozart; in the second place, Beethoven, Brahms and Wagner.

From Bach I learned:

1. Contrapuntal thinking; that is, the art of inventing musical figures which can accompany themselves.
2. The art of developing everything from one basic germ-motif and leading smoothly from one figure into another.
3. Independence from the bar-line and the beat.

From Mozart:

1. Irregularity of phrase-lengths.
2. Formulation of heterogeneous characteristics into a single thematic unit.
3. Deviation from even numbers of measures in the theme and its component parts.
4. The art of forming subordinate ideas.
5. The art of introduction and transition.

From Beethoven:

1. The art of developing themes and movements.
2. The art of variation and transformation.
3. The manifold methods of constructing large movements.
4. The art of writing inconceivably long sections or mercilessly short ones, whichever the circumstances call for.
5. Rhythm: the displacement of figures to different beats.

From Wagner:

1. The possibility of transforming the expressive qualities of themes, and the right way to construct them for this purpose.

2. The relationship between tones and chords.

3. The possibility of treating themes and motifs like ornaments, which can then be set dissonantly against harmonies.

From Brahms:

1. Many of the things that I acquired unconsciously from Mozart—especially uneven numbers of measures, extension and contraction of phrases.

2. Plasticity of formation; not being stingy or cramped when clarity demands more space; carrying out each figure to the very end.

3. Systematic construction of movements.

4. Economy, yet richness.

I also learned much from Schubert as well as from Mahler, Strauss and Reger. I closed my mind against no one and could, therefore, say of myself:

My originality comes from the fact that I immediately imitated everything good that I ever saw. Even if I did not see it first in the works of others.

And I may say this: often enough, I saw it first in my own work.

For I did not merely stick to what I had seen; I took it over in order to possess it; I worked over it and expanded it, and it led me to something new.

I am convinced that, one day, it will be recognized how closely this 'something new' is related to the best models of the past that have been given to us. I lay claim to the merit of having written really new music which, as it rests on tradition, is destined to become a tradition.

24. II. 1931   *Arnold Schönberg*

No. 10. Untitled

It is not at all difficult for the artist to say something about his work if he simply observes inaccurately. Then, according to taste, everything is either classically simple or romantically complicated; a clear path is followed, goals are reached or in sight; mannerism is style, style is personality, personality is the Redeemer or Lucifer—according to taste; in any case, however, everything is so self-evident that the smoothest biographer could hardly write it more smoothly. It is possible that there are artists who carefully live up to their prescribed biographies, who are as loyal to broken laws as others are to the laws they have kept, who are able to make bonds out of liberty but unable to feel free in the knowledge of the bonds of their inner laws! If creators of this sort are artists, one may envy them for the blindness which allows them to see such a smooth path.

I am not so fortunate.

When, after an interruption in my creative work, I am thinking of future compositions, then my future direction lies so clearly before me that I—at least today—can be certain that it will be different from what I have imagined. That I am turning around—perhaps even whirling around—I might still be able to guess. Where I am standing, where I stood—it can only be because of my blindness that I do not realize it. Only one circumstance soon appears: that the new seems as strange and incomprehensible to me as the old once did; that, as long as this condition obtains, the old appears more comprehensible to me, until finally the newest phase apparently becomes more familiar to me and I cease to understand how I was able to write otherwise.

Yes, when one observes carefully, these things gradually become unclear to one. One begins to understand that one is intended, not only not to guess the future (merely to represent it) but also to forget the past (which one has already represented). One gains a feeling that one has truly fulfilled one's duty only when (although one might wish it otherwise) one does not do what was sacred to one in the past and betrays what the future seemed to promise. Only then one begins quietly to enjoy one's blindness, with seeing eyes.

Very seldom, though; and very secretly; for that might betray a delicate secret—there have been moments when one has looked at the completed piece, and the piece still to be completed, and was satisfied.

I cannot say any more about my creative work.

It would be easier to say less; I, too, could proclaim an expressionistic programme.

Better, however, one for others only. I am sure they would fulfil it, and thereby relieve me of any further obligation.

Perhaps I shall do it, one of these days.

But, in the meantime, just one more thing:

I cannot recommend anyone to let himself go this way. It is not supposed to be very advantageous, and ought not to be.

And that one makes oneself interesting by such means is, in the long run, not true either! When one cannot do anything better, it may still, perhaps, be worth while. But woe to him who . . .!

No. 11

Arnold Schönberg   11.X. 1933
Hotel Regina
Place des Pyramides
Paris

Herrn Joseph Malkin
Direktor des Malkin Conservatory
299, Beacon Street
Boston, Massachusetts

Honoured Herr Malkin!

Yesterday, I also wanted to write to you about the courses which I would have liked to give. Since that still may come about, I should like to tell you something about them today.

When I last gave courses in Vienna,★ the following ones in particular proved very successful:

1. Elements of Form, *a course preliminary to* Form and Analysis. *This course could be taken even by beginners in harmony. I arranged it so as to permit the students themselves gradually, through discussions and analyses, to find those elements (after due consideration and observation) which are basic to the art of musical form.*

2. Consultation Period, *also for students of varying degrees of preparation. Here, questions of aesthetics were raised, and the students, guided by me, were to make an effort to find the answers.*

★ AUTHOR's NOTE: the courses referred to were given by Schoenberg (with his pupil, Josef Polnauer, later acting as a substitute) from the autumn of 1917 to the inflation in the summer of 1922. These courses were held in the classrooms of Dr Eugenie Schwarzwald's schools. Schoenberg began to teach at the Malkin Conservatory in Boston soon after his arrival in America in the autumn of 1933.

I. THEORETICAL WORKS

I later added these courses:

3. Bach Analyses, for students who had completed counterpoint. Here, clear explanations of the essence of contrapuntal composition were given. I do not believe that Bach fugues can be analysed more thoroughly.

4. General Analyses: here, no particular area of study was set in advance. The students should have had at least some previous study of form and analysis. But such a course could also be given for non-professionals (of course in a different way).

Of all these courses, Nos. 1 and 3 in particular should prove popular; they should be as interesting to professional musicians as to teachers for, in them, I especially developed the method of leading the student to find himself.

Whether something of the sort can be introduced before I arrive there, I do not know. Perhaps, too, I should have a somewhat more precise idea of what the students in Boston learn easily as well as what they would like to learn!

But I believe that perhaps it is a good idea to have you yourself think over these questions. I hope, then, that we shall easily find the right thing.

For today, I give you my best regards and greetings—your

Arnold Schoenberg

No. 12

In the legacy was found the following plan of instruction (in English) for Schoenberg's teaching at the University of California at Los Angeles:

I. *Monday and Friday, 1–2:* Composition for Beginners.

II. *Friday, 3–5 (2 hours!):* Advanced Counterpoint. *Here I teach: Choralpreludes, simple fugues in 2, 3 and 4 voices, modes, modulations, imitations, double counterpoint and its application to fugues with more than one subject.*

III. *Monday, Wed'nsday and Friday from 2–3:* Advanced Composition. *In this class I teach rather freely, the program depending on the ability, talent and knowledge of the students. Generally I go back to the smaller forms, which in the first year could not be treated thoroughly enough. I try to give the student here a more advanced idea of these forms. If possible the student should also write sonatas.*

IV. *Monday and Wednsday, 2–4:*

once a week: Structural Functions of harmony. This class is an attempt, which I venture for the first time. The purpose is to make the student conscious of the structural effect of harmonies and teach him to take advantage of them and to avoid the dangers they offer.

once a week (the other hour; the time will be arranged): Advanced Analysis. Here I will analize very thoroughly classic masterpieces.

There is also a class 'Special Studies in Music' announced, but this seems to be an error, because I will not teach more than 9–10 hours a week (I am obliged to not more than 6 hours). If I give this class at all it will be a class in which composers have to write.

No. 13. THE MIRACLE SET

Schoenberg always emphasized the fact that the 12-tone row and its treatment represented, for him, no more than a principle of organization for non-tonal music, corresponding to the rôle played by tonality and its laws for tonal music. The row, thus, is contained *a priori* as a melodic element in the musical inspiration; it is 'given', together with all the melodic and harmonic consequences which are to be derived from this inspiration for the piece based upon it. Also, he said that the row so obtained would generally need a few additional corrections, that the composer would have to 'complete its construction' (somewhat in the manner of constructive alterations required by double and multiple counterpoint) so that the idea, and the row as well, would suffice for all possible compositional needs. The various rows in Schoenberg's works show numerous constructive characteristics of this sort.

All the more interesting is the one case (found in the legacy) in which Schoenberg concerned himself with the seemingly abstract formation of an especially constructed row which he called the 'Wunder-Reihe' ('Miracle Set'). The publication of this pattern and of his commentary on it, which he had originally planned, was later abandoned when he found some inaccuracies in it. However, the compositional aim to be achieved may be read clearly in the last paragraph of the commentary. (See FACSIMILE PLATE XXV. Note error in translation in the first paragraph of the German text; 'Krebs', instead of 'Krebsumkehrung', should appear twice, corresponding to the musical example and to the word 'retrograde' in the English original.) The English commentary runs as follows:

As usual, the inversion at the lower fifth of the antecedent furnishes the remaining six tones. It occurred miraculously that the six tones of the inversion in another order, con. 2 became the retrograde of the antecedent, ant. 1. The retrograde of this con. appears to be the transposition of the antecedent A, a whole tone lower, see 2a.

The same procedure, applied to ant. 3, furnishes 4a, consisting of the same six notes in another order. In the same manner the ants. 5, 7, 9 and 11; and the cons. 6, 8, 10, and 12 are produced.

The advantage of this miracle set is that the six antecedents offer the same intervallic relationship, though they consist all of the same six tones. Similarly, every of the remaining five consequents consists of the same tones in a different order as con. 2. Furthermore, so as ant. 1 can be accompanied by ant. 1 inv. or con. 2, all the other five antecedents have the same choice. Moreover: every antecedent can be accompanied by every consequent, by every inversion of every antecedent, and by every antecedent.

This offers a greater variety than double counterpoint of all sorts. Of course you have to invent your theme as ordinarily; but you have more possibilities of producing strongly related configurations, which in sound are essentially different.

II. POEMS - LECTURES - ESSAYS - NOTES

The literary legacy of Schoenberg is extremely extensive. A thorough survey of its contents (especially of the hundreds of articles, essays, etc.) and the ordering of these papers with a view to publication was not possible in the time at my disposal. Such a process should begin with a survey of 2 documents:

1. A list of manuscripts, made under the direction of Schoenberg himself. The first part, comprising Nos. 1–350 (handwritten, in ink) consists of 6 sheets of paper bound in a blue cardboard folder; 8 pages, and a part of a ninth, have been written upon. For each manuscript, the subject-matter, and usually also the date of writing, are noted (see below under 2). This first part, up to No. 350 (written in later, in pencil), comprises, in the main, the essays written between 1922 and 1932 (inclusive) with a few from early years. Loose in the cover are 4 pages (3 of them pasted together) typed on one side of the page, with the continuation of the list (Nos. 351–427). This second part was written in America after 1933 (by Schoenberg, or one of his assistants?), but still includes, in the main, material written before 1933. The greater number of essays written afterwards, in America, is not included in this list.

2. A handwritten outline of the different subject-areas to which the individual essays belong. It may be translated as follows:

> *Aesthetics | (a) Music, theory, also theoretical polemics and theoretical commentaries. All other arts, also commentaries and polemics; also comments on own writings and paintings.*
> *My Theories | Interpretations, explanations, discoveries, suggestions, improvements*
> *Monuments | Portraits (also sympathetic ones), experiences and adventures with persons, the pillory*
> *Miscellaneous thoughts | also political, economic, social*
> *Nature, physics, animals*
> *Questions of language | also commentaries*
> *Aphorisms | Jokes, witticisms, satires, commentaries, polemics, without theoretical significance*
> *Anecdotes | experiences, etc.*
> *Ethics | Philosophy of life, world-view, philosophy, wisdom of life*
> *Biographical material | also on the origin of my works*

In the following list of manuscripts, which also includes all those written after 1933, I could not always hold to this outline of Schoenberg's, especially where he himself had already begun with the practical arrangement of his manuscripts (including, now, those written in America), putting them in order in trunks and cartons. This order differs from that found in the list. It governed my numbering for practical reasons, in order to deal with the manuscripts which were actually at hand and to get a comprehensive survey of the literary legacy.

A. POEMS, TEXTS, FRAGMENTS AND SKETCHES
and early literary efforts

1. TOTENTANZ DER PRINZIPIEN ('Death-Dance of Principles')
Published in: Arnold Schönberg, 'Texte'
Universal Edition, Vienna

Manuscript on $4\frac{1}{2}$ pages of 5 sheets (21×33 cm.) written in ink. Date of completion: *15. I. 1915*. The beginning of the manuscript is headed *III. Satz* (see above, II, B (*e*) 2). The fair copy of the text is written in black ink on 2 sides of a double sheet of paper (21×33 cm.). The title is painted and highly ornate, in Gothic script, with red initial letters. This copy is undated. In comparison with the published version, it is incomplete, for it ends with line 10 of p. 25 of 'Texte' (see above).

2. DIE SCHILDBÜRGER ('The Gothamites')
Comic Opera in Three Acts

18. Juni–28.VII. 1901. Manuscript of the first and second acts written in ink on 56 numbered pages of a notebook. Draft in the form of a detailed plot-sketch (including the fourth scene of the second act) on 7 pages, in ink.

3. ABERGLAUBE ('Superstition'), a fragment

Draft of an opera libretto (2 acts and beginning of third). Manuscript of the plot-sketch written in ink on 17 pages, undated. Sketches of stage-design.

4. BEGINNING of an opera libretto ODOAKER

Manuscript contains 3 scenes of the first act, written in ink on 9 pages, undated.

5. FRAGMENT: PARODIE PFITZNER (Three acts of 'Palestrina's Revenge')

Manuscript written in pencil on 7 pages. Note (translated): *planned for a 'Jolly Evening' of the Society for Musical Private Performances, for which my sense of justice also moved me to prepare several persiflages at my own expense.*

6. DIE JAKOBSLEITER ('Jacob's Ladder')
Published in: Arnold Schönberg, 'Texte'
Universal Edition, Vienna

The manuscript, consisting of 19 pages, bears, at the beginning, the note *IV. Satz* (see above, 'Totentanz der Prinzipien') and the date *18./1. 1915*. It is written in ink, with the corrections in pencil; many alterations have been pasted over (new versions of small sections or of whole paragraphs). On the back of the ninth page is a fairly substantial musical sketch.

There is also a fair copy in ink on 41 numbered pages with the date *26./V. 1917*, as well as a typed copy (31 numbered pages) which shows musical sketches in several places. Finally, there are numerous small note-sheets. Sketches and notes for the 'Jakobsleiter' are found in a 9-page manuscript, written in ink.

7. DIE GLÜCKLICHE HAND ('The Hand of Fate')
Published in: Arnold Schönberg, 'Texte'
Universal Edition, Vienna

First draft in pencil on 8 sheets; date of completion *Ende Juni 1910*. Also, a corrected typed copy, having alternating pages of text and of music-paper with a number of sketches; this is labelled *Compositions-Vorlage*.

8. REQUIEM
Published in: Arnold Schönberg, 'Texte'
Universal Edition, Vienna

At the beginning of the first draft, there is the note *1920 oder 1921? Sch.* Of the 6 pages, the first 3 are written in pencil, the remainder in ink; from time to time, there are musical sketches for specific spots in the text. Date: *15./XI. 1923 Arnold Schönberg*. A typed copy has (as in the printed version) sections numbered from I to XII instead of only to XI (as in the handwritten version). A note of Schoenberg's calls specific attention to this fact.

9. SIX MALE CHORUSES, Op. 35

('Verbundenheit' is missing; it was obviously written earlier—see above, under the discussion of these compositions.) Schoenberg gave this, together with other manuscripts, to Mrs. Charlotte Dieterle in Hollywood. A typed copy also contains 2 musical sketches.

12. VON HEUTE AUF MORGEN ('From Today till Tomorrow')

Three different typed copies, with many corrections. One copy is marked *Handexemplar beim Partiturschreiben mit den letzten Verbesserungen* (copy containing the final corrections). A note on the inside cover points out that the author of the text, 'Max Blonda', is really Schoenberg's wife Gertrud.

11. DER BIBLISCHE WEG ('The Biblical Way'), drama

First sketch, *17./18.VI. 1926*; first draft, *19.VI. 1926* to *5.VII. 1926*, in ink on 31 sheets. A second version is dated *12./VII. 1927* and is written in pencil on 74 pages. There are numerous additional notes and sketches.

On 14 small (10·5 × 17 cm.) loose-leaf notebook pages (in a cardboard cover, and held together with clips) Schoenberg made notes for a revision: 'Sprich zu den Felsen!' ('Speak to the rock!'). P. 16 bears the date *25./4. 1927*; on the 6 following pages is a concise outline of the contents, with dramaturgical notes and with citation of the Bible passages in question.

12. MOSES UND ARON
B. Schotts Söhne, Mainz

The first draft, written in ink on 19 numbered pages, was begun on *3.X. 1928*. End of Part I (i.e., Act I); *8.X. 28*. Part II, 'Das goldene Kalb', was begun on *9./X.* and finished on *10./X. 1928*, Part III on *16.X. 1928*.

There is also at hand the following material: (*a*) a typed copy of the work (originally conceived as an oratorio) with numerous cuts, alterations, and insertions; (*b*) 3 typed stage versions from Schoenberg's later Berlin period, with several additions and changes in pencil. A carbon copy has several drawings (outlines for stage-sketches).

13. MODERNE PSALMEN
B. Schotts Söhne, Mainz

Between the end of September 1950 and the beginning of July 1951, Schoenberg wrote a series of 'Psalms' of religious and philosophical content, which were conceived as a basis for choral compositions. The first 10 psalms are numbered; the numbering of the following 6 is left open. Of these, only 5 are complete; like the first 10, they are dated, and signed individually. The sixth of these (i.e., the sixteenth of the entire set), dated *3.VII. 1951*, is unfinished. These are first drafts. The manuscript comprises 20 loose pages. The first psalm text is written in pencil, while all the others are written in ink.

*

The legacy also contains sketches, beginnings, poems, etc. from Schoenberg's early years.

B. LECTURES

(in this and following sections, asterisks before numbers indicate Schoenberg's original English titles; spelling and punctuation are his.)

[The following lectures and essays were revised and published in 'Style and Idea' (1950): 1. The Relationship of the Text. 2. Gustav Mahler. 3. New Music, Outmoded Music, Style and Idea. 4. Brahms the Progressive. 5. Composition with Twelve Tones. 6. A Dangerous Game. 7. Eartraining through Composing. 8. Heart and Brain in Music. 9. Criteria for the Evaluation of Music. 10. Folkloristic Symphonies. 11. Human Rights. 12. On revient toujours. 13. The Blessing of the Dressing. 14. This is My Fault. 15. To the Wharves. (O.K.)]

1. Gustav Mahler. 30. 10. 1912.
2. Problems of Harmony (48 typed pages). 19. 1. 1927 (revised, New York, 19. 4. 34).
3. Introduction to the 'Glückliche Hand' (for the Breslau performance; 9 typed pages, without music examples). 24. 3. 1928.
4. 'Tonal ou atonal' (Paris, 14 typed pages). 1927.
5. Variations for Orchestra, Op. 31 (analysis for Frankfurt Radio; 17 typed pages, many examples). 22. 3. 1931.
6. Discussion on the Berlin Radio. 30. 3. 1931.
7. Four Orchestral Songs, Op. 22 (analysis for Frankfurt Radio; 20 typed pages, 75 examples). 21. 2. 1932.
8. Brahms (Frankfurt Radio: Schoenberg's last lecture in Germany—see also 'Style and Idea'). 12. 2. 1932.
★9. First American Broadcast ('Zwiegespräch ('Dialogue'); 5 typed pages). 19. 11. 1933.

*10. Adress at a reception in New York. 11. 11. 1933.
*11. First english lecture (New York). Missing. 1933.
*12. Forward to a Jewish Unitary Party. 1. 12. 1933.
*13. Notes to two free lectures (Analyses). 1934.
*14. An adress and a lecture (Jewish situation, Mailam). New York, 29. 4. 1934.
*15. Method of composing with twelve tones. 1934.
*16. Adress: Driven into Paradise. 9. 10. 1935.
*17. When we young Austrian Jewish Artists (Mailam, Los Angeles; 4 typed pages). 29. 3. 1935.
*18. First Californian Broadcast, Interview with Max van Leuwen Swarthout, USC (8 typed pages). 1935.
*19. Broadcast USC over KHJ: What have people to expect from music? 7. 9. 1935.
*20. Success and value (USC Broadcast?) (6 typed pages). 1935.
*21. Some objective reasons require (probably spoken on a meeting of teachers) (7 typed pages). 1936.
*22. At Gershwins funeral (½ typed page). 1937.
*23. How one becomes lonely (Denver). 1937.
*24. Eartraining through composing (Kansas City). 30. 12. 1939.
*25. How can a music student learn [sic: earn] a living (Kansas City) (9 typed pages). 28. 12. 1939.
 26. New and Outmoded Music, or Style and Idea (Prague). 1932.
*27. Notes to a free lecture in UCLA (University of California; Convention of Organists) on: What is good music? 1938.
*28. About my music (UCLA; Alumni Association). 8. 6. 1940.
*29. Six short lectures

    (a) Broadcast from USC (Interview with Swarthout; 6 typed pages with minor corrections).
    (b) What have people to expect from music?
    (c) Driven into Paradise.
    (d) Education for contemporary music.
    (e) Jewish situation (Mailam New York). 1934.
    (f) We young jewish Austrians (Mailam Los Angeles). 1935.
    (g) Succes and value.

C. ARTICLES, ESSAYS

Sketches, notes, critical observations, fragments

1. The Future of the Organ (2 pages). 1904?
2. Why New Melodies? (1 page). 1913.
3. Certainty (2 pages). 1919.
4. Beginning of a letter (to 'Anbruch). (1 page). 1920?
5. Letter to Universal Edition (not sent; 4 pages). 1923.
6. For My Fiftieth Birthday (1 page; Schoenberg on himself). 1924.

C. ARTICLES, ESSAYS

7. Commentary (On the Good). ($\frac{1}{2}$ page). Date?
8. Admission into the Master Class of the Prussian Academy of Arts. 1925.
9. Tonality and Organization (4 pages). 1925.
10. The same, handwritten. 1925.
11. Conviction or Knowledge (8 pages). Date? (See also Section L, No. 33.)
12. The Talking Film (2 pages, handwritten). 1927.
13. The same, typed. 1927.
14. Notes for a free lecture (1 page). 1927?
15. Every Ox (handwritten and typed, 5 pages). 1929.
16. My Public (1 page, sketches). 1930.
17. The same (5 pages). 1930.
18. (a) and (b) Drafts of article for Adolf Loos' 60th birthday. 1930. (c) Letter to the Mayor of Vienna.
19. Article for Loos' birthday book. 1930.
20. On the Study of Composition (11 pages). 1930?
21. On the Teaching of Form (2 pages). Date?
★22. Speeches on the records of the 4 String Quartets. 1936.
23. Studies for 'Kol nidre'. 1938.
24. Draft for 'Plans for a Ministry of Art' by Adolf Loos. 1919.
25. Contributions to a planned 'Abbruch'. 1925.†
26. Drawings, tramway ticket, letter-checks. 1924(40?).
27. Instructions for the engraving of 'Glückliche Hand'. 1924.
28. Foreword and texts for Opp. 27 and 28. 1925/26.
29. Little Manuscripts I.
30. Little Manuscripts II.
31. My war-psychosis and that of others. 1914.
32. Mahler Lecture. 1912.
33. Notes for 'Problems of Harmony'. 1927.
34. Notes for the lecture 'Variations for Orchestra' (Frankfurt). 1931.
35. Little Manuscripts (The Viennese String Quartet).‡ Date?
36. Notes on the lecture 'Limitations of Copyright'. Date?
★37. On George Gershwins funeral (1 page). 1937.
38. George Gershwin (4 pages). 1937.
★39. Letter to L. Liebling (not sent; copy missing). 1937.
40. (a) for a book on Alban Berg (7 pages). 1936. (b) Explanation why this was not printed. 1940.
★41. Fragment: Teaching without a method. 1939.
★42. Preface to the recording of the String Quartets (7 pages). 1937.
★43. Teaching and modern trends in music. 1938?
★44. About the Kol nidre. 1938.

† TRANSLATOR'S NOTE: this was doubtless intended as a take-off on the magazine 'Anbruch' to which Schoenberg was a frequent contributor.

‡ TRANSLATOR'S NOTE: the 'Wiener Streichquartett' was later to attain world renown as the Kolisch String Quartet.

II. POEMS—LECTURES—ESSAYS—NOTES

★45. The technic of the opera composer (Stichworte für einen Vortrag ('Keywords for a lecture')). 1939.

46. Circular letter for my 60th birthday (to friends). (2 pages). 1934.

47. The same (report to more distant acquaintances). (3 pages). 1934.

48. Comment: conductors (1 page). 1934.

★49. A four point Program for Jewry. 1938.

★50. Art and the moving pictures (7 pages). 1940.

51. 'Wien, Wien, nur du allein' ('Vienna, Vienna, thou alone . . .')† (2 pages). 1939.

52. For the 50th anniversary of Mahler's death (fragment and letters; 4 pages). 1936.

53. (a) and (b) Letters to Mrs. McCormick (not sent). 1938. (c) Information on Greissle, (d) Information on Görgi (4 pages).‡

54. Notes for Brahms lecture, Frankfurt Radio (18 pages). 1933.

★55. Notes for: 'Eartraining through composing' and 'How can a student . . .' 1938.

★56. Notes and draught to Method of composing with 12 tones. 1934.

★57. Manuscript 'Success and value' (9 pages). 1935.

★58. Manuscript: 'When we young austrian Jewish' (4 pages). 1935.

★59. Fragment of a speech in German to be spoken at a reception in New York (5 pages). 1933.

★60. Notes on the Kol nidre and the four point program (8 pages). 1938.

★61. Fragment on my music (2 pages). Date?

★62. 2 Fragments on Jewish affairs (15 pages). 1937?

★63. Fragment on organization of music department at UCLA. 1937.

64. Draft of the statutes of the Mahler Society. 1921.

65. Sketches for 'Moses und Aron' (3 pages). 1926.

66. Sketches for a drama. 1928.

67. Diary of War Clouds. 1914.

68. Attempt at a diary (early 1912; 28 pages).

69. Sketches for 'Seraphita'. 1918?

70. Music of 'Friends of the Party', and other fragments. 1908?

71. My music and 'On Opera'. Before 1930.

72. Directions for printing 'Erwartung'. 1914.

73. My music typewriter, outline for patent (drawing). 1909.

74. New Music (mine, see also No. 71). (14 pages, notes.) 1928?

75. Busoni's 'Aesthetics', with commentaries. 1909?

76. Criteria of Musical Value, draft. 1927.

77. Comments on theories. 1929.

78. Streetcar ticket. 1928?

79. Announcement (courses) and drafts of letters. 1934?

80. Two fragments (a) of an opera. 1909?
                (b) of the 'Jakobsleiter'. 1910?

★81. Abbreviations UCLA (für den Musikunterricht ('for music instruction')). 1938.

† Translator's Note: in this sketch, Schoenberg set scurrilous, satirical words of his own to the well-loved Viennese sentimental song.

‡ Translator's Note: these are Schoenberg's son-in-law and eldest son, respectively

C. ARTICLES, ESSAYS

★82. Ideas, Notes, Sketches, Fragments. Date?

83. Aphorisms. 1912.

84. (*a*) for Karl Kraus,† (*b*) against K.K. (4 pages).

85. Aphorisms. Date?

86. Draft of a polemic article (against a 'Fackel' article: 'Kitsch, Dilettantismus, Form' ('Trash, Dilettantism, Form')). Date?

87. The Relationship to the Text. 1912?

88. According to the Facts (2 pages). Date?

89. Franz Liszt ('Allgemeine Deutsche Musikzeitung' X/1912). 1912.

90. Plan for a music magazine (3½ pages.) Date?

★91. There is no escape (1 page). 1940.

92. Seven Fragments. Ca. 1900.

93. Aphorisms (in 'Die Musik'). 1910/11.

94. International military security for peace. 1917.

95. Manuscript: Problems of Teaching the Arts. 1911?

★96. Encouraging the lesser master: a contribution to a book edited by José Rodriguez (7 pages). 1940.

★97. Notes to 96.

98 to

107. Directions for printing and engraving, forewords, notes and texts for Opp. 27 and 28.

108. A notebook with ideas (also musical ones).

109. Text of a birthday canon for Dr. D. J. Bach. Date?

110. Conditions for teaching (never accepted). Date?

111. My Contemporaries (probably for an American magazine). Date?

112. 'Beethoven-Kuratorium', Academy of Arts in Berlin. Date?

113. Sketches for 'Moses und Aron'. Date?

★114. Folkloristic symphonies. 1947.

115. Symphonies from Folk-Songs. 1947. (German.)

★116. Is it fair?/Date?

117. 'On revient toujours' ('One always returns'). 1948.

★118. Blessing, Todays manner, O.K., Maturity. Date? (see 'Style and Idea').

★119. Thanks to the National Institute of Arts and Letters. 1947.

★120. Criteria for the evaluation of music.

★121. My evolution (englisch)—Rückblick (deutsch). Date?

122. Human Rights. Date? (see 'Style and Idea').

★123. 1. To become recognized; 2. Alban Berg; 3. Ehrenbürger . . . [Honorary Citizen]; 4. Letter to Fassett; 5. My attitude towards politics; 6. The task of the teacher./Date?

★124. (*a*) The story of the third trombone.

(*b*) For the Broadcast of the String Trio. 1949.

(*c*) In answer to Koussevitzkys article 'Justice to composers'.

(*d*) Tennis symbols.

(*e*) Letter of thanks (75. birthday).

† TRANSLATOR'S NOTE: Kraus was the noted Viennese satirist and editor of 'Die Fackel' ('The Torch') which appeared between 1899 and 1936.

125. (Obviously skipped in numbering.)
126. (*a*) Bach (I, II, III, IV).
    (*b*) Cadenza.
  ★ (*c*) Politics.
    (*d*) Foreword to the Columbia record of 'Pierrot Lunaire'.
★127. (*a*) Analysis of Kammersymphonie opus 9.
    (*b*) For my broadcast.
    (*c*) Pumpernickel.
    (*d*) My way.
    (*e*) Three pieces for piano.
    (*f*) Some letters.
128. Napoleon-Patience (in German).
129. Programme Notes.
130. (*a*) Cadenza; (*b*) Gurrelieder; (*c*) Tone-Colour Melodies ('Klangfarbenmelodien'). 1951.
131. ★1. Every strike. 1951.
   ★2. Peace treaties. 1951.
    3. Body Temperature. 1950.
132. Letter of thanks for the election to the honorary presidency of the Israel Academy of Music.
133. (*a*) Little Muck. ★(*b*) If I were today . . . (*c*) World première of my Variations. ★(*d*) When for 8 weeks I lived in Barcelona.
134. Skipped in numbering.
135. Wiesengrund.
136. Modern Psalms.
★137. Beginning of a lecture to have been broadcast by BBC.
★138. (*a*) Copyright law (unfinished). (*b*) Subordination (unfinished). (*c*) A few lines about the tragic death of Rolf Hoffmann.
★139. Notes remarks.
★140. Sketches for a highway.
141. ★(*a*) Israel exists again. (*b*) 'Hymne' (German). 1949.
★142. To the San Francisco Round-Table on modern art (4½ typed pages). Undated.
143. Letter to Olin Downes (with music examples), unfinished (2½ typed blueprint pages). Undated. Schoenberg attacks a review by Downes, then the music critic of the 'New York Times', covering a performance of Mahler's Seventh Symphony under Mitropoulos.
★144. Foreword to a Broadcast of the Capitol Recording of Pelleas and Melisande. 17. 2. 1950 (1 typed page).
★145. Copyright. Undated. (2 typed pages.)
146. Subordination. Undated. (1½ typed pages.)
147. Bruno der Walter von Stolzings Vogelweide. Undated. (1 typed page.)
★148. For the Cincinnati performance of the Gurrelieder. 12. 1. 1951. (2½ typed pages.)
★149. New friends of Music. November 1940. (2 typed pages; conversation between Schoenberg and Mr. Sergio over NBC Radio, New York, at the time of the world première of the Second Chamber Symphony under Fritz Stiedry.)

C. ARTICLES, ESSAYS

150. The Concept of Form. Undated. (2½ typed pages.)
151. Mahler's Ninth Symphony. (2½ handwritten pages, with 2 music examples.) 1917.
*152. How I came to compose the Ode to Napoleon. Undated. (3 handwritten pages.)
*153. Music expresses message to mankind. Undated. (8 handwritten pages.)
*154. Two fragments; Attempts of writing a new Textbook of harmony. Undated. (6 handwritten pages.)
*155. My attitude toward politics. 16. 2. 1950. (1½ typed pages.)
156. Sir Henry Wood. 8. 2. 1944. (1 typed page, 2 handwritten pages.)
*157. Music and Morality. Undated (about 1950). (1 typed page, 2 handwritten pages.)
*158. Untitled, begins: *A composer who is writing for an audience does not think in music* . . . 14. 7. 1949. (1½ typed pages.)
*159. The modes. Undated (about 1950). (2½ handwritten pages.)
160. Vienna, concerning speech-formations. 6. 2. 1949. (2 typed pages.)
*161. Music is a composition of tones and rythms. Undated (about 1950). (3 handwritten pages.)
*162. Connection of musical ideas. Undated (about 1950). (3½ handwritten pages.)
*163. Formalism. 13. 2. 1949. (3 handwritten pages, unfinished.)
*164. Leadingtone. Undated (about 1950). (1 typed page.)
165. Rudolf Kolisch. 11. 3. 1950. (1 handwritten page.)
*166. To Mr. Fendler. (3½ handwritten pages, 14. 3. 1949, and 1½ handwritten pages, 18. 2. 1949, with postscript of 25. 2. 49.)
167. Untitled. Schoenberg here concerns himself with the problem of the artistic creative process, emphasizing the subconscious and the unforeseeable. Undated. (1½ handwritten pages; see above, Appendix to 'Theoretical Works', No. 10.)
*168. Musicians judge about performers. Undated. (1 handwritten page.)
169. Untitled: Remarks on a letter from Edwin Franko Goldman (then director of the Goldman Band) requesting the composer to express his opinion of the artistic and cultural value of the band. 17. 1. 1934. (1 handwritten page—English and German.)
170. The Helper in Need. Undated (perhaps about 1919?). (1 handwritten page.)
171. Zemlinsky. 1. 7. 1921. (2 large handwritten pages, about 3 typed pages.)
*172. Maturity. 3. 3. 1948. (3 typed pages; identical with 'Selbstanalyse'.)
*173. Composition with twelve tones. Undated (after 1945). (3½ typed pages.)
174. A Musical Institute.—Plan and Two Exposés. Beginning of August, 1934. (27 handwritten pages, plan; exposés, 4 handwritten and 2 typed pages.)
175. (*a*) Polemic against Casella. 1936? (8 handwritten pages.)
    *(*b*) Rigoletto and Kammersymphony compaired by an analysis. (2 music examples with text, 1 handwritten page.) 1936?
*176. Performers. Undated (after 1945). (3 typed pages, 7 handwritten pages.)
*177. Chromaticism. Undated (after 1945). (2 handwritten pages = 1 typed page with 1 music example.)
*178. Against the specialist. Undated (after 1945). (5 handwritten pages = 1½ typed pages.)
*179. Tonality. Undated (after 1945). (2½ typed pages.)

*180. Form (fragment). Undated (after 1945). (1½ typed pages.)

*181. Fragment (untitled): Problems of teaching. Undated (after 1945). (4 handwritten pages.)

182. On ornamentation, Negro, gypsy and other primitive rhythms, and birdsong (with many notes). 21. 11. 1922. (17 large handwritten pages, not completed.)

*183. A 'theory' of forths. (Fragment of a correction of Tovey.)

184. Fragments. *A. The conserver. 1934. (17 handwritten lines, in German.)

*B. Why no great American music? 28. 6. 1934. (10 typed pages, in German.)

The indication 'Fragment' on the cover is not exactly accurate, at least for B. This article, stimulated by W. J. Henderson's essay of the same name in the 'American Mercury' of July, 1934, seems to be complete in its present form. With it, we find Henderson's article, as well as numerous notes for Schoenberg's article.

185. Notebook (7 pages) with notes on Form, Conservatism. 1947.

186. Fragments. *A. The manners of the construction of a phrase. Undated. (7 small, short handwritten pages.)

*B. Criterions of value. Undated. (3 handwritten pages in German, 1 typed in English.)

*C. Competition of knowledge. Undated. (4 handwritten pages.)

D. Music examples (4) for A.

187. Fragments. *A. 'My music is supposedly not emotional.' Undated. (2 handwritten pages.)

B. Tennis. Undated. (2 handwritten pages.)

*C. To my dead friends. Undated (after 1945). (2 handwritten pages.)

188. Specifications for writing of parts. Undated. (1½ typed pages.)

*189. What constitutes musicianship? Undated. (9 handwritten pages of notes.)

190. On Instrumentation. Undated (about 1945?). (3½ handwritten pages.)

*191. Fragment. Bachs Counterpoint. Undated. (24 handwritten pages with music examples; also, 8 notebook pages.) Organization of a book. Each of the 24 pages has its own (chapter) heading.

192. Untitled. On problems of band music. Undated. (1 typed page.)

*193. Index to Fundamentals of musical Composition. Undated. (1 bound, complete folder of typed pages; also, handwritten plan for this—a notebook.)

194. Untitled: concerning the occasion and reasons for writing a band composition (Op. 43A).

*195. For the Broadcast of the String Trio, May 1949. (1 typed page.)

*196. For my Broadcast, 23. 8. 1949. (1½ typed pages.)

In connection with an observation of Olin Downes in the 'New York Times'. Downes was surprised by a report that 12-tone music was extending its sphere of influence in Western Europe, while 'here it is considered as a dying art'. Schoenberg believed that the reason for this was the desire of certain circles in America to 'corriger la fortune'.

*197. For the Broadcast, 22. 8. 1949. (½ typed page; announcement from Schoenberg to those interested in his music.)

C. ARTICLES, ESSAYS

198. Plan for a 'School for sound, recordings and transmission', a suggestion to the Academy of Motion Pictures, Art and Science. Undated. (9 handwritten pages.) With this are 4 handwritten pages containing the draft of a course for composers, arrangers and orchestrators.
199. Plan for an 'Arnold Schoenberg School of Composition'. Undated. (1½ typed pages.)
200. Untitled: Attempt to develop a musical terminology. Undated. (½ typed page and many notes.)
*201. (Fragment) Turn of time (Zeitwende). 1948. (2 typed pages—not identical with 173—on 12-tone composition.)
202. Fragment, untitled; on the task of the artist. Undated (after 1945). (1½ handwritten pages.)
203. Music Philology. 16. 2. 1948. (1 handwritten page.)
204. Radio interview of Schoenberg with Mr. Gripenwaldt on KOWL (Santa Monica) concerning his creative work. 7. 7. 1948. (6 typed pages.)
*205. Esthetics. Undated. (An invitation of the Cleveland Museum of Art and of the Carnegie Corporation, New York, to take part in a conference on esthetics is dated April, 1941.)
    *A. Esthetics is pure science (1 typed page).
    B. Reasons for the proposed foundation of a 'Forum of Esthetics and the Arts' which is to bring about exchange and contact among the arts and the sciences, and is to do away with the estrangement of life from nature, of investigation from theory. (Fragment; 2 typed pages, and notes.)
206. Letters, comments, articles and notes concerning the Arnold Schoenberg–Thomas Mann controversy about 'Doktor Faustus' (unpublished; 1948).
207. Untitled. Comment on National Socialism. Undated. (1 handwritten page.)
208. Untitled. Questions of priority. Undated. (8 small handwritten pages.)
*209. In the Austrian Army.
    (a) Undated. (2 handwritten pages.)
    (b) 2. 1. 1944 (1 handwritten page.)
    *(c) Petition to be freed from service. 10. 4. 1944. (2 handwritten pages.)
210. Dr. Egon Wellesz. 10. 4. 1944. (5 handwritten pages.)
*211. My sense of measures and forms. Undated. (1 handwritten page, unfinished.)
212. ASCAP. Undated. (2 handwritten pages.)
213. Toscanini. Letter to Olin Downes (not sent), 27. 8. 1944. (2 handwritten pages.)
214. Hindemith (unfinished). Undated. (3 handwritten pages.)
215. Koussewitzki–Toscanini. 11. 8. 1944. (20 handwritten pages.)
*216. To all my critics. 23. 8. 1945. (1 handwritten page.)
217. Anton von Webern. Undated. (1 handwritten page.)
218. Schopenhauer. 24. 9. 1944. (2 handwritten pages.)
    Nos. 207–218 are (partly fragmentary) drafts planned for an autobiography.
*219. To the birthday of Broadcasts of contemporary music. Undated. (1 typed page.)
220. Notes on various subjects, e.g.: *Is it the new look? (1949); *I do not write for morons (Schwachsinnige)—On inspiration and conscious work.
221. Answer to Koussevitzky's article 'Justice to composers'. 9. 5. 1949. (1 handwritten page.)

II. POEMS—LECTURES—ESSAYS—NOTES

*222. Who am I? Preface to the UCLA lecture, October, 1949 (1 typed page).

223. Letter to the mayor of Vienna after the granting of honorary citizenship (after 1945; 1 handwritten page), as well as Schoenberg's speech made at the time of the presentation of this document by the Austrian Consul in Los Angeles.

224. Little Manuscripts (between 1930 and 1934)
  - A. 1, 2, 3. Text for a chorus.
  - B. Note on commentaries to be written, etc.
  - C. Comments in Heyse's 'Grammatik' (merely a reference).
  - D. Art not revolutionary.
  - E. Triplets and quadruplets in Brahms and Bach.
  - F. Aphorism: Butter on the head ('Butter auf den [dem] Kopf').
  - G. Draft (fragment) of a lecture in Princeton: Melody and Harmony. (9 handwritten pages.)
  - H. My Canons (incomplete)—merely a listing.
  - I. Suggestion to Furtwängler. (2 handwritten pages; political.)
  - K. Christmas 1930.
  - L. Constructed Music. (4 handwritten pages.)
  - M. Admission of Students (Malkin Conservatory).

225. Analysis of 'Pelleas und Melisande' (2 typed pages, 10 examples). 1949.

226. Analysis of 'Chamber Symphony', Op. 9 (4 typed pages in English, 10 examples). 1949.

227. Analysis of 'Verklärte Nacht', Op. 4 (2 typed pages, 16 examples). 1950.

*228. Some problems for the educator (15 typed pages). Undated.

*229. (a) About new music (from a lecture in Prague, New and antiquated music). (4 typed pages.)
  - (b) Something about Bach. (2½ typed pages.)
  - (c) About Romanticism. (1½ typed pages.)
  - (d) The Radio, the artist and the majority (2½ typed pages; from a Radio discourse delivered in Frankfurt, Analysis of Variations for orchestra opus 31).
  - (e) What is a 'Finale'? (from the same lecture). (3½ typed pages.)
  - (f) My public (see also No. 16). (7 typed pages.)

230. Introduction to 'Three Piano Pieces', Op. 11 (1 typed page). 1949.

D. MUSIC

This folder bears the note (translated): *Many of the polemical articles included here belong (at least in part) to Monuments, Aphorisms, Aethics, Biography.*

1. Art-Golem. Thoughts on a German Art-Golem. 15. 7. 1922. (1 handwritten page.)
2. Music Historians. About 1915. (1 handwritten page, typed copy.)
3. Repetition. Undated (1913–14?). (1 handwritten page.)
4. Repetitive Whistling (unfinished); *This is directed against 'declamation'*. 1913–14? (1 page, handwritten and typed.)
5. Ostinato. 13. 5. 1922. (½ page, handwritten and typed.)

6. Fundamentals, Musical. 25. 3. 1923. (12 typed lines.)
7. The principal difference between me and the polytonalists. 21. 4. 1923. (1 typed page.)
8. Short formulation of the purpose of the 'Method of Composition with Twelve Tones' (in contrast to Hauer). 8. 5. 1923. (1 typed page.)
9. Cosmic Laws. 9. 5. 1923. ($\frac{1}{2}$ typed page.) Concerns J. M. Hauer.
10. On 'Composition with 12 Tones'. 9. 5. 1923. (2 typed pages.)
11. Source-Poisoner Riemann. 11. 5. 1923. (2 typed pages.)
12. Transposition (on transposing instruments). 12. 5. 1923. (2–3 typed pages.)
13. Answer to Dr. Max Unger, Leipzig, in response to his questions concerning 'absolute pitch', relative and absolute methods of hearing. 3. 3. 1923. (4 typed pages.) (See Appendix to 'Theoretical Works', No. 7.)
14. Erudition. Part of 'Unity, or The Logic of Musical Forms'. 25. 5. 1923. (1 typed page.)
15. Untitled. On directions for performance. 30. 5. 1923. (1 typed page.)
16. Symmetry. 1. 6. 1923. (9 typed lines.)
17. Schenker, Polemics. 6. 6. 1923. ($\frac{1}{2}$ typed page.)
18. Untitled. Thoughts on the polyphonic style of writing. 11. 6. 1923. ($\frac{1}{2}$ typed page.)
19. On Notation. On accidentals and their resolutions. 26. 6. 1923. (1 typed page.)
20. (a) My technique of marking indications for performance. 6. 7. 1923. ($\frac{1}{2}$ typed page.)
   (b) Repetition. ($\frac{1}{2}$ typed page.)
21. Misunderstanding of Counterpoint. Suggested by Hermann Wetzel's review of Otto Fiebach's 'Die Lehre vom strengen Kontrapunkt' in 'Die Musik'. 6. 7. 1923. ($\frac{1}{2}$ typed page.)
22. Slurs. 7. 7. 1923. (1 typed page; concerns musical meanings of slurs.)
23. Theoretician's Brain. Comment on a review by Korngold. 9. 7. 1923. (1 typed page.)
24. Directions for Performance. 16. 7. 1923. (1 typed page.)
25. Ornaments and Construction. 20. 7. 1923. (1 typed page.)
26. On Metrics. 11. 8. 1923. ($1\frac{1}{2}$ typed pages.) Observations on an article by Th. Wiehmayer: 'An Explanation. Hugo Riemann's Metric Accentuation-Scheme', in the May, 1923, issue of 'Neue Musik-Zeitung'.
27. Law of Parallels. Traunkirchen, 20. 8. 1923. (5 typed lines, with music example.)
28. Young People and I. Between August 19 and 21, 1923; two postscripts dated 25. 9. 1923. (About 4 typed pages.)
29. Imitators. Traunkirchen, 24. 8. 1923. (Concerning a Kuhlau sonatina; a bit over 1 typed page.)
30. The Sawers-Off at Work. 29. 9. 1923. (1 handwritten page.)
31. Historical Parallels. Traunkirchen, 5. 9. 23. (1 typed page.)
32. New Music. Vienna, 29. 9. 23. (3 handwritten pages.)
33. Hauer's Theories. Begun 9./9. 23. (4–5 typed pages.)
34. Polytonalists. Mödling, 29. 11. 23. (1 typed page.)
35. I and my contemporaries. Mödling, 5. 12. 23. (4 handwritten pages.)
36. Musical Picture Notation. Mödling, 10. 11. 23. ($\frac{1}{2}$ typed page.)
37. Leap Over the Shadow. Mödling, 21. 12. 23. (About 4 typed pages; concerning Krenek's 'Sprung über den Schatten'.)

38. Secrets of Art. 22./12. 23. (½ typed page.)
39. Fuga = Flight. Mödling, 10. 1. 24. (½ typed page.)
40. Study of Form. Mödling, 29. 1. 24. (3–4 typed pages.)
41. Study Score. Mödling, 1. 2. 24. (½ typed page.)
42. Jens Quer. (Pseudonym which Schoenberg used when writing for the Viennese music magazine 'Pult und Taktstock'.) Undated.
43. Foreword to Webern's short quartet pieces. Mödling, June 24.
44. Jens Quer on the orchestra of the future. March 1924. (Handwritten and typed, 2 pages.)
45. Jens Quer reports again. December 1924. (About 3 typed pages.)
46. Correction by J.Q. 31. 12. 24. (10 typed lines.)
47. No heading. *Unfortunately I am responsible not only for atonal, but also for polytonal music.* 12. 12. 24. (1 handwritten page.)
48. For 'Presentation of the Musical Idea'. 12. 11. 1925. (3 handwritten pages.)
49. No heading. *I thank Herr Bruno Weigl.* Vienna, 5. 10. 25. (1 handwritten page.)
50. 'The Singularity of Johann Strauss.' 25. 10. 25. (1 small handwritten page.) Parallel to Nestroy.
51. Telegram to the Chicago Daily News in answer to its question as to whether jazz music has influenced German music. Undated. (10 typed lines.) *Not more so than gypsy music in its day.*
52. What is the value of studying harmony? 10. 2. 26. (10 handwritten lines.)
54. Kleiber conducts Bruckner. 11. 4. 26. (13 handwritten lines.)
54. No heading. *Klemperer is considered a great innovator in Berlin* . . . 7. 3. 28. (1 large handwritten page.)
55. Oedipus, by Stravinsky. 24. 2. 28. (1 handwritten page.)
56. The Future of Opera. (24. 12. 27; 2 handwritten pages, in response to a survey by the 'Neues Wiener Tagblatt'.)
57. On Metronomization. 25. 10. 26. (2 typed pages, plus 1 handwritten page dated 8. 11. 26.)
58. Investigation of Dissonances. Undated. (8 handwritten lines.)
59. My blind alley. 23. 7. 26. (1 handwritten page.)
60. The Restaurant Owner. (24. 7. 26; 1 handwritten page.) Attacking a statement by Stravinsky, *who makes fun of musicians who (while he wants only to compose the* music of the present) *are striving to write the* music of the future.
61. Opinion on a new musical notation. *Perhaps 1927 ???*
62. Krenek for light music. 26. 2. 26. (2 handwritten pages.) Comment on Krenek's article in the yearbook 'Musik in der Gegenwart', in which he defends light music.
63. Octave-Sounds and? (illegible; perhaps 'Gänge'—progressions). 17. 12. 25. (2 small handwritten pages.)
64. Old forms in new music. 1. 12. 27. On the same sheet: Modern variation form. 10. 7. 28. (1 handwritten page.)
65. Creative Agonies . . . 7. 4. 28. (2 handwritten pages.)
66. Musical Dynamics. 5. 4. 29. (1 handwritten page.)
67. Arrangement of a textbook of counterpoint. Barcelona, 24. 11. 31. (2 small handwritten pages.)

D. MUSIC

68. The original form of the cambiata. Barcelona, April 1932. (1 small handwritten page.)
69. Phrasing. 7. 12. 31. (2 handwritten pages.)
70. Linear Counterpoint. Barcelona, 2. 12. 31. (8 handwritten pages.)

    It was always clear to me that there is something that looks like counterpoint, sounds like counterpoint, but is not counterpoint—this is the beginning of Schoenberg's commentary, which takes its point of departure from Kurth's book of the same name.
71. Instrumentation. Barcelona, 23. 11. 31. (7 handwritten pages.)
72. No heading. Commentary and observation on an essay (subjoined), by Otto Reiner: 'Der Kritiker Robert Schumann' ('Vossische Zeitung', November 6, 1931). ($1\frac{1}{2}$ handwritten pages.)
73. 'Reverberation' ('Raumton'), vibrato, radio, etc. 5. 2. 31, Berlin. (5 handwritten pages; observations on the problems of vibrato and of choral sound.)
74. Constructive details in 'Verklärte Nacht'. *Discovered during a sleepless night. Barcelona 1932.* (2 handwritten pages with music examples.)
75. Notation—accidentals. 18. 1. 31. (1 handwritten page.)
76. Durchführung (i.e., 'development'). 22. 7. 32. ($\frac{1}{2}$ handwritten page.)
77. From a recommendation for the Academy. 4. 12. 29. (1 small handwritten page.)
78. Italian National Music. 25. 9. 27. (2 handwritten pages; an attack on the creation of a national music—e.g., by Respighi.)
79. Respighi—a 'Selfian' ('Selberaner'). 26. 9. 27.
80. No heading, undated. Note on the word 'Kammermusik'. (9 handwritten lines.)
81. Postscript to the foreword of the 'Satires'. 26. 9. 27. (5 handwritten lines.)
82. On Wilhelm Werker's studies concerning the symmetry of the fugue, etc., in Bach. 20. 9. 26. (1 handwritten page.)
83. Old and new counterpoint. Vienna. 10. 6. 28. (2 handwritten pages.)
84. Bach and the 12 tones. 23. 7. 32. (1 small handwritten page.)
85. Linear Counterpoint—Linear Polyphony. Undated; see No. 70. (5 small handwritten pages.)
86. Comments on the article 'Die kompositorische Situation von 1930' by H. F. Redlich in the June, 1930 number of the Viennese music magazine 'Anbruch'. Undated.
87. Comments on 'Fortschritt und Reaktion' ('Progress and Reaction') by Ernst Krenek, in the same issue of 'Anbruch'. (A total of 8 small handwritten pages.)
88. Our Musical Writing. 21. 6. 31 and 16. 11. 31. (One small handwritten page for each of these dates.)
89. National Music. 24. 2. 31. (11 handwritten pages; closes with an account of Schoenberg's development from the mainstream of German music. See Appendix to 'Theoretical Works', No. 9.)
90. For 'Presentation of the Musical Idea'. 16. 8. 31. (2 handwritten pages.)
91. Sketches for a foreword to the composition textbook. 17. 8. 31. (1 small handwritten page.)
92. Waltershausen. 11. 7. 31. (6 handwritten pages.)
93. On a new method of musical notation. (Recommendation to the Academy of Arts; undated.)
94. Difficulties of comprehension. Undated. (12 handwritten lines.)

95. Questionnaire: Influence of Jazz. Undated. (1 small handwritten page, identical with No. 51.)

96. The Question(naire) [Die (Rund-) Frage] as to how one stands to Beethoven. Undated. (2 small handwritten pages.)

97. Tonality. 3. 8. 32. (2 handwritten pages; note on the first: *ohne Datum, 1923 oder 1924.*)

98. For 'Presentation of the Idea'. Undated. (12 handwritten lines.)

99. Draft of a lecture in the 'Society for Acoustics and Phonetics' (not delivered). (1 page, handwritten and typed.)

100. On the teaching of performance. Undated. (1 typed page.)

101. Development of Harmony. Undated (a short postscript is dated 7. 8. 32). (2 handwritten pages.)

102. No heading: about Reger's Violin Concerto. Note: *scheinbar 1923* ('apparently 1923'). Unfinished. (1 handwritten page.)

103. Rhythmics. 30. 6. 25. Only 6 handwritten lines, with postscript (translated): *Probably just a plan? but somewhere I wrote a fairly good definition.*

104. Comment on a subjoined newspaper article: 'Igor Stravinsky on his music', a conversation with N. Roerig (New York). (About 30 handwritten lines.)

105. On the teaching of performance. *About 1923 or 24.* (18 typed lines.)

106. The future of the organ. *About 1906 or 07 at latest; this was planned as a long article.* (2 handwritten pages.)

107. Folk-Music and Art-Music. *Undated, in any case some time before the Foreword to the 'Satires'.* (2 large handwritten pages.)

108. On the study of form. Undated. (1½ handwritten pages.)

109. Letter to Dr. Stiedry, 31. 7. 1930, concerning Schoenberg's Bach orchestrations. (2 handwritten pages; see also above, Section I, B, 'Orchestrations'.)

110. Letter to Mr. Ibach (answer to a questionnaire on the effect of the radio on musical culture). 31. 7. 1930. (2 handwritten pages.)

*111. Analysis by ear (letter to Olin Downes, music critic of the 'New York Times', concerning the latter's review, 'New Music by Arnold Schoenberg', of a performance of the 'Suite for String Orchestra'). 18. 10. 1935. (6 handwritten pages.)

112. *(a) Teaching. Undated. (1 handwritten page.)
(b) Counterpoint in the 19th and 20th centuries.
(c) Preliminary observations.

*113. Notes: Preface to Suite [for String Orchestra]. See above, Section I, B.

114. The musician Weill. 1928. (4 handwritten pages; comment on the newspaper article of the same name by Kurt Weill—the name of the newspaper is not mentioned.)

115. Schubert. 1928. (1 typed page with handwritten addition.)

116. No heading. 1928. (3 handwritten pages; concerning Hindemith's assertion that 'the musician of today has no more technical problems to solve'.)

117. Notes on the concept of 'artistic value'.

118. Kroll's nonsensical introduction. 1932. (1½ typed pages; the introduction is to Bach's 'Well-Tempered Clavier'.)

119. Definition of (a) rhythm, (b) counterpoint, (c) canon. 1932. (1 handwritten page.)

E. AESTHETICS

120. The photographic intelligence of the 'greatest living musician'! 1935. (2 handwritten pages; about Toscanini and the inferiority of objective reproduction of works of art.)
121. Notes on [the preparation of] 'The Piano Reduction'.
122. The 25th Anniversary of Mahler's Death. 1936. (5 handwritten pages.)
123. Examples of 6-, 7-, 8- and 9-voiced chords which resolve into tonal chords according to the principles of leading-tone progression. Undated.
124. Fugue (comment on Marc André Souchaux's 'The Theme in the Fugue of Bach'). 1936. (1 handwritten page.)
125. Notes on: Symphonic Form. Undated. ($\frac{1}{2}$ handwritten page.)
126. Origin of Music. 1930. ($\frac{1}{2}$ handwritten page.)
*127. The concept of form in music. Undated. ($4\frac{1}{2}$ handwritten pages.)

E. AESTHETICS

1. The Study of Form. 1924. (6 small typed pages.)
2. Art for the Community. 1928. (1 handwritten page.)
3. Inspiration. 1926. ($1\frac{1}{2}$ handwritten pages.)
4. Music for the People and Music of the Revolution. 1929. (4 handwritten pages.)
5. Pathos. 1928. (2 handwritten pages.)
6. Anti-Criticism, Praise of Reason. 1927. (1 handwritten page.)
7. Heart and Brain. 1927. ($\frac{1}{2}$ handwritten page.)
8. Depth. 1927. (1 handwritten page.)
9. Theatre Crisis (unfinished). 1931. (4 handwritten pages.)
10. Feelings of Beauty. 1931. ($\frac{1}{2}$ handwritten page.)
11. Spiritual—sensual. 1931. ($\frac{1}{2}$ handwritten page.)
12. Stuckenschmidt. 1931. (7 handwritten pages; about H. H. Stuckenschmidt's article in the 'Vossische Zeitung': 'Brecht, Operngesetze' / 'Anmerkungen zur Oper'.)
13. For the drama 'Der biblische Weg'. 1927. (1 handwritten page.)
14. 'Speak to the rock'. 1927. (1 handwritten page.)
15. Should the composer learn from the critic?—Sketch for a discussion. Undated. (1 handwritten page.)
16. Welcome to the talking film. (3 versions, 1927; *I worked a lot on this stuff.*)
17. Recommendation of the Prussian Academy of Arts, Poetry Section, for extension of copyright—handwritten comments on this.
18. For 'Presentation of the Idea'. 1932. (1 handwritten page.)
19. On the teaching of performance. Undated. (1 typed page.)
20. Art and Revolution (unfinished). 1919 or 1920. (3 large handwritten pages.)
21. False Alarm. About 1910? (5 handwritten pages.) A later, undated postscript (translated): *I did not finish this article at that time, because the more I thought about it the worse I found Pfitzner's brochure to be, so that I considered it superfluous to oppose it. But perhaps it would have been the right thing to do after all? See also the comments in the brochure.* (See below, Section M. 8.)

22. Article on Loos, 1926. (2 handwritten pages; on the Viennese architect Adolf Loos, a friend of Schoenberg's.)
23. On 'Criteria of the Value of the Musical Work of Art'. Undated. (1 handwritten page.)
24. Theatre of Poetry. 1931. A lengthy comment noted on a circular calling for money for an 'Ensemble Theatre of Poetry' under the leadership of Karl Kraus, the founding of which was being planned at that time.
25. Consideration of the Public (incomplete). Undated. (2 handwritten pages.)
26. Answer to Ibach. 1930. (1 handwritten page.)

F. MY THEORIES

(Interpretations, explanations; also discoveries, suggestions, improvements)

1. Genius. 1935. (4 large handwritten pages.)
2. America and Japan. 1937. (13 handwritten note-pad sheets.)
3. State. 1932. ($\frac{1}{2}$ handwritten page with an adverse comment added in 1940.)
4. Politics. 1932. (4 handwritten pages.)
5. Power, Majority, Fascism, etc. 1932. (6 handwritten pages.)
6. World Economics. (*a*) Letter to ??
   (*b*) Suggestion for a resolution of the crisis. Undated, but before 1933. (7 handwritten pages.)
7. Observations of the newborn child. 1932. (1 handwritten page.)
8. Economic Matters. 1932. (1 handwritten page.)
9. Greetings. 1933. (2 handwritten pages.)
10. O Man! 1928. (1 handwritten page.)
11. Ös Tachinierer! (Viennese dialect: 'You cowards!'). 1932. (2 handwritten pages.)
12. Nearby Mountains. 1932. ($\frac{1}{2}$ handwritten page.)
13. Illuminated Darkness. 1932. (1 handwritten page.)
14. At the Oculist's. 1932. (3 handwritten pages.)
15. Temperature and Pulse. 1925. (2 handwritten pages.)
16. Steel – Sharpness. 1925. (3 handwritten pages.)
17. Be Careful—A Postscript. 1927. ($\frac{1}{2}$ handwritten page.)
18. Pumpernickel. 1927. (1 handwritten page.)
19. Animals. 1927. (2 handwritten pages.)
20. Illnesses. 1927. (4 handwritten pages.)
21. Clothing. 1927. ($1\frac{1}{2}$ handwritten pages.)
22. Little Ideas. 1927. (6 handwritten pages.)
23. Disorders in Vienna, 1922. 1928. (1 handwritten page.)
24. Typewriter Table. Undated. (1 handwritten page.)
25. Besieged Fortress. 1923. (1 large typed page.)
26. The Bourgeoisification of the Proletariat. 1923. (2 typed pages.)

G. MONUMENTS

1. Little Zaches. Mödling, 19. Mai 1923. (½ typed page.) Note: *not to be published, only in case of necessity as a defence. Arnold Schönberg 20. 7. 32.*
2. Untitled; also concerned with Klein Zaches. 27. 4. 23. (9 typed lines.)
3. St. Stephen's. 18. 4. 23. (8 typed lines.)
4. Letter to Webern. 28. 5. 23 (not sent). (9 typed lines.)
5. Rösch. 17. 7. 23. (5 handwritten lines.)
6. No heading: concerns a statement of Richard Strauss to Hindemith. Mödling, November 23.
7. Herr Hofrat Triebenbacher. 15.1.24. Mödling. (½ typed page.)
8. A Settling of Accounts. 21. 2. 24. Postscript, 21. 7. 32. (1 typed page and 1 handwritten page.)
9. The lecture 'held' by Krenek. Undated. (1 handwritten page.)
10. Florizel's Spirits. 13. 8. 29. Comment on an article in the 'Neues Wiener Journal', 'The Conductor from the Realm of Spirits', by Florizel von Reuter. (1 handwritten page.)
11. Letter to the editor of the '8-Uhr-Abendblatt' (Berlin). (1 typed page.)
12. Herr Muck—*no Hauff fairy tale, but still a German story.* 12. 2. 1928, postscript of 21. 7. 32. (2 large handwritten pages.) A dispute with the conductor Karl Muck.
13. Congratulations to Bach. 28. 7. 24. (1 handwritten page.)
14. Julia Culp. 28. 5. 28. Settlement on the basis of a letter of the singer to Dr. Hugo Botstiber, Vienna. This has to do with Schoenberg's vain efforts to get her to return his orchestrations of Beethoven's 'Adelaide' and of three Schubert songs. They must be considered as lost.
15. On Franz Schreker. March or April 1931. (1 handwritten page.)
16. Schreker. 9. 5. 29. (1 handwritten page.)
17. Klemperer. 3. 5. 30. (½ typed page.)
18. Letter to Mme. René Dubost, Paris. 9. 10. 28 (not sent).
19. The 'Allgemeine Deutsche Musikverein', 24. 5. 28. Postscript on 6. 12. 28. (1½ handwritten pages.)
20. Dr. Graf—Monn Arrangements. 11. 5. 28. (3 handwritten pages.) Detailed justification of Schoenberg's realization of the figured bass. Parallel with Mozart's arrangement of 'Messiah'.
21. Stylistic Gems of my Lying Enemies. Berlin, 8. 4. 29. (2 handwritten pages.)
22. Decsey. 28. 9. 27. (½ typed page.)
23. Hanns Eisler. 8. 7. 28 and 13. 7. 28. (1½ handwritten pages.)
24. Herr Petschnig. 7. 7. 27. (6 handwritten pages.)
25. Florizel's Spirits. 16. 12. 31. (3 handwritten pages and a newspaper clipping, 'A Vision Solves a Burglary', by Dr. Eugen Krüger, 'Wiener Journal', 13. 12. 31.)
26. de Falla. Barcelona, 1. 12. 31; postscript 23. 7. 32. (1 handwritten page).
27. Herr von Milenkovic (Max Morold). 25. 11. 31. (2 handwritten pages.)
28. What one ought not to forget. 2. 12. 31. (3 handwritten pages.)

29. The Universal Edition. Supplement to my correspondence. 5. 7. 27 and 13. 5. 28. (1 handwritten page.)
30. Envy. 22. 10. 28. (1 handwritten page.)
31. Hermann Wolff's brother. 13. 5. 28. (1 handwritten page.)
32. Herr Lendvai. 13. 5. 28. (1 handwritten page.)
33. Herr Weissmann. 27. 3. 28. (1 handwritten page.)
34. Dr. Alfred Einstein. 31. 3. 28. (1 handwritten page.)
35. The Copy-Cat ('Der Ab-Seher'). 18. 4. 28.
36. Bondy. 17. 9. 30. (1 handwritten page, added to on 31. 7. 32.)
37. Paul Stefan the Biographer. Undated. Observations on Stefan's article 'Music in Post-Empire Austria' (?)
38. Attempt at a memorial for Hertzka. May 1932. (3 handwritten pages.)
39. Exaggerated Individualism. Undated. (1 handwritten page.)
40. Biographer No. 2/2. 1. 26. ($\frac{1}{2}$ handwritten page.)
41. Herr Prof. Lach. Undated. (4 handwritten pages.)
42. Untitled; commentary on the subjoined article 'What is Progress in Music?' by Reinhold Conrad Muschler. 8. 12. 32. (1 handwritten page.)
43. Untitled: an analytical study of the theme of Bach's 'Musical Offering', taking as its point of departure a (subjoined) review by Dr. Erich Urban. Undated but marked *offenbar 1928 oder 29?* ('evidently 1928 or 29?'). (1 handwritten page.)
44. Elsa. 1928. ($\frac{1}{2}$ handwritten page; on Dr. Elsa Bienenfeld, music critic of the 'Neues Wiener Journal'.)
45. So the young people chattered. Undated. (1 handwritten page.)
46. Toscanini. 18. 7. 37. (2 handwritten pages.)
47. Stefan George. 12. 10. 32. (1 handwritten page.)
48. Webern. 10. 8. 1940. (1 handwritten page.)

H. MISCELLANEOUS

1. Seminar for Composition (Schwarzwald, Vienna). 1. 9. 1917. ($1\frac{1}{2}$ handwritten pages.)
2. Rumour-Spreaders of Ruin ('Untergangs-Raunzer'). (1 typed page; 9. 6. 1923.)
3. Relationship. 16. 4. 1923. (16 lines.)
4. Israelites and Jews (with a newspaper report from 'Der Tag', Berlin, on 'Münchner Versammlungen'). 5. 7. 1923. (1 typed page.)
5. The Antagonist, a political marginal note. 26. 9. 1923.
6. Comment on the reprint of the contribution 'Music' to the 'Plans for a Ministry of Art'. January, 1924.
7. Observation on the Concert-Gebouw (*a glance back at the time when art was dependent on vitally interested patrons*). Undated (about 1927). (11 typed lines.)
8. Society of the Authors of the Universal-Edition (invitation to help form one). Undated.
9. National Plan of Attack of the Nordic Race. Beginning of 1932. (1 small handwritten page.)
10. The Teachers. 25. 8. 1928. (4 handwritten pages.)

H. MISCELLANEOUS

11. My Style. An attack on the subjoined reprint 'Krise des Geschmacks' ('Crisis of Taste') from the 'Berliner Börsen-Courier'. 1. 1. 1931. (1 small handwritten page.)

12. The Electric Tram and the Autobus. (*told this to Rufer yesterday; but to Trude long ago, only didn't write it down then.*) 19. 1. 1930 or 1931. (2 handwritten pages.)

13. Notes on a short speech before the Committee for the Introduction of the 50-year Copyright. Berlin. 2. 5. 1927.

14. Suggestion for the foundation of an International School of Style. March, 1927. (2 typed sheets.)

15. Professionalism. April, 1928. (10 handwritten lines.)

16. On Criticism. 15. 11. 1930. (2 small handwritten pages.)

17. Economic Matters. 2. 11. 1930. (10 handwritten pages.)

18. Development. 24. 12. 1931. (½ handwritten page.)

19. Socio-Economics. 26. 11. 1931. (10 handwritten pages.)

20. On: Spanish Tennis. March, 1932. (½ typed page.)

21. Observations and Thoughts on a Music-Typewriter. Undated. (6 handwritten pages.)

22. Characteristics of Logic. 29. 2. 1932. (2 handwritten pages.)

23. Sketches for a satirical article. Undated. (11 regular pages and 6 small pages, handwritten.)

24. Streetcar Ticket. Letter to the management of the Berlin Streetcar Company with carefully worked-out sketches and explanations for a streetcar transfer. 12. 1. 1927.

25. Against the Scourge of Robbers. 1922 or 1923. (1 typed page.)

26. Prerequisites for Admission, Master Class of the Prussian Academy of Arts. Undated.

27. Clipping from 'Berliner Illustrirte Zeitung'. No. 20, with handwritten marginal notes on pictures of the Nazi leaders. 1933.

28. Notes on a 'People's Music School'. About 1910.

29. Plan of stage arrangement for the 'Gurre-Lieder'. About 1914 (1918)?

30. Suggestion to Universal Edition, for securing 'subscribers to new music'. 1918 or 1919?

31. Much or little experimentation ('probieren'). Observations suggested by the subjoined article 'Much or little rehearsal' ('proben') by Furtwängler in the 'Neues Wiener Journal', 19. 2. 1931.

32. Untitled. About tennis-playing. Undated (about 1927). (3 handwritten pages.)

33. Observations on the sentence: 'The idea can wait, for it is timeless.' (*Der Gedanke kann warten, denn er hat keine Zeit.*) Undated, between 1928 and 1933. (1 handwritten page.)

34. The new way of music teaching. 24. 3. 1929. (1½ handwritten pages.)

35. Glaserer. (*a*) 18. 2. 1933, (*b*) 25. 9. 1933, (*c*) 27. 12. 1933. (*b*) and (*c*) are comments on German racial theories. (½ handwritten page each.)

36. ?

37. Drawings for (*a*) a bookbinding press, (*b*) a music typewriter, (*c*) a telephone connection, (*d*) the classification of the Jews.

★38. Why do we make it so difficult to our children and especially to our babies? Undated. (1 handwritten page; unfinished.)

    N.B.: The following numbers, 39–76, were found in the legacy, obviously still unclassified, in a carton. I have included them here under 'Miscellaneous'. Some of these are duplicates of material listed elsewhere in our classification.

*39. A four point program. 1939. (37 typed pages.)

40. The Jewish Question. Arcachon, 12. and 13. 8. 1933. (13 handwritten pages.)

41. Notes on Jewish politics. 1933.

42. PUJ (essays on the Jewish question, begun in December 1933).

43. To the swimmers of the Hakoah, Vienna. 1933. (1 page.)

*44. A lecture (adress). 1933. (5 pages.)

45. A new 'Realpolitik' (4 pages) and other articles. April, 1934.

46. The Jewish government in exile.

47. Protection of intellectual property. 1933. (3 pages.)

48. Program for the assistance and development of the [Jewish] party.

49. Einstein's false politics. 1933.

50. Speech for the reception in Chicago. Undated.

51. Speech for the reception in New York. 11. 11. 1933.

*52. Driven into Paradise.

*53. What have people to expect . . .

*54. Some objective reasons.

*55. Letter to Chancellor of University of Chicago (Mr. Hutchins?). (On the possibility of organizing a music department.)

*56. Preface and Introduction of Counterpoint (textbook). 1934. ($1\frac{1}{2}$ handwritten pages.)

*57. Musical Idea (unfinished). 1934. (1 handwritten page.)

*58. Outline to 'Verzierungen, etc.' Undated. (1 handwritten page, in German.)

*59. Classes at USC.

60. Mechanical Musical Instruments (in German). 1926. ($4\frac{1}{2}$ large typed pages.)

61. Piano Reduction. 1923. ($1\frac{1}{2}$ typed pages.)

*62. Folkloristic Symphonies. 1947. (12 handwritten pages.)

*63. The share of the heart and that of the brain in the music. First draft. 18. 1. 1946.

64. Drafts of letters: (a) to D. J. Bach, after 1933
                        (b) to the Prussian Academy of Arts.

65. 60th-birthday thank-you letter (2 handwritten pages).

66. Boheme. 6. 5. 28. (2 handwritten and typed pages.)

67. Untitled. Influence of the arts on politics? (National anthems.) May, 1928. (2 typed pages.)

68. International School for the Formation of Style. Suggestion for its foundation (first draft, 1920). March, 1927. (2 typed pages.)

69. Draft of a foreword to the 'Suite for String Orchestra'. (2 handwritten pages, 1 typed.)

70. Foreword to the 'Concerto for String Quartet and Orchestra', after Handel. (1 typed page; published on the sleeve of the Columbia record.)

71. Letter to Schreker (50th birthday); published in 'Anbruch'. March, 1928.

72. My 50th birthday. (2 typed pages.)

73. A New Twelve-Tone Notation (in 'Anbruch', January, 1925).

74. The Present State of Music. 1929. ('Querschnitt'). (1 handwritten page.)

75. My Opinion of Contemporaries. (Courrier musical, or Musical Courier?). December, 1923. ($2\frac{1}{2}$ typed pages.)

76. Interview with Myself. October, 1928. (7 typed pages.)

J. LANGUAGE

1. . . . pleasantly disappointed . . . ('angenehm enttäuscht')
   . . . no laurels plucked . . . ('keine Lorbeeren gepflückt')
   . . . elevated ranks . . . ('gehobene Stände')
   'Painful lawsuit for H . . .' ('Peinlicher Prozess für H. . . .'). 1932.
2. Work for me—workman ('Arbeit für mich—Arbeitnehmer'). 1932.
3. Remained—stayed. ('Verblieben—geblieben'.) 1932.
4. The most faithful customs examination ('Loyalste Zollrevision'). 1932.
5. New Words ('Geburtlichkeit, Verfestigung, Schaubild'). 1932. (These neologisms might be translated as 'birthship', 'reconfirmation', 'show-picture'.)
6. The honorably confessing thief ('Der ehrlich zugebende Dieb').
7. (a) Hundreds and thousands ('Aberhundert—Abertausend'). 1927/29.
   (b) 'That is not meant' ('Das ist nicht gesagt').
   (c) The Same ('Derselbe').
   (d) Advertising Language ('Die Sprache der Reklame').
   (e) Quality Goods ('Qualitätsware').
   (f) Seven Bargain Glove Days ('Sieben billige Handschuhtage').
   (g) The German-est ('Die Deutschesten').
   (h) Tennis Language.
   (i) Karpath.
   (k) Weissmann.
8. Gems of Style ('Stilblüten'). 1927.
9. Pithy Elsa ('Die kernige Elsa'). 1927.
10. Landing on Water ('Wasserlandung'). 1925.
11. Fugue = Flight. 1924.
12. From an open letter of Herr Ludendorff. 1923.
13. New Land of the Palette. 1923.
14. On the 'superfluous periods'. 1923.
15. November Criminals; Speech-Corrupters. 1923.
16. 'Schupo–Sipo–Arbeitgeber—Arbeitnehmer' (nicknames for policemen; employer—employee). 1923.

K. ETHICS (Moral)

1. Cultural Leaders. 1932. (2 handwritten pages.)
2. Hero or Martyr. 1932. (4 handwritten pages.)
3. The Utility of the False. 1924. (1 typed page.)
4. Credibility of the Truth. 1932. (1 handwritten page.)
5. Schopenhauer and Socrates. 1927. (2 handwritten pages.)

6. Love Thy Neighbour As Thyself. 1926. (2 handwritten pages.)
7. Development - Progress. 1932. (1 handwritten page.)
8. Letter to a Pianist. 1925. (2 typed pages.)
9. Attitude towards Zionism. 1924. (1 typed page.)
10. Theoreticians' Habits. 1924. (2 typed pages.)
11. The Wealthy Jew. 1923. (½ typed page.)
12. Vienna Concert Society ('Wiener Konzertvereinsgesellschaft'). 1923. (½ typed page.)
The legacy also contains:
A folder 'Aphorisms, Jokes, Witticisms, Satires, Commentaries (without theoretical significance), Polemics'.
60 small and larger pieces of paper with notes of all sizes.

L. PUBLISHED ARTICLES

(also aphorisms, dedications, etc.)

1. On Music Criticism. ('Der Merker', I/2). (6 pages.)
2. Foreword to the programme of the performance of the 'Gurrelieder' with 2 pianos in Vienna. (16 lines.)
3. Problems of Teaching The Arts. ('Musikalisches Taschenbuch'.) (6 pages.)
4. Gustav Mahler. (Periodical in which published not clear here; Vienna, 1911.) (1¼ pages.)
5. Franz Liszt's Work and Personality. ('Allgemeine Musikzeitung', special issue on Liszt.) 1912.
6. 'Parsifal and Copyright'. (Periodical in which published and date not given here.) (7 pages.)
7. Sleepwalkers. ('Pan', 1912.) (2 pages; with this, a criticism by Leopold Schmidt, Berlin.)
8. Answer to Leopold Schmidt's reply. ('Pan'.) (2¼ pages.)
9. Aphorisms. ('Gutmanns Konzertkalender', 1911/12.) (3 pages.)
10. Aphorisms. ('Gutmanns Konzertkalender'.) (1 page.)
11. Aphorisms. (Place of publication not noted.) (5 pages.)
12. String Quartet, Op. 7; analysis with music examples. ('Die Musik', June, 1918.) (3 pages.)
13. Plans for a Ministry of Art. (Verlag Richard Lanyi, Vienna, 1919.)
14. Recognition. ('Arbeid en Resultaat', 1919.) (½ page.) On Willem Mengelberg.
15. On the Problem of Modern Composition Teaching. ('Deutsche Tonkünstler-Zeitung', Jahrg. 27, Heft 21, 5. November 1919.) (2¼ pages.)
16. 'Idées d'Arnold Schönberg sur la musique, Dialogue'. ('La Revue Musicale', 10ème année, No. 1.) (5 pages.)
17. Answer to a questionnaire of the '8-Uhr Abendblatt' ('Berliner National-Zeitung'), 26. 5. 1928. (About 35 lines.)
18. Answer to a questionnaire of the 'Deutsche Allgemeine Zeitung', 10. 8. 1930: 'Berlin or Vienna? Supremacy as European musical capital'. (34 lines.)

19. Schoenberg answers a questionnaire of the 'Berliner Tageblatt', 13. 5. 1928: 'The Dying Bohemian'. He points out that the title given his answer, 'Result: the end of Bohemianism', was not provided by him.

20. A New Twelve-Tone Notation (reprint from 'Anbruch', Vienna, January, 1925). (7 pages; music examples and chart.)

21. Thanks (place of publication not mentioned; October, 1924). (17 lines.)

22. Canon for Concert-Gebouw (place of publication and date not given). (See above, Section II, A (d).)

23. Canon for the 'Genossenschaft Deutscher Tonsetzer' (place of publication and date not given; see also preceding item).

24. A very instructive speech by Felix Mottl. ('Pult und Taktstock', Vienna; date not given on this manuscript of 1½ pages.)

25. Mechanical Musical Instruments. ('Pult und Taktstock', 3. Jahrg., Heft 3/4.) (4½ pages.)

26. The Future of Orchestral Instruments. ('Pult und Taktstock', Heft 8, December, 1924.)

27. Jens Quer reports. ('Pult und Taktstock', same issue.) (3 pages.)

28. Cue Numbers. ('Pult und Taktstock'; number and date of issue not given on this manuscript of 1½ pages.)

29. Alban Berg. ('Die Theaterwelt', Düsseldorf, 10. 4. 1930. (1 page.)

30. My Public. ('Querschnitt', Berlin, April, 1930.) (3 pages.)

31. Answer to a questionnaire from an unnamed French music magazine, in the form of a letter to Robert Lyon. Undated. (12 lines.)

32. Tonality and Form. (Not extant; note by Schoenberg: 'published in English only'.)

33. Conviction and Knowledge. ('Jahrbuch der Universal Edition', Vienna, 1926. Not here.) (9 pages.)

34. Canon for Hermann Abraham's 85th birthday (no indication where published). (See above, Section II, A (d).)

35. My Models. (Manuscript not at hand; *sent to a French magazine*.)

36. Modern Music on the Radio. ('Radiowelt Wien', X. Jahrg., Heft 15, 8. 4. 1933.) (2 pages.)

37. 'Zagadnienia Nowoczesnej Nauki Kompozycji' ('Nowa Muzyka', Warsaw). A translation of No. 15; see above.

38. Problems of Harmony. ('Modern Music', Vol. XI, No. 4, May–June 1934.) (21 pages.)

39. Seminar for Composition (subjects and prerequisites for admission to the seminar which Schoenberg established in the Schwarzwald School, Vienna, in 1918).

40. Foreword to Webern's Bagatelles for String Quartet. (Magazine '23', Vienna; special issue for Webern's 50th birthday, No. 14, February, 1934.)

41. Dedication to Karl Kraus ('Der Brenner', III. Jahrg., Heft 18). (6 lines.)

42. Introduction to the four Quartets (in English, without indication of place of publication or date). (4 pages.)

*43. How can a music student earn a living? (MTNA 'Proceedings', 1939.) (4½ pages.)

*44. Ear training through composing (original place of publication not mentioned; 1940). (7 pages; see also 'Style and Idea').

*45. Art and the Moving Pictures. ('California Arts and Architecture', April, 1940.) (4 pages.)

M. ARTICLES ABOUT ME

(and other subjects; with comments)

Schoenberg often wrote his comments in the margins of the articles in question, while at other times he wrote them on pasted-on or inserted sheets of paper.

1. Casella, 'Harmony, Counterpoint, etc.' (Pro-Musica Quarterly, March–June 1926). With this, a long essay by Schoenberg.

2. Comments on Fritz Jöde's 'Music and Society', on Fritz Thöne's 'The Situation of the Reproductive Musician', and, in great detail, on Hindemith's 'Demands on the Amateur'. ('Musik und Gesellschaft', edited by Dr. Hans Boettcher, published by Schotts Söhne and G. Kallmeyer, Jahrg. 1, Heft 1.)

3. Klaus Pringsheim, 'The Atonalists'. ('Die Weltbühne', XXII/2, 12. 1. 1926.) Extensive comments.

4. Alexander Maria Schnabel, 'The New Formation of Music'. ('Die Musik', XV/8.)

5. Emil Petschnig, 'German Opera'. ('Die Musik', XV/3.)

6. Heinrich Schenker, 'Johann Sebastian Bach'. ('Well-Tempered Clavier', Book I, C minor prelude.) ('Die Musik', XV/9.)

7. Elsa Bienenfeld, 'Arnold Schönbergs "Kammersymphonie"'. ('Neues Wiener Journal', 25. 7. 1918.) Comment on this review, opposing Paul Bekker, who is cited in it.

8. Hans Pfitzner, 'The Menace of Futurism'. (See also under 'Aesthetics', No. 21.)

9. Alfredo Casella, 'Modern Music in Italy'. ('Modern Music', League of Composers, Vol. XII/1, Nov.–Dec., 1934.)

10. Ernst Toch, 'Melodielehre' (Verlag Max Hesse, Berlin, 1923). Detailed comments.

11. L. Dunton Green, 'On Inspiration'. ('The Chesterian', Vol. IX/68, Jan.–Feb. 1928.)

12. Edwin v.d. Null, 'Moderne Harmonik' (Kistner & Siegel, Leipzig, 1932). Thorough commentary on the book.

13. J. M. Hauer, 'Sphärenmusik'. ('Melos', III/3.) This is rather an article than a commentary.

14. Answers to a questionnaire of the music magazine 'Der Merker' (IX/13/14) on Schoenberg's simplified study and conducting score, written by Siegfried Ochs, Artur Nikisch, Felix v. Weingartner, Max v. Schillings, Bruno Walter, and Wilhelm Furtwängler. Schoenberg's comments on these.

15. Comments in Heinrich Schenker's 'Der Tonwille' (1. Heft, 1921) on the following articles:

    (a) On the Mission of German Genius
    (b) The 'Urlinie'
    (c) Beethoven, Fifth Symphony
    (d) J. S. Bach, 'Well-Tempered Clavier', Book I, Prelude in E flat minor
    (e) Franz Schubert, 'Ihr Bild'

From the commentary on (b): *The presentation on one line will never succeed! Very simply: because a composition just does not happen to exist in one dimension only! Schenker's 'Urlinie' is, at best,* one *cross-section of the whole! But one must make* many *such cross-sections. The artfulness of art consists in one's not noticing its component parts; that is its simplicity.*

That the smallest component parts are simple is no merit of the author's; he cannot help it.

But, even apart from that, he did not compose those smallest component parts—rather, he composed the whole piece. The piece consists of its smallest component parts only—when one takes it apart.

16. J. M. Hauer, 'Atonale Musik'. ('Die Musik', XVI/2, Nov. 1923.) Detailed comments.
17. Comments on the following articles published in 'Die Musik', April, 1929:
    August Halm, 'On the Value of Musical Analyses'.
    Adolf Weissmann, 'German and Foreign Musical Creativity'.
    Justus H. Wetzel, 'On Artistic Formation'.
18. Comments on contributions by conductors to a discussion on 'Metronomization' ('Pult und Taktstock', March–April, 1926).
19. Comment on Alfredo Casella's introduction to his own 'Partita' for piano and orchestra ('Pult und Taktstock', May–June, 1926).
20. Comments on H. H. Stuckenschmidt's 'Erik Satie' and Krenek's statement on Casella's article 'Scarlattiana' ('Anbruch', Vienna, XI, 2, 1929).
21. Comments on the following articles in 'Anbruch', X, 9/10:
    Ernst Krenek, 'Voice and Instrument'.
    Theodor Adorno, 'Situation of the Song'.
22. H. H. Stuckenschmidt, 'Hanns Eisler'. ('Anbruch', X, 5, 1928.)
23. Klaus Pringsheim, 'Neue Musik?' ('Die Weltbühne', XXII/3, January, 1926).
24. Paul Bekker, 'Schönbergs "Erwartung"', a study in the special 'Anbruch' issue for Schoenberg's 50th birthday. Comments on this as well as on the 'Anecdotes' recounted by Hanns Eisler.
25. Egon Wellesz, 'Probleme der modernen Musik'. ('Anbruch', VI, Nov.–Dec., 1924.)
26. Comments on articles by Alexander Jemnitz and Percy Grainger in the Jazz Issue of 'Anbruch', VII, April, 1925.

OIL PAINTINGS
WATER-COLOURS
DRAWINGS

OIL PAINTINGS, WATER-COLOURS,
AND DRAWINGS FOUND IN THE LEGACY

The Conquered	Water-colour, 35·5 × 25·5; signed 22. IV. 1919
The Conqueror	Water-colour, 31·5 × 26; signed April 1919
Gaze	Oil, 31 × 22·5, on wood; signed 1910
Christ, Vision	Water-colour, 21 × 11; signed 1910
Tears	Oil, 29 × 23, on canvas
Blue Gaze	Oil, 21 × 24; signed
Red Gaze	Oil, 23 × 29; signed 26. 3. 1910
Hands	Oil, 64 × 40; signed 1910
Thinking	Oil, 22 × 25
Red Gaze	Oil, 24 × 32; signed Mai 1910
Gaze	Oil, 29 × 20, on canvas; signed 1910
Blue Self-Portrait	Oil, 31 × 22, on wood; signed 1910
Green Self-Portrait	Oil, 33·5 × 24·5; signed 1910
(on the reverse: Woman's Head)	
Yellow Self-Portrait	Missing
Self-Portrait (rear view, full figure)	Oil, 50 × 45; signed 1911
Gustav Mahler, Vision	Oil, 45 × 45; signed 1910
Christ, Vision	Oil, 50 × 36·5
Critic I	Oil, 45 × 31·5
Critic II	Oil, 30 × 23
Satire, Vision	Oil, 31 × 24, on wood; signed
Art-Patron, Vision	Oil, 37·5 × 32
Flesh	Water-colour, 22 × 29
Night (Landscape)	Oil, 58·5 × 74, on canvas; signed 1910
Comfort (title doubtful)	Oil, 33·5 × 22, on canvas
Dr. W., portrait	Oil, 49·5 × 42, on wood
Dr. P. St. (twice)	Crayon, 39 × 19·5 and 33 × 20·5; signed
Portrait of a Woman	Oil, 32 × 22, signed
Portrait of a Woman	Oil, 68 × 55, on canvas
Landscape	Oil, 51 × 38
Alexander v. Zemlinsky	Oil, 49·5 × 34
Georg Schönberg (son)	Oil, 50 × 48, on wood
Three pictures for 'Die glückliche Hand'	22 × 30, 25 × 36, 22 × 30
Gertrud Schönberg (daughter)	Oil, 36 × 26
Self-Portrait	Oil, 33·5 × 22, signed Mai 1910
Self-Portrait	Pen-drawing, 18 × 12, signed 1933

The Conqueror, The Conquered	Sketches, crayon, 23 × 16
Self-Portrait	Water-colour, 36 × 24·5
Self-Portrait	Oil, 29 × 23, on canvas
Self-Portrait	Oil, 31 × 24·5
Self-Portrait	Crayon, 40 × 30
Portrait of a Woman	Water-colour, 40·5 × 26·5
Vision	Oil, 24 × 18
Vision	Water-colour, 32 × 47·5
Portrait of a Boy	Oil, 33 × 24
Five sketches for 'Die glückliche Hand'	Water-colours and drawings (figures and stage-settings)
Garden in Mödling	Oil, 71·5 × 50
Self-Portrait	Pen-drawing, shaded, 45 × 31·5; signed 1908
Self-Portrait	Water-colour (black and white), 40 × 30; signed
Self-Portrait	Pen-drawing, 28 × 21·5; signed 1927
Group in the Garden	Oil, 50 × 37
Portrait	Oil, 57·5 × 42·5, on canvas; signed
Landscape	47·5 × 41, very darkened and discoloured water-colour. (on reverse: sketches for a Christ)
Picture of a Woman	41 × 28·5; signed 1925
Gaze	Oil, 31 × 35·5
Vision	Oil, 29 × 18
Two sketches for 'Erwartung'	Crayon, 32 × 26; water-colour, 17 × 10
Portrait of a Man	Oil, 34 × 28
Portrait of a Man	Oil, 37 × 30; on reverse: Landscape
Gaze	Oil, 25·5 × 16
Vision	Oil, 25 × 16; on reverse: Grotto
Landscape	Water-colour, 46 × 23
Vision	Oil, 32 × 29
Self-Portrait	Water-colour, 23 × 18·5
Self-Portrait	Water-colour, black and white, 41 × 18·5; signed 1919
Picture of a Woman	Oil, 142 × 84, on canvas
Two Self-Portraits	Pen-drawing, charcoal, India ink, 29 × 23; 1935
Three Self-Portraits	Pen-drawing, charcoal, India ink, 24 × 20; 1936
Landscape	Oil, 49 × 56
Self-Portrait	Oil, 21 × 15
Portrait of a Boy	Oil, 50 × 32
Self-Portrait	Oil, 41 × 30·5
Portrait of a Woman	Oil, 37 × 24·5
10 Caricatures	Charcoal or crayon, 28 × 21·5, 9 signed, 1935; hand-written signed commentary, August, 1940.

Oil Paintings in the possession of Mrs. Jalowetz

Hatred	17·5 × 12

OIL PAINTINGS, WATER-COLOURS, DRAWINGS

Mahler's Funeral	17·5 × 14·5
Self-Portrait	15·5 × 11

Letter from Wassili Kandinsky to Schoenberg, 16. 11. 1911.

Dear Mr. Schönberg,

Your letter made me very happy. Fine—so many concerts ! When will the one in Munich be ? I'm looking forward to it tremendously. A whole evening in Paris—quite splendid! I could get something into the newspapers there through Le Fanesmil [?]. Would you like that ? I'm happy, too, that you have such a pleasant place to live. *Perhaps* we shall come to Berlin in January. Now, 'Der Blaue Reiter'! That won't appear till the middle of January— perhaps even at the end of the month. And therefore you have a good month to finish your article. *First* number without Schönberg! No, I won't have that.

. . . .

In your pictures (which I received from the shipper only yesterday; we returned to Munich only two days ago) I see a *great* deal. Two sources: (1) 'My' realism, i.e., how things *are* and, at the same time, the *inner resonance* which they create. This is what I foretold in my books, as 'fantasy in the hardest material'. This is antipodal to my art and . . . in the end, grows from the same root. A chair lives, a line lives—in the long run, it all amounts to the same thing. I am very fond of this sort of 'fantasy'—especially after your pictures! The 'Self-Portrait', the 'Garden' (not the one I wanted, but also a very good one). (2) The second source— materialized, romantic, mystical sound (also the sort of thing that I do) I do not like so well when the principle is applied in *this* way. And yet . . . these things are good, too, and interest me very much. Kokoschka, too, saw this second source three years ago—he had the 'plus' element of 'strangeness'. Thus I am 'interpreted'; while I like to see it, it doesn't excite me inwardly. This is too binding and precise for me. If something of the sort stirred in me, I should simply *write* (never paint!): 'he had a white face and black lips.' That is sufficient for me—i.e., that really means *more* to me! I feel ever more strongly that there must be some empty space in every work, so that one is not too tied down! Perhaps this is no 'eternal' law, but only a law for 'tomorrow'. I am modest and shall content myself with 'tomorrow'. Oh yes !

Please write me, too, what effect my things at the 'New Secession' have on you. Really, I was always sure that *you* would understand and feel Münter (something that happens, in general, far too seldom). Oh yes, these good old elephants' hides! I am lucky; I beat the dear little animals black and blue. Here, your means and mine coincide completely. So let us (you ? me ?) make hell plenty hot for the Berliners! The fellows should sweat and get out of breath. Naturally, we'll not have to see to that *on purpose*. I have a friend who unintentionally squeezes your hand so hard when he greets you with 'Grüss Gott' that everybody yells *Ouch!* Then he immediately begs pardon. But our manners aren't that good!

I have a great deal of work. And many wishes as a painter. Why is there so little time ? I, too, have been feeling very strongly that we shall all 'live' many more lives. That is, physically. And this long, long road.

I press your hand warmly and both of us greet you and your wife. Has the little girl recovered completely ?

Your KANDINSKY

OIL PAINTINGS, WATER-COLOURS, DRAWINGS

From a letter of Kandinsky to Schoenberg, 13. 1. 12:

Long ago, I asked you about the prices for your pictures, and whether we might keep some of them for our D.B.R. ['Der Blaue Reiter'] exhibition. Long ago, too, I sent everything to Budapest (at the wish of Paris v. Gütersloh, who arranged an exhibition there) with the following exceptions: (1) We have hung 'Selbstportrait', 'Landschaft', and 2 'Visionen'; (2) You did not want to have the portrait 'Dame in Rosa' sent there (it is still at my house). From group (1), I removed the 'Landschaft', at your wish (it is at Thannhauser's); the other three travelled with our exhibition to Cologne and are quite determined to voyage further, too. These pictures made quite a good impression in our show. And whoever told you that I do not like your pictures? It's only that the origin of the 'Visions' is not clear to me and I should be happy to hear something about it *soon*. It is very important for my article in the 'B.R.'!!

....?

Your letter about going to the N. Secession pleased us very much—especially the detailed interesting comments on our (also Marc's) pictures. But naturally I must argue with you, just the same. Mathematically, 4 is to 2 as 8 is to 4. Artistically—no. Mathematically, $1 + 1 = 2$; artistically, $1 - 1$ can also be 2. In the second place; are you against orchestral doublings? Now, that is merely enlargement (and, therefore, complication) of the artistic means. But, in the third place, my aim is *oftentimes* to prevent the onlooker from glancing over the pictures in a moment, simply by enlarging their dimensions. In the fourth place: dimension itself is a force, a means. This chandelier* and this one* are entirely different.

★

That the Schoenberg–Kandinsky friendship survived all the years is proved by a long letter of two closely-spaced typed pages which Kandinsky wrote to Schoenberg on 1. 7. 36 from Neuilly-sur-Seine, after he had received a short note from him through a Mr. Danz. Kandinsky reports in detail on his life during the last years, on Paris, and on the fate of artists during this period. He closes as follows:

Do you still remember, dear Mr. Schönberg, how we became acquainted? It was on the *Starnberger See*—I came on the steamer, wearing my short *Lederhosen*, and suddenly saw a drawing in black and white—you were dressed all in white and only your face was sunburned nearly black. And, later, the summer in Murnau? All our contemporaries of those days sigh deeply at recollections of that bygone time and say, 'Those were the good old days'. And they were really good, better than good. How wonderfully everything pulsed with life then! how impatiently we awaited our victories of the spirit! I am still waiting for them, and with the greatest confidence. Only, now I know that it will take a long, long time.

The report that you wanted to have from me has become long and detailed. I shall wait for your 'revenge'. In the meantime, heartiest greetings, also to your wife, in which my wife joins just as cordially.

Your
KANDINSKY

---

* Sketches of the identical chandelier in 2 different sizes.

RECORDINGS
MICROFILMS

RECORDINGS

(in the legacy, according to Schoenberg's listing)

1. Gurrelieder
2. Verklärte Nacht
3. Pierrot lunaire
4. I. Orchestral Variations   II. Discussion with Strobel   III. Letter to Stiedry
5. Pierrot—Orchestral Songs, Op. 22—Von Heute auf Morgen
6. Brahms, G minor Piano Quartet, orchestrated
7. Chamber Symphony No. 2
8. Piano Concerto
9. Variations for Band
10. Second Chamber Symphony (for 2 pianos), Clara Silvers and Leonard Stein
11. Concerto for String Quartet and Orchestra
12. Ode to Napoleon
12a. Septet Op. 29, Suite
14. Wind Quintet (incomplete)
15. ISCM Concert (75th birthday); 1. Trio; 2. Songs: 'Der verlorene Haufen, Abschied';
    3. Phantasy for Violin with Piano Accompaniment; 4. Ode to Napoleon
16. First String Quartet
17. Second String Quartet
18. Third String Quartet
19. Fourth String Quartet
    played by the Kolisch Quartet

This listing includes both commercial and private recordings. Additional discs and tapes of Schoenberg's works are found in five packages.

Long-Playing Records

First String Quartet (ALCO)
Third String Quartet (DIAL)
First Chamber Symphony (DIAL)
Serenade (ESOTERIC)
Pelleas und Melisande (CAPITOL)
Five Orchestral Pieces (Winfried Zillig, Radio Frankfurt)
Ode to Napoleon (Leibowitz)
String Trio (recorded at Berlin RIAS)

Discs or tapes of lectures delivered by Schoenberg

Thanks to the Institute of Arts and Letters
Music examples for 'My Evolution'

Schoenberg, Speech
Lecture at Koldofsky's world première of the String Trio (KFWB)
Lecture and analysis, Variations for Orchestra, Op. 31 (Radio Frankfurt)

MICROFILMS
(of original manuscripts)

1. Dance around the Golden Calf (score); text of 'Moses und Aron'
2. Phantasy for Violin with Piano Accompaniment, Op. 47
3. 'Die Jakobsleiter', score
4. 'Die glückliche Hand', score
5. 'Moses und Aron', score from the fourth scene onwards, incomplete
6. Suite for String Orchestra; also, in photocopies, 36 sketch-sheets

COMPLETE LIST OF WORKS
CHRONOLOGICAL LIST OF WORKS
DATES OF WORLD PREMIÈRES

ABBREVIATIONS

AMP	Associated Music Publishers, New York City
B	Verlag Richard Birnbach, Berlin
B & B	Bote und Bock, Berlin
Boe	Boelke-Bomart, Inc., Hillsdale, N.Y.
EBM	Edward B. Marks Music Corporation, New York City
F & F	Faber and Faber, Ltd., London
G	H. W. Gray Co., New York City
H	Wilhelm Hansen, Copenhagen
Hhf	Heinrichshofens Verlag, Wilhelmshaven
Is	Israeli Music Publications
	(Representatives: Leeds Music Corp., New York City
	J. & W. Chester Ltd., London
	Heugel & Co., Paris
	Carisch S.A., Milan
	Hug & Co., Zürich
	Broekmans & Van Poppel, Amsterdam
	Wilhelm Hansen, Copenhagen)
P	C. F. Peters Corporation, New York—London—Frankfurt
PhL	Philosophical Library, New York City
Sch M	Schotts Söhne, Mainz
Sch NY	G. Schirmer, New York City
Shi	Edition Shilkret, Malverne, Long Island, N.Y.
UE	Universal Edition, Vienna—London
WN	Williams & Norgate, Ltd., London

COMPLETE LIST OF WORKS

A. WORKS WITH OPUS NUMBERS

(N.B.: arrangements and piano reductions not attributed to a publisher in this list were, in each case, brought out by the publisher of the original composition.)

Opus 1 Two Songs, for baritone and piano (B)

2 Four Songs, for voice and piano (B)

3 Six Songs, for medium voice and piano (B)

4 String Sextet 'Verklärte Nacht' ('Transfigured Night') for 2 violins, 2 violas and 2 'cellos (B)
Arrangement for string orchestra (1917) by the composer (UE)
Revised version for string orchestra (1943) by the composer (AMP)

5 'Pelleas und Melisande', symphonic poem for orchestra (UE)
Arrangement for piano four hands (Heinrich Jalowetz)

6 Eight Songs, for voice and piano (B)

7 First String Quartet in D minor (B)
Arrangement for piano four hands (Felix Greissle)

8 Six Songs, for voice and orchestra (UE)
Reduction for voice and piano (Anton Webern)

9 First Chamber Symphony, for 15 solo instruments (UE)
First arrangement for orchestra by the composer (UE)

9B Second arrangement for orchestra by the composer (Sch NY)
Arrangement for flute (or second violin), clarinet (or viola), violin, 'cello and piano (Anton Webern, UE)
Arrangement for piano solo (Eduard Steuermann, UE)
Arrangement for piano four hands by the composer (manuscript)
Arrangement for piano four hands (Felix Greissle, UE)

10 Second String Quartet in F♯ minor, with voice (UE)
Arrangement for string orchestra by the composer
Arrangement for piano four hands (Felix Greissle)
Reduction for voice and piano of third and fourth movements (Alban Berg)

11 Three Piano Pieces (UE)
'Concert Interpretation' of No. 2 by Ferruccio Busoni

12 Two Ballads, for voice and piano (UE)

13 'Friede auf Erden' ('Peace on Earth'), for mixed chorus a cappella (Sch M)
Instrumental accompaniment to the above (*ad lib.*)

14 Two Songs, for voice and piano (UE)

15   Fifteen Verses from 'Das Buch der hängenden Gärten' ('The Book of the Hanging Gardens') by Stefan George, for soprano and piano (UE)

16   Five Orchestral Pieces (P)
New, 'reduced' version (for normal-sized orchestra) by the composer
Arrangement for chamber orchestra (Felix Greissle)
Arrangement for two pianos (Anton Webern)

17   'Erwartung' ('Expectation'), monodrama for soprano and orchestra (UE)
Reduction for voice and piano (Eduard Steuermann)

18   'Die glückliche Hand' ('The Hand of Fate'), drama with music (UE)
Reduction for two pianos (Eduard Steuermann)

19   Six Little Piano Pieces (UE)

20   'Herzgewächse' ('Foliage of the Heart') for high soprano, celesta, harmonium and harp (UE)
Piano reduction (Felix Greissle)

21   'Pierrot lunaire', melodramas for a speaking voice, piano, flute (alternating with piccolo), clarinet (alternating with bass clarinet), violin (alternating with viola), and 'cello (UE)
Piano reduction with voice (Erwin Stein)

22   Four Songs, for voice and orchestra (simplified study and conductor's score; UE)

23   Five Piano Pieces (H)

24   Serenade, for clarinet, bass clarinet, mandolin, guitar, violin, viola, 'cello and baritone voice (H)
Arrangement for piano four hands (Felix Greissle)
Arrangement for piano, violin and 'cello (Felix Greissle)
Fourth movement (Sonnet of Petrarch) for man's low voice, reduction with piano accompaniment (Felix Greissle)
The same, arrangement for violin, solo 'cello and piano (Felix Greissle)

25   Suite for Piano (UE)

26   Quintet for flute, oboe, clarinet, horn and bassoon (UE)
Arrangements: Sonata for violin (or flute) and piano (Greissle)
Sonata for clarinet and piano (Greissle)
Reduction for piano four hands (Greissle)

27   Four Pieces for Mixed Chorus (UE)

28   Three Satires for Mixed Chorus (UE)

29   Suite for piano, piccolo clarinet, clarinet, bass clarinet, violin, viola and 'cello (UE)

30   Third String Quartet (UE)

31   Variations for Orchestra (UE)

32   'Von Heute auf Morgen' ('From Today till Tomorrow'), opera in one act (text by 'Max Blonda', *recte* Gertrud Schoenberg; Sch M)
Piano reduction (with voice parts) by the composer

33A Piano Piece (UE)

33B Piano Piece (formerly published by New Music Society of California; rights of publication now vested in Gertrud Schoenberg)

B. WORKS WITHOUT OPUS NUMBERS

34   'Begleitungsmusik zu einer Lichtspielszene' ('Accompaniment to a Film-Scene'), for orchestra (Hhf)
35   Six Pieces for Male Chorus (B & B)
36   Concerto for Violin and Orchestra (Sch NY)
      Piano reduction (Felix Greissle)
37   Fourth String Quartet (Sch NY)
38A   Second Chamber Symphony (Sch NY)
38B   Arrangement of the same for two pianos, by the composer (unpublished)
39   Kol Nidre, for speaker, mixed chorus and orchestra (Boe)
40   Variations on a Recitative for Organ (G)
      Arrangement for two pianos (Celius Dougherty)
41   'Ode to Napoleon' (Lord Byron), for reciter, string quartet and piano (Sch NY)
41B   The same, for reciter, string orchestra and piano
42   Concerto for Piano and Orchestra (Sch NY)
      Reduction for two pianos (Eduard Steuermann)
43A   Theme and Variations for Band (Sch NY)
43B   The same, arranged for orchestra
44   Prelude, for orchestra and mixed chorus (Shi)
45   String Trio (Boe)
46   'A Survivor from Warsaw', for reciter, male chorus and orchestra (Boe)
47   Phantasy for Violin with Piano Accompaniment (P)
48   Three Songs, for voice and piano (Boe)
49   Three Choruses (German folksongs of the 15th and 16th centuries) for mixed chorus a cappella (EBM)
50A   'Dreimal tausend Jahre' ('Thrice a Thousand Years'), for mixed chorus a cappella (Sch M)
50B   'De Profundis' (130th Psalm), for six-part mixed chorus a cappella (Is)
50C   Modern Psalm, for reciter, mixed chorus and orchestra (unfinished; Sch M)

B. WORKS WITHOUT OPUS NUMBERS
(including arrangements and orchestrations)

'Gurrelieder', for soli, reciter, mixed chorus and orchestra (UE)
   Excerpt: 'Song of the Wood-Dove', for voice and chamber orchestra
   Piano reduction, with vocal parts (Alban Berg)
'Die Jakobsleiter', oratorio for soli, mixed chorus and orchestra (unfinished; text published by UE)
'Moses und Aron', opera in 3 acts (final act unfinished; Sch M)
   Piano reduction, with vocal parts (Winfried Zillig)
Suite for String Orchestra (Sch NY)
Concerto for 'Cello and Orchestra, after the harpsichord concerto in D major by G. M. Monn (Sch NY)
   Piano reduction by the composer

Concerto for String Quartet and Orchestra, freely adapted from Handel's Concerto Grosso Op. 6, No. 7 in B flat major (Sch NY)

J. S. Bach: Two Chorale Preludes, arranged for large orchestra (1: 'Schmücke dich, o liebe Seele' ('Deck Thyself, O Soul, with Gladness'); 2: 'Komm Gott, Schöpfer, Heiliger Geist' ('Come God, Creator, Holy Ghost')) (UE)

J. S. Bach: Prelude and Fugue in E flat major ('St. Anne'), arranged for large orchestra (UE) Also, reduced version by Erwin Stein

Johannes Brahms: Piano Quartet, Op. 25, in G minor, arranged for orchestra (Sch NY)

Three German Folksongs (15th and 16th centuries), for four-part mixed chorus, a cappella (P)

Four German Folksongs (15th and 16th centuries), for voice with piano accompaniment (P)

G. M. Monn: Symphony in A major, 'Cello Concerto in G minor, Cembalo Concerto in D major. J. C. Mann: Divertimento in D major. Realization of the figured basses by Schoenberg (Denkmäler der Tonkunst in Österreich)
    Piano reduction of Monn's 'Cello Concerto in G minor (UE)

Johann Strauss: 'Emperor Waltz', arranged for flute, clarinet, string quartet and piano (Sch M)

Carl Löwe: 'Der Nöck' ('The Water-Sprite'), for voice and orchestra (UE)

Beethoven: 'Adelaide', for voice and orchestra (MS. lost)

Schubert: Three Songs (titles unknown), for voice and orchestra (MS. lost)

C. UNPUBLISHED WORKS

(completed)

Eleven Songs (the 11th unfinished) from the earliest period
Six Pieces for Piano Four Hands (only 3 still exist) (1894)
Ten Songs (1897–1909)
String Quartet in D major (1897)
Presto for String Quartet (or string orchestra?) from the early period
Alla marcia (E flat major) for piano, from the early period
Gavotte and Musette for String Orchestra (in the olden style; 1897)
Untitled: Three little pieces for chamber orchestra (the third unfinished; 1910)
Numerous canons, vocal and instrumental (mostly 1922–1949)
'Die Jakobsleiter', oratorio (unfinished, 1917)

D. MISCELLANEOUS

(unpublished)

Eight 'Brettelieder' (1901); 7 for voice and paino, 1 for voice, snare-drum, trumpet, piccolo, and piano

Johann Strauss: 'Roses from the South', for string quartet, piano and harmonium

E. THEORETICAL WORKS

Ferruccio Busoni: 'Berceuse élégiaque', for flute, clarinet, harmonium, piano and string quintet (about 1920)

Franz Schubert: 'Serenade', for clarinet, bassoon, mandolin, guitar and string quartet (1921)

'Der deutsche Michel', for male chorus (1916?)

'The Iron Brigade', march for piano and string quartet (1916)

Christmas Music, for 2 violins, 'cello, piano and harmonium (1921)

E. THEORETICAL WORKS . OTHER WRITINGS

'Harmonielehre' (UE)—Theory of Harmony (PhL)

Models for Beginners in Composition (Sch NY)

Structural Functions of Harmony (WN)*—'Die formbildenden Tendenzen der Harmonie' (Sch M)

'Die Lehre vom Kontrapunkt' (text in English; unfinished, manuscript; part of this in preparation as Preliminary Exercises in Counterpoint, F & F)

Fundamentals of Musical Composition (in preparation, F & F; German translation by Rudolf Kolisch, in preparation, Sch M)

Style and Idea (PhL).† Essays, edited and translated by Dika Newlin

'Der musikalische Gedanke und die Logik, Technik und Kunst seiner Darstellung' ('The musical idea and the logic, technique, and art of its presentation') (unfinished)

'Instrumentationslehre' (unfinished)

* In U.S.: W. W. Norton, Inc.
† In England: WN.

CHRONOLOGICAL LIST OF WORKS

1897	String Quartet in D major
1897 (98 ?)	Two Songs, Op. 1
1899	Four Songs, Op. 2
1899	String Sextet, Op. 4
1899–1903	Six Songs, Op. 3
1900–1911	'Gurrelieder'
1903	Symphonic Poem 'Pelleas und Melisande', Op. 5
1903–1905	Eight Songs, Op. 6
1904	Six Orchestral Songs, Op. 8
1905	First String Quartet in D minor, Op. 7
1906	First Chamber Symphony in E major, Op. 9
1907	Two Ballads for voice and piano, Op. 12
1907	'Friede auf Erden', mixed chorus a cappella, Op. 13
1907–1908	Second String Quartet in F♯ minor, Op. 10
1907–1908	Two Songs, Op. 14
1908–1909	Fifteen Songs after Stefan George, Op. 15
1909	Three Piano Pieces, Op. 11
1909	Five Orchestral Pieces, Op. 16
1909	'Erwartung', monodrama, Op. 17
1911	Six Little Piano Pieces, Op. 19
1911	'Herzgewächse', Op. 20
1912	'Pierrot lunaire', Op. 21
(1908)–1913	'Die glückliche Hand', drama with music, Op. 18
1913–1916	Four Orchestral Songs, Op. 22
1917 (–1922)	'Die Jakobsleiter', oratorio
1920–1923	Five Piano Pieces, Op. 23
1920–1923	Serenade, Op. 24
1921	Suite for Piano, Op. 25
1922	Song of the Wood-Dove from 'Gurrelieder', for chamber orchestra
1922	J. S. Bach, Two Chorale Preludes, arranged for orchestra
1923–1924	Quintet for Winds, Op. 26
1924–1926	Suite (Septet) for piano, 3 winds and 3 strings, Op. 29
1925	Johann Strauss, Emperor Waltz, arranged for chamber ensemble
1925	Four Pieces for Mixed Chorus, Op. 27
1925	Three Satires for Mixed Chorus, Op. 28
1925–1926	Appendix to Op. 28

1926–1928	Variations for Orchestra, Op. 31
1927	Third String Quartet, Op. 30
1928	J. S. Bach, Prelude and Fugue in E flat major, arranged for orchestra
1928	Piano Piece, Op. 33a
1928	Three German Folksongs (15th and 16th centuries), arranged for mixed chorus a cappella
1928–1929 (Jan. 1)	'Von Heute auf Morgen', opera, Op. 32
1929	Four German Folksongs (15th and 16th centuries), arranged for voice and piano
1929–1930	Accompaniment to a Film-Scene, Op. 34
1929–1930	Six Pieces for Male Chorus, Op. 35
1931	Piano Piece, Op. 33b
1930–1932	'Moses und Aron', opera
1932–1933 (Jan. 4)	Concerto for 'Cello and Orchestra, after the harpsichord concerto of G. M. Monn
1933	Three Songs, Op. 48
1933	Concerto for String Quartet and Orchestra (after Handel)
1934	Suite for String Orchestra
1934–1936	Violin Concerto, Op. 36
1935	First Chamber Symphony, arranged for orchestra, Op. 9B
1936	Fourth String Quartet, Op. 37
1937	Brahms, Piano Quartet in G minor, arranged for orchestra
1938	'Kol nidre', for speaker, mixed chorus and orchestra, Op. 39
1939	Second Chamber Symphony, Op. 38 (begun 1906)
1941	Variations for Organ, Op. 40
1942	Ode to Napoleon, for speaker, piano and string quartet, Op. 41
1942	Concerto for Piano and Orchestra, Op. 42
1943	Theme and Variations for Band, Op. 43A; version for orchestra, Op. 43B
1945	Prelude for Orchestra and Mixed Chorus, Op. 44
1946	String Trio, Op. 45
1947	A Survivor from Warsaw, for speaker, male chorus and orchestra, Op. 46
1948	Three Folksongs for mixed chorus a cappella, Op. 49
1949	Phantasy for Violin with Piano Accompaniment, Op. 47
1949	'Dreimal tausend Jahre', for mixed chorus a cappella, Op. 50A
1950	'De Profundis', Psalm 130, for mixed chorus a cappella, Op. 50B
1950	Modern Psalm (text by the composer), for mixed chorus, speaker and orchestra, Op. 50C

Undated, and therefore not included in this list, are the orchestration of Carl Löwe's 'Der Nöck' and the realization of the continuo of the works by G. M. Monn and J. C. Mann, which were probably done about 1910 or 1911.

DATES OF WORLD PREMIÈRES

(a) Works with opus numbers

String Sextet, 'Verklärte Nacht', Op. 4:
1903, Vienna, Rosé Quartet and members of the Vienna Philharmonic.

'Pelleas und Melisande', Op. 5:

January 26, 1905, Vienna, 'Wiener Konzertvereinsorchester' (joined with the 'Wiener Tonkünstlerorchester' after 1918 as 'Wiener Symphoniker'), conducted by Schoenberg.

First String Quartet in D minor, Op. 7:
February 5, 1907, Vienna, Rosé Quartet.

First Chamber Symphony, Op. 9:
Early 1907 in Vienna, Rosé Quartet and wind ensemble of the Vienna Philharmonic.

Second String Quartet in F♯ minor, Op. 10:
December, 1908, Vienna, Rosé Quartet and Marie Gutheil-Schoder, soprano.

Three Piano Pieces, Op. 11:
January 14, 1910, Vienna ('Verein für Kunst und Kultur'), Etta Werndorff.

Fifteen Songs after Stefan George, Op. 15:
January 14, 1910, Vienna, Martha Winternitz-Dorda.

Five Orchestral Pieces, Op. 16:
September 3, 1912, London, conducted by Sir Henry Wood.

'Erwartung', monodrama, Op. 17:
June 6, 1924, Prague (Neues Deutsches Theater), conducted by Alexander von Zemlinsky; Marie Gutheil-Schoder, soprano.

'Die glückliche Hand', drama with music, Op. 18:
October 14, 1924, Vienna (Volksoper), conducted by Fritz Stiedry, stage direction by Fritz Turnau. The cast: Alfred Jerger (The Man), Hedy Pfundtmayr (The Woman), Josef Hustinger (The Gentleman).

'Pierrot lunaire', Op. 21:
October 16, 1912, Berlin, conducted by Schoenberg. Albertine Zehme, reciter; Eduard Steuermann, piano; Jakob Maliniak, violin and viola; Hans Kindler, 'cello; H. W. de Vries, flute and piccolo; K. Essberger, clarinet and bass clarinet.

Four Orchestral Songs, Op. 22:
February 21, 1932, Frankfurt am Main, Radio Orchestra, conducted by Hans Rosbaud; Hertha Reinecke, soprano.

Serenade, Op. 24:
July 20, 1924, Donaueschingen, conducted by Schoenberg.

Wind Quintet, Op. 26:
September 13, 1924, Vienna, wind group of the Vienna Philharmonic, conducted by Felix Greissel.

Suite, Op. 29:
December 15, 1927, Paris, conducted by Schoenberg.

Third String Quartet, Op. 30:
September 19, 1927, Vienna, Kolisch Quartet.

Variations for Orchestra, Op. 31:
December 2, 1928, Berlin, Berlin Philharmonic conducted by Wilhelm Furtwängler.

'Von Heute auf Morgen', opera in one act, Op. 32:
February 1, 1930, Frankfurt am Main (Municipal Theatre), conducted by William (Hans Wilhelm) Steinberg, stage direction by Herbert Graf. The cast: Else Gentner-Fischer (Wife), Elisabeth Friedrich (Girl-Friend), Benno Ziegler (Husband), Anton M. Topitz (Singer).

Accompaniment to a Film-Scene, Op. 34:
1930, Berlin, orchestra of the Kroll Opera conducted by Otto Klemperer.

Concerto for Violin and Orchestra, Op. 36:
December 6, 1940, Philadelphia, Philadelphia Orchestra conducted by Leopold Stokowski; Louis Krasner, violin.

Fourth String Quartet, Op. 37:
January 9, 1937, Los Angeles, Kolisch Quartet.

Second Chamber Symphony, Op. 38:
December 15, 1940, New York, orchestra of the New Friends of Music conducted by Fritz Stiedry.

'Kol nidre', Op. 39:
October 4, 1938, Los Angeles, conducted by Schoenberg.

Ode to Napoleon, Op. 41:
November 23, 1944, New York, New York Philharmonic conducted by Artur Rodzinski; Mack Harrell, speaker; Eduard Steuermann, piano.

Concerto for Piano and Orchestra, Op. 42:
February 6, 1944, New York, NBC Symphony conducted by Stokowski; Eduard Steuermann, piano.

Theme and Variations for Orchestra, Op. 43B:
October 20, 1944, Boston, Boston Symphony Orchestra.

Prelude for Orchestra and Mixed Chorus, Op. 44:
November 18, 1945, Los Angeles, conducted by Werner Janssen.

String Trio, Op. 45:
March, 1947, Harvard University, Cambridge, Mass.

A Survivor from Warsaw, Op. 46:
1948, Albuquerque, New Mexico, Albuquerque Orchestra conducted by Kurt Frederick.

Phantasy for Violin with Piano Accompaniment, Op. 47:
September 13, 1949, Los Angeles; Adolf Koldofsky, violin; Leonard Stein, piano.

'Dreimal tausend Jahre', for mixed chorus a cappella, Op. 50A:
October 29, 1949, Fylkingen (Sweden), Lilla Chamber Chorus conducted by Eric Ericson.

'De Profundis', for mixed chorus a cappella, Op. 50B:
January 29, 1954, Cologne, chorus of the West German Radio conducted by Bernhard
    Zimmermann.

Modern Psalm (text by composer) for speaker, mixed chorus and orchestra, Op. 50C:
May 29, 1956, Cologne, chorus and orchestra of the West German Radio conducted by Nino
    Sanzogno.

(b) Works without opus numbers

String Quartet in D major:
1897, Vienna, Fitzner Quartet.

'Gurrelieder', for soloists, mixed chorus and orchestra:
February 23, 1913, Vienna, Philharmonic Chorus and 'Wiener Tonkünstlerorchester' (joined
    with the 'Wiener Konzertvereinsorchester' after 1918 as 'Wiener Symphoniker') con-
    ducted by Franz Schreker.

G. M. Monn, 'Cello Concerto in G minor (continuo realized by Schoenberg):
November 11, 1913, Vienna, Vienna Philharmonic conducted by Franz Schalk; Pablo Casals,
    'cello.

J. S. Bach, Two Chorale Preludes arranged for orchestra:
December 7, 1922, New York, New York Philharmonic conducted by Josef Stransky.

J. S. Bach, Prelude and Fugue in E flat major arranged for orchestra:
November 10, 1929, Vienna, conducted by Anton Webern.

Suite for String Orchestra:
May 18, 1935, Los Angeles, Los Angeles Philharmonic conducted by Otto Klemperer.

Concerto for String Quartet and Orchestra (after Handel, Concerto Grosso Op. 6, No. 7):
September 26, 1934, Prague, Kolisch Quartet and Radio Orchestra conducted by Karl B.
    Jirak.

Concerto for 'Cello and Orchestra in D major (after G. M. Monn, Harpsichord Concerto):
December 7, 1935, London, Emanuel Feuermann with London Philharmonic Orchestra.

Brahms, Piano Quartet, Op. 25, arranged for orchestra:
May 7, 1938, Los Angeles, Los Angeles Philharmonic conducted by Otto Klemperer.

Dance Around the Golden Calf (from the opera 'Moses und Aron'):
July 2, 1951, Darmstadt, orchestra and chorus of the 'Landestheater' conducted by Hermann
    Scherchen.

DATES OF WORLD PREMIÈRES

'Moses und Aron', opera in 3 acts:

March 12, 1954, concert première; Hamburg, orchestra and chorus of the North-west German Radio, conducted by Hans Rosbaud; Hans Herbert Fiedler (Moses), Helmut Krebs (Aron).

June 6, 1957, stage première; Zürich (Municipal Theatre), conducted by Hans Rosbaud, stage direction by Karl Heinz Krahl; Hans Herbert Fiedler (Moses), Helmut Melchert (Aron).

Untitled: three little pieces for chamber orchestra:

October 10, 1957, Berlin, Academy of Arts; played by members of the Berlin Philharmonic without conductor.

'Die Jakobsleiter', oratorio (unfinished):

Première of the beginning (180 measures): January 12, 1958, Hamburg, orchestra and chorus of the North German Radio, conducted by Hans Rosbaud. At the same concert, which was the 50th jubilee programme of 'Das neue Werk', two other fragments from the legacy received their premières: 'Israel Exists Again', for mixed chorus and orchestra, and the Sonata for Organ.

Première of whole work: June 16, 1961, Vienna (Grosser Konzerthaussaal), orchestra and chorus of the West German Radio, Cologne, and chorus of the North German Radio, Hamburg, conducted by Rafael Kubelik. The soloists: Ilse Hollweg, Günther Reich, Thomas Stewart, Josef Traxel, Julius Patzak, Hans Herbert Fiedler, Helmut Krebs.

APPENDIX

DOCUMENTS CONCERNING THE EMPLOYMENT AND DISMISSAL OF ARNOLD SCHOENBERG BY THE PRUSSIAN ACADEMY OF ARTS IN BERLIN

The Prussian Minister
for Science, Art and Education
U IV Nr. 13113

Berlin, W.8. September 17, 1925
Unter den Linden 4

It is necessary for me to express my lively pleasure that the negotiations concerning your employment as the director of a Master School for Musical Composition at our Academy of Arts have been successfully completed.

After consultation with the Minister of Finance, I herewith inform you of my consent to your appointment as of October 1 of this year, according to the agreement made between you and my representative Professor Kestenberg on August 28, 1925, in Vienna, with the following conditions:

1. Under Heading 2 of the contract, I authorize the payment of a monthly salary to you for the duration of your teaching activity, said salary to be reckoned as follows:

   (a) Highest legal pay for salary group B4— 962·50 RM
   (b) Legal recompense for housing costs — 133·— „
   (c) Special bonus — 300·— „
   Total: 1395·50 RM

   To this is added the (variable) special municipal payment, presently 5%; in addition, the special benefits for wife and children are guaranteed.

2. Should you be appointed as a regular civil-service employee during the period of this contract, the special sum of 300 RM monthly listed under (c) will be subtracted from the above-mentioned salary.

3. In the case of new regulations for the salaries of civil-service employees, we reserve the right to alter the sum listed under 1.

For the record, I send you herewith the certified copy of the agreement of August 28, 1925.

For the duration of your teaching position, you will bear the title of Professor.

I am also honoured to inform you that, in your capacity as director of a Master School, you are simultaneously a member of the Senate of the Academy of Arts. As such, you are to receive a special payment of 900 RM yearly.

For the purpose of assuming your official duties and of induction into the Senate, may I request that you report to the President of the Academy of Arts on October 1 of this year? He will authorize the necessary procedures for payment of your salary.

The special bonus of 300 RM together with the special municipal payment of 5% will be paid by the treasury of the Building and Finance Director (here, *Invalidenstrasse*), while the remainder of your salary and your fee as Senator will be paid directly by the treasury of the Academy of Arts.

Representing the Minister
(signed) Lammers

To
the composer Herr Arnold Schönberg
       in Altaussee/Austria
         Certified copy with U IV 13113.

Between Herr Arnold Schönberg, composer in Vienna/Mödling, Bernhardgasse 6, and the undersigned representative, the following agreement is reached, subject to the approval of the Minister for Science, Art and Education:

(1) Herr Arnold Schönberg agrees to take charge of a Master School of Musical Composition at the Academy of Arts in Berlin between October 1, 1925, and September 30, 1930.

Herr Schönberg is granted the right to request the change from a contractual position to a State position during the first two years of the contract. The Prussian Office of Education will consider this request.

(2) For his work, Herr Schönberg will receive a monthly salary, the exact amount of which is yet to be determined. This salary shall not be less than 1400–1500 marks monthly, i.e., a yearly salary of 16800–18000 marks.

(3) Herr Schönberg agrees to teach in Berlin six months a year during the period of his contract. It is up to Herr Schönberg to determine the time of teaching. Also, the form of teaching may be freely determined by him.

(4) For the duration of the contract, Herr Schönberg will bear the official title 'Professor'.

(5) The costs of moving his household, first in part and later entirely, from Vienna to Berlin will be reimbursed to Herr Schönberg according to official specifications and according to his necessary expenditures.

(6) The Office of Education will concern itself with assisting Herr Schönberg in finding a place to live. Also, it will take care of the arrangements for necessary teaching materials and additional teaching assistants.

(7) Should Herr Schönberg be prevented in any contractual year from fulfilling his obligations as teacher by concert or lecture tours outside Europe, he will make every effort to make up the missed teaching time in the following academic year.

(signed) Arnold Schönberg
(signed) Leo Kestenberg

Vienna, August 28, 1925.

Arnold Schönberg   Berlin, March 20, 1933
Berlin W 50
Nürnberger Platz 3

To the
Prussian Academy of Arts,
Berlin.

In the meeting of 1. III at the Academy, formulations were made known from which it was evident that my remaining in a leading position here is no longer desired.

Pride, and the awareness of my achievement, would have moved me to voluntary resignation long ago.

For: when I followed the lure of the flattering summons to the Academy, this happened because my ambition as a teacher was spurred, and my duty to disseminate my knowledge was held up to me; and because I knew what I am in a position to do for students.

But I achieved that, and more: whoever was my pupil gained a sense of a serious and moral concept of art which, if he knows how to maintain it, will do him honour in all circumstances of life! I believe that it is unnecessary to diminish my accomplishment by the listing of petty details.

In any case: when I was called upon, I was not dragged from obscurity; I was shown no undeserved honour.

And: I had pupils, so many that I could enjoy a very respectable standard of living as a private person.

But, as a result of this summons, I gave up my former position and moved here with my entire household goods.

One who stands, as I do, unimpeachable from the political and moral viewpoint, who has been deeply wounded in his honour as an artist and a man by being deprived of his sphere of influence, ought not to be threatened, on top of all this, with the ruin of his economic status, the destruction of his possibilities of making a living.

Therefore I take the liberty of requesting the payment to me in cash of the amount still owing me according to my contract (which still has to run till 30. IX. 1935), as well as of the costs of my moving away, and, at the same time, the permission to take this sum out of the country. For I shall be forced to use the next years in building up a new existence.

Hoping for a favourable decision, I sign myself most respectfully yours—

(signed) Arnold Schönberg
Director of a Master Class
for Musical Composition

Prussian Academy of Arts   May 23, 1933
Berlin W 8, Pariser Platz 4
J. Nr. 499
          Registered!

Honoured Colleague!

The Minister for Science, Art and Education has empowered me, through the act of May 17 of this year—UI Nr. 51950—to grant you immediate leave from your position as director of a Master School of Musical Composition. The further disposition of this matter remains in the hands of the Minister.

With respectful regards,
The President
(signed) Max v. Schillings

Professor Arnold Schönberg
    Berlin W 50
        Nürnberger Platz 3

APPENDIX

Prussian Academy of Arts
Berlin W 8, Pariser Platz 4
J. Nr. 991

September 18, 1933

At the request of the Minister of Science, Art and Education, I release you herewith from your agreement of May 15, 1930 with Ministerial Councillor Kestenberg, on the basis of Section 3 of the second order for carrying out the law for the reform of the professional civil service, May 4, 1933, in the form of the order covering July 7 to October 31, 1933.

Representative of the President
(signed) A. Kraus

To
The Director of a Master School of Musical Composition
Professor Arnold Schönberg
Arcachon (Gironde), France
Villa Strésa, Avenue Rapp

INDEX OF NAMES

INDEX OF NAMES

INDEX OF NAMES

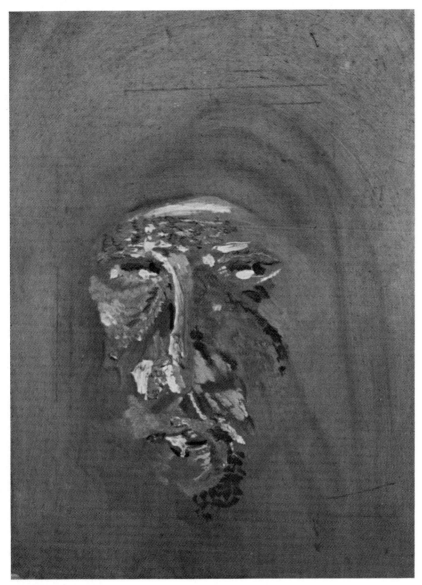

I. Vision

II. Self portrait

III. Vision of Christ

IV. The Critic

V. Self portrait

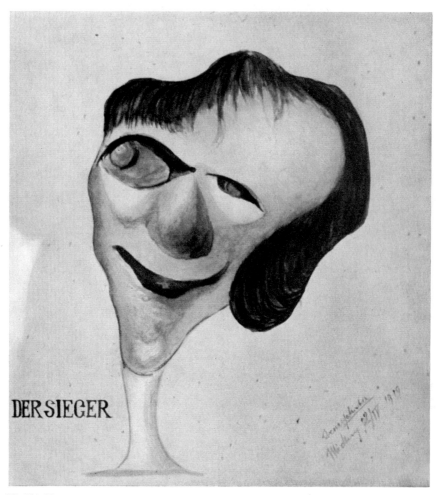

VI. The Victor

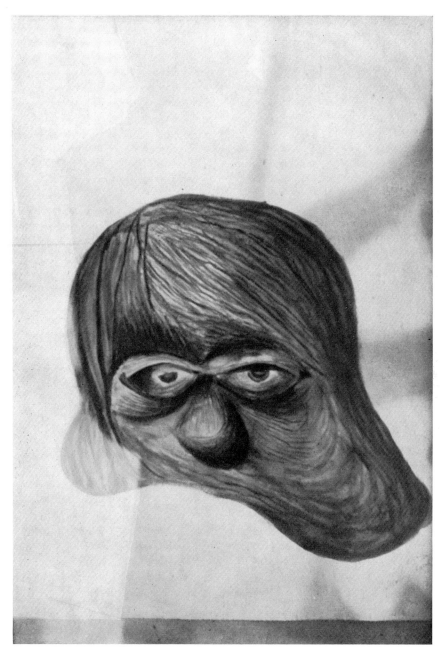

VII. The Vanquished

VIII. Gustav Mahler

IX. Red Glance

X. Self portrait

XI. Schoenberg's study in Los Angeles

XII. The Schoenberg Hall, University of California, Los Angeles